ELECTRONIC CIRCUITS FOR TECHNICIANS

ELECTRONIC CIRCUITS FOR TECHNICIANS

LLOYD TEMES, B.E.E., M.E.E.
Brooklyn Tech

McGRAW-HILL BOOK COMPANY

NEW YORK   ST. LOUIS   SAN FRANCISCO   LONDON
SYDNEY   TORONTO   MEXICO   PANAMA

ELECTRONIC CIRCUITS FOR TECHNICIANS

Library of Congress Catalog Card Number 70-81914
63485
1234567890 VHVH 7654321069

This book was set in Caledonia by Progressive
Typographers, and printed on permanent paper and
bound by Von Hoffman Press, Inc.   The designer
was Edward Zytko; the drawings were done by
Harry Lazarus.   The editors were Alan W. Lowe
and Albert Shapiro.   Adam Jacobs supervised the
production.

To Roberta, Karen, and Peter

PREFACE

This book is written for use in two-year technical programs found in junior and community colleges and technical institutes. It provides for the training of engineering technicians.

Mathematical explanations are provided wherever pertinent. Since most of the literature the student will be called upon to study on his own in his future career as an engineering technician will be of a mathematical nature, he should build an appreciation of such material and an ability to handle it. All mathematical explanations are presented with simple algebra and a bit of geometry. At no point in this text is calculus used. Thus, the only mathematics required of the student is what would normally be included in a high school course in intermediate algebra.

The student is expected to bring a knowledge of dc and ac circuitry to the course of study presented here. A basic knowledge of thermionic emission and the mechanics of operation of transistors will prove helpful. A course using a book such as "Basic Electronics" by Grob (McGraw-Hill, 1965) would serve as an excellent prerequisite to this text, since it provides the fundamental background in devices and an intensive study of ac and dc circuit analysis. However, the student who has not had a background in thermionic emission or transistor physics will be able to master the material in this book since this text takes an engineering approach to the material.

Active devices are presented as components whose action is described by the characteristic curves and parameters supplied by the manufacturer. From the engineering point of view, it is sufficient to have a functional description of the device such as that provided by characteristic curves when designing or analyzing circuits.

Vacuum tubes, transistors, and MOSFETs are presented side by side and are treated as special cases of the active device. In this age of rapid innovation, the student must develop a means of handling any device whose characteristics can be presented by a graph and/or parameters regardless of what the device is called.

In all parts of the text the material is constantly motivated by the design of better circuits for given functions. The reader is presented with enough background at each stage so that he can analyze and design working hardware.

Whenever a new concept or principle is introduced, a numerical illustrative problem is presented at that point, so that the student can see an immediate application. The text contains approximately 60 illustrative problems. If necessary, more than one illustrative problem is presented to show the similarity or dissimilarity of the different points of view. Many illustrative problems include a quick review by recalling all the information pertaining to a particular topic in a design. Each illustrative problem is designed to provide an example of the proper problem-solving technique. In many of the illustrative problems complete designs and analyses are performed.

The text is profusely illustrated, containing approximately 400 line drawings.

Wherever feasible fundamental circuit theory is stressed. Throughout the text Thévenin's and Norton's theorems as well as Kirchhoff's two laws are constantly being emphasized. Whenever possible these laws and theorems are recalled and applied.

This text can also serve as a basis for a course for industrial arts and vocational teachers in a teachers college setting.

LLOYD TEMES

CONTENTS

UNIT 𝕋ℍℝ𝔼𝔼   **PULSES AND THEIR APPLICATIONS**

1

THE HALF-WAVE-RECTIFIER CIRCUIT

Various kinds of equipment respond to the average value of the electric signal presented to them. A dc motor, for example, will rotate only if the voltage being applied to it has a nonzero average value. Most electronic equipment, such as amplifiers, requires a dc source of energy to provide it with operating power. Of course we are familiar with the fact that the most commonly available electricity is the mass-produced 60-Hz 120-volt-rms sine wave. In taking the average value of such a sine wave we see that because it has a negative value for each and every positive value, it has an average value of zero. Thus it is not, in its present form, able to power a dc motor or to serve as a power source for the operation of electronic equipment. In order to provide for the needs of the dc motor and electronic equipment the designer either must specify battery operation or provide circuitry which can operate on the readily available ac signal and produce a waveshape whose average value is some nonzero quantity.

How can we convert the sine wave of Fig. 1-1a into a waveshape whose average value is not zero? If we could remove the portion below the horizontal axis and retain the portion above the horizontal axis, or vice versa, we would have a waveshape whose average value was other than zero (see Fig. 1-1b). How can we implement this in hardware? The first thought is to provide a switch that is closed during one half the cycle and open during the remaining half of the cycle. Obviously we cannot provide a hand-operated switch to perform this function because the operator

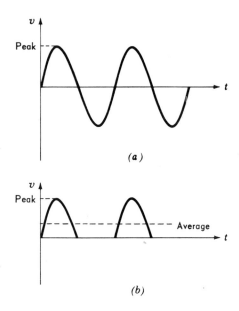

FIGURE 1-1 (a) *Sine wave.* (b) *Sine wave with negative portion removed.*

would not be able to move fast enough, and even if he could, we would not want to tie up an operator with such a menial task. Is there a switch capable of responding automatically at the great speed required? Yes. A diode permits large currents to flow in one direction but not in the other direction. The diode may be of the semiconductor type, the vacuum-tube variety, or of the gas- or vapor-filled variety. The present trend is toward the design of power supplies with semiconductor diodes wherever possible. Under normal operating conditions semiconductor diodes last for indefinitely long periods of time, take up relatively little space, and require no filament supply.

THE CIRCUIT CONFIGURATION

Figure 1-2 is a schematic diagram of a circuit which can be used to convert the power company's sine wave to a waveshape having a nonzero average value. This circuit is called a *half-wave rectifier*. Its major shortcoming is that we seem to be limited by the amplitude of the power company's waveshape. However, adding a transformer allows us the freedom to choose the peak values we desire. The transformer also isolates the circuit from power-company ground, thereby eliminating the risk of the metal chassis being at a high voltage with respect to house ground. Thus frequently with high-quality equipment 1:1 transformers may be used

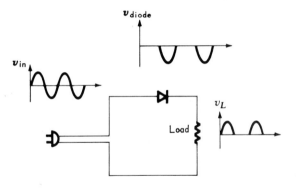

FIGURE 1-2 *Half-wave-rectifier circuit.*

to provide ground isolation even though no step up or down in voltage is required (see Fig. 1-3).

PEAK, RMS, AND AVERAGE VALUES

What relationship exists between the rms, the peak, and the average values of waveshapes involved in the half-wave-rectifier circuit? The relationship between the peak value of a sine wave and its rms value is

$$\text{Peak} = \text{rms} \times \sqrt{2}$$

Why, you may ask, does such a relationship exist? The relationship was originally developed in order to permit comparison of the heating values of ac and dc electricity. It was found that a sine wave whose peak value was $\sqrt{2}$ times a particular dc level provided the same amount of heat as the dc value when passed through resistive devices. Thus another quantity, in addition to peak values, came into use to describe sine waves. In mathematical studies it was found that the relationship existing between *any waveshape* and its effective heating value compared to a dc level was the same relationship which mathematicians call the *root mean square* of the waveshape, thus the rms value. So the rms value of a sine wave is the value of that dc level which can generate as much heat as the sine wave can when passed through a resistor. For a pure sine wave the rms value is equal to $\sqrt{2}$ times its peak value.

If not otherwise specified, sine-wave voltage and current values are assumed to be rms values. The 120-volt sine wave

FIGURE 1-3 *Half-wave-rectifier circuit with isolation transformer.*

THE HALF-WAVE-RECTIFIER CIRCUIT 5

provided by most power companies in the United States is 120 volts rms, having a peak value of $120\sqrt{2}$, or 169 volts,

Now, what about average values? We have already decided that the pure sine wave in Fig. 1-1*a* has an average value of zero, but what about the half-wave-rectified sine wave of Fig. 1-1*b*?

To find the average value of the waveshape shown in Fig. 1-1*b* we should choose many equally spaced points and determine the average value of the waveshape at these points. Do not forget to include all those points at which the waveshape is equal to zero. In doing this we find

$$\text{Average} = \frac{\text{peak}}{\pi}$$

for a half-wave-rectified sine wave.

COMPONENT SPECIFICATION

Obviously connecting just any transformer to just any diode will not provide a particular desired average output voltage. How do we specify requirements for the component parts of a rectifier? To simplify our initial approach to power-supply design we will assume that we are dealing with ideal diodes and ideal transformers. That is, we will assume that neither the transformer nor the diode is absorbing power from the circuit. They are assumed to have zero resistance and thus have no internal voltage drop during the *conduction portion* of the cycle. Further studies of power supplies in later chapters, however, will include these drops.

TRANSFORMER REQUIREMENTS

Refer to Fig. 1-4 and assume that we are interested in providing an average output voltage of 100 volts to the load R_L. To do this the peak value of the output voltage must be $\pi \times 100$, or 314 volts. Recalling that we have assumed that the forward voltage drop across the diode will be negligible during the conduction portion

FIGURE 1-4 *Half-wave rectifier feeding a 500-ohm load.*

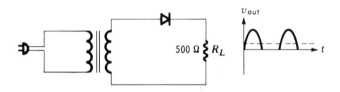

of the cycle and referring to Kirchhoff's voltage law, which states that the sum of all the voltage drops must equal the sum of all the voltage rises in a closed electric loop at every instant of time, we find that at the time when the peak value of output voltage is occurring, the voltage across the transformer secondary must equal the peak output voltage, which in this case is 314 volts. However, transformer secondaries are not rated according to peak values of voltage but according to rms values. So we must now divide this peak voltage value by $\sqrt{2}$ in order to determine its rms value; thus $314/\sqrt{2}$ equals 222 volts. The voltage specification for the transformer is therefore 120:222 volts rms.

Another specification required for transformers serving in rectifier circuits is the average current which will be passed through the transformer secondary windings. Again studying the circuit of Fig. 1-4, we find that the average current passed through the transformer is the same as the average current passed through the load R_L (series circuit). Let us now determine the value. Using Ohm's law, we find

$$I_{av} = \frac{100}{500} = 200 \text{ ma}$$

What about a factor of safety? We really do not want to push our components right up to the edge of their ratings.

By specifying a larger current rating for the average current of the transformer, we provide a certain amount of safety without changing the output conditions of the circuit. A reasonable rule is to specify component requirements so that they are operated at only 80 percent of their rated values. In order to do this we merely divide the requirements by 0.8, getting a slightly larger value. Thus in the case under discussion we will specify a minimum rating for average current capabilities for the transformer secondary as follows:

$$\frac{I_{av \text{ anticipated}}}{0.8} = I_{av \text{ min rating}}$$
$$\frac{200 \text{ ma}}{0.8} = I_{av \text{ min rating}}$$
$$250 \text{ ma} = I_{av \text{ min rating}}$$

The transformer we are seeking must therefore have an average secondary-current rating of *at least* 250 ma. The total specification for the transformer then is:

120:222 volts rms
250 ma average secondary current

Obviously we do not want to change the voltage ratings of the transformer because this will change our output voltages.

DIODE REQUIREMENTS

Now that we have specified the transformer requirements, let us turn to the diode. First we must specify the minimum value we can allow for the average current rating of the diode. We already know this because of our calculations for the transformer: $I_{\text{av min rating}} = 250$ ma. Next we must determine the minimum allowable value for peak-value rating of the current waveshape. Examining the voltage waveshape across the load resistor R_L and knowing that at every instant in time the current must be related to the voltage according to Ohm's law, we realize that the current waveshape differs from the voltage waveshape only in magnitude

$$I_{\text{peak}} = \frac{V_{\text{peak}}}{R_L}$$

In the case being considered

$$I_{\text{peak}} = \frac{314}{500} = 628 \text{ ma}$$

Of course this same value could have been determined by using the relationship existing between the average value of the current waveshape, which is a half-wave-rectified sine wave, and its peak value.

Now let us take into account our 0.8 derating factor

$$I_{\text{peak min rating}} = \frac{628 \text{ ma}}{0.8} = 784 \text{ ma}$$

Thus we are seeking a diode whose current ratings are *greater than* a 250-ma average and a 784-ma peak.

The peak value we have been referring to is usually called *recurrent peak rating* in manufacturer's specifications.

Now that we have specified the current ratings for the diode, is there any voltage rating which must be considered? As far as forward voltage drop is concerned, we have assumed an ideal diode having zero forward voltage drop. The *critical voltage stress* on the diode occurs when the diode is functioning as an *open switch* and is not passing current. In that case the *full transformer voltage* appears across the diode. (Remember Kirchhoff's voltage law: In a closed electric loop the sum of the voltage rises must be equal to the sum of the voltage drops.) When no current flows, there is

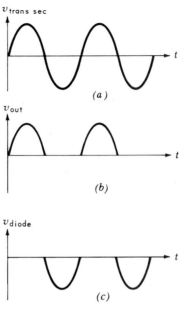

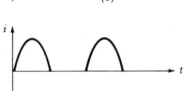

FIGURE 1-5 *Waveshapes encountered in a half-wave-rectifier circuit. (a) Voltage across the transformer secondary; (b) output voltage; (c) voltage across the diode; (d) current.*

zero drop across the load, leaving the full transformer voltage to be taken across the diode which is acting as an open switch.

Figure 1-5 depicts a set of synchronized graphs for all wave-shapes encountered in the half-wave-rectifier circuit. The greatest back voltage stress on a diode is called the *peak inverse voltage* or *peak reverse voltage* usually referred to as PIV or PRV. It is necessary to specify the minimum allowed PIV rating for the diode we are seeking.

Knowing that the PIV to which our diode will be subjected in the half-wave rectifier is equal to the peak voltage across the transformer, we know that in the example we are considering PIV = 314 volts.

Allowing for our 0.8 derating factor, we get

$$PIV_{\text{min rating}} = \frac{314}{0.8} = 392 \text{ volts}$$

Thus the diode we are seeking must have a PIV rating of *at least* 392 volts.

Illustrative Problem 1-1
A 20-kilohm load is to be fed by a half-wave-rectifier supply which has a 120:120-volt transformer.

(a) Draw a schematic representation of the circuit described above.
(b) What is the peak value of the output voltage?
(c) Draw the waveshape of the voltage which appears across the load.
(d) What is the average voltage level of the output?
(e) What is the peak value of the current which flows through the load?
(f) What is the average level of the current through the load?
(g) What is the value of the PIV that appears across the diode?
(h) Calculate the minimum required PIV rating of a diode for use in this circuit.
(i) What is the minimum average current rating required of the diode?
(j) Determine the minimum required peak current rating of the diode.

SOLUTION
Given: 120:120 transformer; $R_L = 20$ kilohms; half-wave rectifier
Find:

(a) Schematic	(b) $V_{\text{peak out}}$
(c) Waveshape across R_L	(d) $V_{\text{av out}}$
(e) I_{peak}	(f) I_{av}
(g) PIV	(h) Manufacturer's rated PIV
(i) Manufacturer's rated I_{av}	(j) Manufacturer's rated I_{peak}

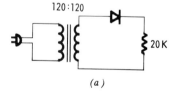

120:120

20 K

(a)

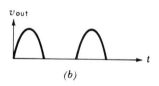

(b)

FIGURE PROB. 1-1

(a) See Fig. Prob. 1-1a.
(b) $\sqrt{2}V_{\text{rms}} = V_{\text{peak}}$
$\sqrt{2} \times 120 = 169$ volts
$V_{\text{peak}} = 169$ volts
(c) See Fig. Prob. 1-1b.
(d) $V_{\text{av}} = \dfrac{V_{\text{peak}}}{\pi} = \dfrac{169}{\pi} = 53.9$ volts

(e) $I_{\text{peak}} = \dfrac{V_{\text{peak out}}}{R_L} = \dfrac{169}{20 \times 10^3} = 8.5$ ma

(f) $I_{\text{av}} = \dfrac{V_{\text{av out}}}{R_L} = \dfrac{53.9}{20 \times 10^3} = 2.68$ ma

(g) $\text{PIV} = V_{\text{peak trans sec}} = 169$ volts

(h) Minimum manufacturer's PIV rating $= \dfrac{\text{actual PIV}}{0.8}$

$$= \dfrac{169}{0.8} = 213 \text{ volts}$$

(i) Minimum manufacturer's I_{av} rating $= \dfrac{2.68}{0.8}$ ma $= 3.35$ ma

(j) Minimum manufacturer's I_{peak} rating $= \dfrac{8.5}{0.8}$ ma $= 10.6$ ma

PROBLEMS

1-1 Describe two kinds of equipment which cannot respond properly if fed *directly* from an ac source.

1-2 How can a sine wave be altered so as to provide a waveshape having an average value other than zero?

1-3 What functions does a transformer perform in a rectifier supply?

1-4 A sine wave has a peak value of 200 volts.
 (a) What is its rms value?
 (b) What is its average value?
 (c) Determine the average value of the waveshape which results when this sine wave is passed through a half-wave-rectifier circuit.

1-5 What is meant by the term "peak inverse voltage"?

1-6 A half-wave-rectifier circuit is to provide an average voltage of 50 volts at its output.
 (a) Draw a schematic diagram of the circuit.
 (b) Sketch the output voltage waveshape.
 (c) Determine the peak value of the output voltage.
 (d) Sketch the voltage waveshape that appears across the transformer secondary.
 (e) What is the rms voltage across the transformer secondary?

1-7 A half-wave rectifier is required which is to supply an average current of 350 ma to a 75-ohm load.
 (a) Sketch the output current and voltage waveshapes.
 (b) Calculate the peak current that flows in the circuit.
 (c) Determine the average voltage across the load.
 (d) Find the peak voltage across the load.
 (e) Specify the requirements for the transformer and the diode to be used in this circuit.

1-8 A 120:75-volt transformer and a diode whose ratings are PIV = 225 volts, $I_{\text{av}} = 400$ ma, and $I_{\text{peak}} = 3$ amp are to be used in a half-wave-rectifier circuit.

(a) Draw a schematic diagram of the half-wave-rectifier circuit.

(b) How large is the peak voltage available across the secondary of the transformer?

(c) Sketch the following waveshapes:
1. Voltage across the transformer secondary
2. Voltage across the load
3. Voltage across the diode
4. Current

(d) How large is the PIV presented to the diode?

(e) Considering the 0.8 safety factor discussed in this chapter, can the diode safely withstand the PIV presented to it?

(f) Which of the current ratings limits the operation of the circuit? What is the average current that can be safely drawn from the circuit (remember the 0.8 safety factor)?

(g) Calculate the average output voltage available across the output of the circuit.

(h) Determine the minimum safe resistance that can be put across the output of the circuit.

1-9 A half-wave rectifier is providing an output of 2 amp average at 50 volts average.

(a) Draw the output current and voltage waveshapes.

(b) Determine the peak values of the output current and voltage.

(c) Calculate the load resistance.

(d) What is the average power being taken by the load? *Hint:* It is *not* equal to $I_{av} \times V_{av}$.

2 FULL-WAVE-RECTIFIER CIRCUITS

In studying the output waveshape of the half-wave rectifier we see that current flows for only half the cycle. For many applications this is not desirable. For example, in the case of dc motor operation this causes uneven torque generation. For smooth torque development less variation in current is required.

THE CENTER-TAPPED-TRANSFORMER TYPE OF FULL-WAVE RECTIFIER

Can we use two half-wave-rectifier circuits operating alternately and provide the waveshape of Fig. 2-1? We can design such a circuit using two half-wave-rectifier circuits as shown in Fig. 2-2. Figure 2-3 depicts the same circuit as Fig. 2-2 with only slight variation in order to supply a neater looking diagram. Figure 2-4 again is a diagram of the same circuit with only the circuit components moved slightly. In order to differentiate this circuit from other types of full-wave-rectifier circuits it is referred to as the *center-tapped-transformer* type of full-wave rectifier.

WAVESHAPES

Before examining the required rating of the components, let us investigate the various waveshapes encountered in the center-tapped-transformer type of full-wave power supply. The circuit shown in Fig. 2-4 permits us to see what happens during the half-

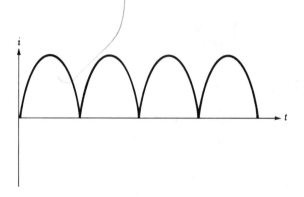

FIGURE 2-1 *Full-wave-rectified sine wave.*

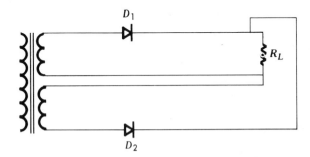

FIGURE 2-2 *Two half-wave rectifiers arranged to operate alternately.*

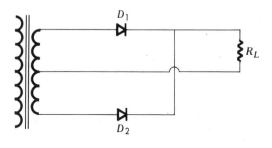

FIGURE 2-3 *The center-tapped-transformer type of full-wave-rectifier circuit.*

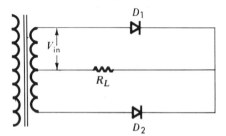

FIGURE 2-4 *An alternate schematic of the center-tapped-transformer type of full-wave-rectifier circuit.*

cycle when the voltage at the top of the transformer is positive with respect to the bottom. The top of the transformer secondary is positive with respect to the center tap, while the bottom of the transformer secondary is negative with respect to the center tap. When this happens, current will flow in D_1, the upper diode of Fig. 2-4, but not through D_2, the lower one. Thus, during this portion of the cycle only the upper half of the transformer is connected to the load by the upper diode acting as a closed switch. The lower section of the transformer is disconnected from the load because the lower diode is acting as an open switch. When the polarity of the input voltage changes, making the top of the transformer negative with respect to the bottom of the transformer, the bottom diode D_2 conducts, connecting the bottom half of the transformer to the load, and diode D_1 does not conduct, thereby disconnecting the upper half of the transformer from the load. Returning to the waveshapes, refer to Fig. 2-5. For purposes of discussion we will refer to the voltage from the center tap of the transformer to one end as V_{in}, as indicated in Fig. 2-4. In specifying the transformer it is necessary to require a secondary voltage of $2V_{in}$, which must be center-tapped. The voltage waveshape across the load and the current waveshape through the load are also shown in Fig. 2-5. Note that if we continue to consider the forward voltage drop across the diodes as negligible, we will have the peak voltage across the output, equal to the peak voltage of half the transformer secondary V_{in}. Note the waveshapes of the currents through the diodes, shown in Fig. 2-5. Since only *one diode* conducts at a time, each has current flowing through it during half the time the *load* has current flowing through it.

The most unexpected aspect of this analysis appears when we consider the PIV which each of the diodes experiences. To do so let us examine the outermost loop of the circuit of Fig. 2-4 and then apply Kirchhoff's voltage law: in a complete electric loop the sum of the voltage rises must equal the sum of the voltage drops. This outer loop consists of the complete transformer secondary and the two diodes. Consider the situation that takes place during that half-cycle of the input during which the upper terminal of the transformer secondary is positive with respect to the lower terminal. During this time interval the upper diode D_1 is acting as a closed switch and therefore has negligible voltage across it. The only other components left in the loop being discussed is the lower diode D_2 and the complete transformer secondary. According to Kirchhoff's voltage law, the full transformer-secondary voltage must be dropped across the nonconducting diode, providing the last two

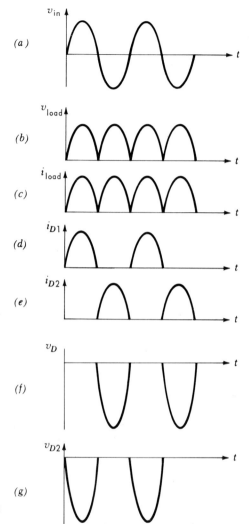

FIGURE 2-5 *Waveshapes encountered in the center-tapped-transformer type of full-wave-rectifier circuit. (a) Input voltage; (b) load voltage; (c) load current; (d) current through diode D_1; (e) current through diode D_2; (f) voltage across diode D_1; (g) voltage across diode D_2.*

waveshapes shown in Fig. 2-5. Note that these two wave-shapes have peak values which are twice as large as the output voltage peak. Thus, one of the disadvantages of this type of power supply is that the PIV is twice as large as the peak of the output voltage.

What relationship exists between the peak and the average values of a full-wave-rectified sine wave? Obviously such a relationship should show that the average value of the waveshape is twice as large as it would have been if the waveshape had been only half-wave-rectified. Thus

$$\text{Average of full-wave-rectified sine wave} = 2 \times \frac{\text{peak}}{\pi}$$

DESIGN SPECIFICATIONS

Let us again consider specifying the requirements for components. Recall that our aim in the last chapter was to provide an average current of 200 ma at an average voltage of 100 volts.

Transformer Requirements   For the full-wave-rectified sine wave across the output to have an average value of 100 volts it must have a peak value of $\pi/2 \times 100$, which is equal to 157 volts. Assuming ideal diodes, and thus negligible forward voltage drop across the diodes, the peak voltage across *half* of the transformer secondary must be 157 volts. Converting this to rms, we obtain $157/\sqrt{2}$, or 111 volts. Thus the voltage requirement for the required transformer is 120:222 volts rms center-tapped. Another way of specifying the same voltage requirement is 120:111-0-111 volts rms.

What about the minimum current rating required of the transformer? Since all the current which is passed on to the load must also pass through the transformer secondary (series circuit), the average current passing through the transformer secondary equals 200 ma. Taking the derating factor into account provides $200/0.8 = 250$ ma. Therefore the minimum current rating permitted for the transformer needed in this circuit is 250 ma average.

Diode Requirements   Now, what about the diodes? Since each diode is conducting for half the cycle and resting for the other half, the average current which passes through each of the diodes is equal to half the average current which passes through the load. Thus each diode will have an average current of 100 ma pass through it. The minimum current rating for each diode must therefore be 100/0.8, or 125 ma.

What must the minimum recurrent peak current rating for the diodes be? At the instant that the load takes its peak value only one of the diodes is conducting. Thus the recurrent peak current which passes through each of the diodes is equal to the peak of the output current.   Thus,

$$I_{\text{peak out}} = I_{\text{peak diode}} = \frac{\pi}{2} \times 200 \text{ ma} = 314 \text{ ma}$$

$$I_{\text{peak diode min rating}} = \frac{314}{0.8} = 393 \text{ ma}$$

What about the PIV that each of the diodes must be prepared to experience?   Recall that each of the diodes must be prepared to handle the peak voltage that appears across the *full* transformer secondary.   This is twice the peak voltage across the load.   The actual PIV then is 157×2, or 314 volts, which thus requires a minimum PIV rating of 314/0.8, or 393 volts.   The specifications for the components necessary for building a center-tapped type of full-wave-rectified supply which meets our load requirements of 200 ma at 100 volts average are

Transformer
     Voltage ratio 120:222 rms center-tapped
     Minimum required average secondary current rating = 250 ma
Two diodes   Minimum required current rating:

$$I_{\text{av}} = 125 \text{ ma}$$
$$I_{\text{peak}} = 393 \text{ ma}$$
$$\text{PIV}_{\text{min rating}} = 393 \text{ volts}$$

Illustrative Problem 2-1
A center-tapped-transformer type of full-wave rectifier is to be designed using a pair of solid-state diodes.   The circuit is to supply an average voltage of 60 volts to a 500-kilohm load.

(*a*)   Draw a schematic representation of this circuit.
(*b*)   Calculate the peak value of the output voltage.
(*c*)   Determine the required transformer voltage requirements.
(*d*)   Calculate the average current to be delivered to the load.
(*e*)   Determine the average current through each of the diodes.
(*f*)   Determine the peak current through each of the diodes.
(*g*)   Calculate the PIV presented to each diode.
(*h*)   Find the minimum ratings required of diodes used in this circuit.

SOLUTION
Given: Center-tapped full-wave rectifier; $V_{\text{av out}} = 60$ volts; $R_L = 400$ kilohms
Find:
(*a*)   Schematic   (*b*) $V_{\text{peak out}}$
(*c*)   Transformer voltage requirements

(d) $I_{\text{av out}}$ (e) $I_{\text{diode av}}$

(f) $I_{\text{diode peak}}$ (g) PIV

(h) Diode minimum ratings

(a) See Fig. Prob. 2-1.

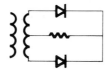

FIGURE PROB. 2-1

(b) $\dfrac{2V_{\text{peak out}}}{\pi} = V_{\text{av out}}$

$V_{\text{peak out}} = \dfrac{\pi}{2} V_{\text{av out}} = \dfrac{\pi}{2} \times 60$

$\boxed{V_{\text{peak out}} = 94.2 \text{ volts}}$

(c) $V_{\text{peak trans sec}} = 2V_{\text{peak out}} = 2 \times 94.2 = 189 \text{ volts}$

$V_{\text{rms trans sec}} = \dfrac{V_{\text{peak trans sec}}}{\sqrt{2}} = \dfrac{189}{\sqrt{2}}$

$\boxed{V_{\text{rms trans sec}} = 133 \text{ volts}}$

Transformer voltage requirements 120:133 center-tapped. This specification can also be written as 66.5-0-66.5 volts.

(d) $I_{\text{av out}} = \dfrac{V_{\text{av out}}}{R_L} = \dfrac{60}{500 \times 10^3}$

$\boxed{I_{\text{av out}} = 120 \ \mu\text{a}}$

(e) $I_{\text{av diode}} = \dfrac{120 \times 10^{-6}}{2} = 60 \times 10^{-6}$

$\boxed{I_{\text{av diode}} = 60 \ \mu\text{a}}$

(f) $I_{\text{diode peak}} = I_{\text{out peak}} = \dfrac{V_{\text{out peak}}}{R_L}$

$I_{\text{out peak}} = \dfrac{94.2}{500 \times 10^3} = 18.8 \times 10^{-5}$

$\boxed{I_{\text{diode peak}} = 188 \ \mu\text{a}}$

(g) $\quad \text{PIV}_{\text{fw-rect ckt}} = 2V_{\text{peak out}}$
$$\text{PIV} = 2 \times 94.2$$

$$\boxed{\text{PIV} = 188 \text{ volts}}$$

(h) $\quad \text{Required } I_{\text{av diode rating}} = \dfrac{60 \times 10^{-6}}{0.8 \quad \text{safety factor}}$

$$\boxed{\text{Required } I_{\text{av diode rating}} = 75 \times 10^{-6} \text{ amp}}$$

$$I_{\text{diode peak}} = 188 \times 10^{-6}$$

$$\boxed{\text{Required } I_{\text{diode peak rating}} = \dfrac{188 \times 10^{-6}}{0.8} = 236 \ \mu\text{a}}$$

$$\text{PIV}_{\text{min rating}} = \dfrac{188}{0.8}$$

$$\boxed{\text{PIV}_{\text{min rating}} = 236 \text{ volts}}$$

THE BRIDGE RECTIFIER

Compared to the component requirements for the half-wave-rectifier circuit, the center-tapped full-wave circuit requires diodes having twice the PIV rating of those used in the half-wave circuit. Also, the transformer-secondary voltage must be twice as large in the center-tapped transformer type. Another major consideration when comparing the two circuit types is that the most expensive item in the circuit is the transformer. In the case of the half-wave rectifier it is possible to eliminate the transformer and instead feed the circuit directly from the line. However, in the center-tapped full-wave rectifier the transformer is needed to provide the necessary center tap. Is it possible to design a full-wave-rectifier circuit in which we can feed the circuit directly from the line and not

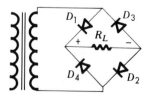

FIGURE 2-6 *The bridge-rectifier circuit.*

20 **POWER SUPPLIES**

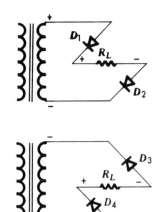

require so large a PIV rating of the diodes? Such a circuit does exist and is called a *bridge-rectifier circuit.* A schematic diagram of the bridge-rectifier circuit is shown in Fig. 2-6. Note that although the transformer is not essential to the operation of the circuit, it has been included in Fig. 2-6. To provide a voltage other than that available at the line, it is necessary to provide a transformer.

CIRCUIT ACTION

When the top of the transformer secondary of Fig. 2-6 is positive with respect to the bottom, current flows through diode D_1, the load, and diode D_2. When the polarity of the transformer changes, the top becoming negative with respect to the bottom of the transformer, current flows through diode D_3, the load, and diode D_4. One of the most significant points of the circuit operation is that in both cases the current enters on the same side of the load and thus keeps the polarity of the load resistor fixed, as shown in Fig. 2-6. The separate paths taken by the current during each half of the cycle are shown in Fig. 2-7.

WAVESHAPES AND COMPONENT SPECIFICATIONS

Next we will examine the waveshapes encountered in this circuit. The waveshapes to be discussed appear as Fig. 2-8. As expected, each pair of diodes conducts alternately, and therefore each diode carries only half the average current taken by the load.   The voltage across the load is full-wave-rectified, and if we again assume negli-

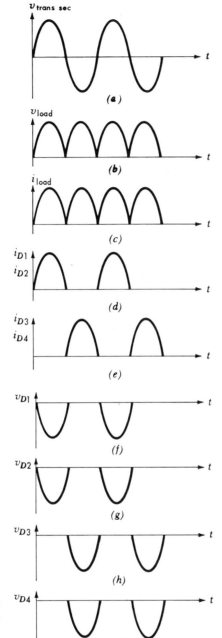

FIGURE 2-8 *The wave-forms encountered in the bridge-rectifier circuit. (a) Transformer-secondary voltage; (b) load voltage; (c) load current; (d) current through diodes D_1 and D_2; (e) current through diodes D_3 and D_4; (f) voltage across diode D_1; (g) voltage across diode D_2; (h) voltage across diode D_3; (i) voltage across diode D_4.*

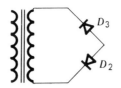

FIGURE 2-9   *The Kirchhoff loop used in determining the PIV.*

gible forward voltage drop across the diodes, the output voltage peak is equal to the peak of the voltage across the secondary of the transformer. What about the voltage across the diodes? Recall we wished to eliminate the high PIV requirements of the center-tapped type of full-wave rectifier.

The loop shown in Fig. 2-9 provides the most insight into the voltage across the diodes. At any time during the cycle one of the diodes is conducting and can therefore be considered a closed switch or short circuit. Applying Kirchhoff's voltage law around this loop, we conclude that the PIV experienced by each of the diodes is equal to the peak value of the transformer-secondary voltage. The transformer-secondary voltage will be equal to the peak output voltage. Thus another advantage of this circuit over the center-tapped-transformer type is a reduced PIV.

Applying the techniques used in the design of the half-wave and the center-tapped types of full-wave-rectifier circuits, we find the following requirements for components to be used in the construction of the bridge circuit. The output requirements of the bridge circuit are the same as the other circuits: 200 ma at 100 volts average.

Transformer
    120:111 volts rms
    Minimum required average secondary current rating = 250 ma
Four diodes
    $I_{av\ min\ rating}$ = 125 ma
    $I_{peak\ min\ rating}$ = 393 ma
    $PIV_{min\ rating}$ = 196 volts

Illustrative Problem 2-2
A full-wave bridge rectifier is required which can provide 50 ma average current at 150 volts average.   Disregard the forward drops in the transformer and the diodes.

(*a*)   Determine the peak output voltage.
(*b*)   Find the required transformer voltage specifications.
(*c*)   How large is the output current peak?

(*d*) Determine the average current through each diode.
(*e*) Find the peak current through each diode.
(*f*) Find the PIV presented to each diode.
(*g*) Allowing for an 80 percent derating factor, specify the requirements for diodes to suit this design.

SOLUTION
Given: $V_{\text{dc out}} = 150$ volts; $I_{\text{dc out}} = 50$ ma
Find:
(*a*) $V_{\text{peak out}}$
(*b*) Transformer voltage specifications

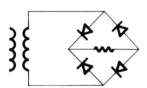

FIGURE PROB. 2-2

(*c*) $I_{\text{peak out}}$ (*d*) $I_{\text{diode av}}$
(*e*) $I_{\text{peak diode}}$ (*f*) PIV
(*g*) Diode ratings

(*a*) $\dfrac{2V_{\text{peak out}}}{\pi} = V_{\text{dc out}}$

$V_{\text{peak out}} = \dfrac{\pi(150)}{2}$

$\boxed{V_{\text{peak out}} = 236 \text{ volts}}$

(*b*) $V_{\text{peak trans sec}} = V_{\text{peak out}} = 236$ volts

$V_{\text{rms trans sec}} = \dfrac{V_{\text{peak trans sec}}}{\sqrt{2}} = \dfrac{236}{\sqrt{2}} = 167$ volts

$\boxed{120 : 167 = \text{transformer voltage specifications}}$

(*c*) $\dfrac{2I_{\text{peak out}}}{\pi} = I_{\text{dc out}}$

$I_{\text{peak out}} = \dfrac{\pi}{2} I_{\text{dc out}} = \dfrac{\pi}{2} 50 \times 10^{-3}$

$\boxed{I_{\text{peak out}} = 79 \text{ ma}}$

24   POWER SUPPLIES

(d) $I_{\text{diode av}} = \frac{1}{2}I_{\text{dc out}} = \frac{1}{2}(50 \times 10^{-3})$

$$\boxed{I_{\text{diode av}} = 25 \text{ ma}}$$

(e) $I_{\text{peak diode}} = I_{\text{peak out}}$

$$\boxed{I_{\text{peak diode}} = 79 \text{ ma}}$$

(f) $\text{PIV} = V_{\text{peak trans sec}}$

$$\boxed{\text{PIV} = 236 \text{ volts}}$$

(g)
$$0.8I_{\text{av rated}} = I_{\text{av actual}}$$
$$I_{\text{av rated}} = I_{\text{av}} \frac{25 \times 10^{-3}}{0.8} = 31.3 \text{ ma}$$
$$0.8I_{\text{peak rated}} = I_{\text{peak actual}}$$
$$I_{\text{peak rated}} = \frac{79 \times 10^{-3}}{0.8} = 98 \text{ ma}$$
$$\text{Minimum PIV rating} = \frac{\text{PIV actual}}{0.8} = \frac{236}{0.8} = 295 \text{ volts}$$

$$\boxed{\begin{array}{l} \text{Required ratings: PIV} = 295 \text{ volts} \\ \qquad\qquad\quad I_{\text{av}} = 31.3 \text{ ma} \\ \qquad\qquad\quad I_{\text{peak}} = 98 \text{ ma} \end{array}}$$

DIODE STACKING

If we want to use diodes whose rated PIV is lower than that required by the circuit, more than one diode may be connected in series. The rated PIV of the *stack* is then equal to n times the rated PIV of each one of the diodes in the series, where n is the number of diodes which have been connected in series. This assumes that the voltage divides equally between all the diodes in the series stack. To ensure this equal voltage division in series stacks, swamping resistors are placed in parallel with the diodes. The swamping resistors are very high in value (on the order of megohms) and pass only a very small amount of current (see Fig. 2-10).

Diodes may also be arranged in parallel, increasing the rated current capacity. Rated I_{peak} and rated I_{av} are multiplied by n, the number of diodes in parallel, to determine the rating of the parallel stack. No component analogous to the swamping resistor is required for parallel arrangements.

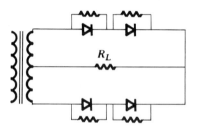

FIGURE 2-10 *A center-tapped-transformer type of full-wave rectifier with series-stacked diodes and swamping resistors.*

PROBLEMS

2-1 A center-tapped-transformer type of full-wave-rectifier circuit is to supply 50 volts average to a load.
  (a) Calculate the peak output voltage.
  (b) How large is the peak voltage from the center tap to each end of the transformer?
  (c) Determine the peak voltage from end to end of the secondary of the transformer.
  (d) Find the rms voltage from end to end across the transformer secondary.
  (e) Determine the required minimum average current rating for the transformer if the load is a 10-ohm resistance.

2-2 Determine the actual PIV that appears across a diode being used in a center-tapped-transformer type of rectifier circuit that is providing an average voltage of 400 volts.

2-3 Specify the minimum required ratings for all the components required for use in a full-wave center-tapped-transformer type of rectifier circuit which is to supply 150 ma average current at an average voltage of 75 volts.

2-4 Sketch and annotate all current and voltage waveshapes for the center-tapped-transformer rectifier circuit which is to supply 150 ma average at 75 volts average.

2-5 What advantages can be gained by using a full-wave bridge rectifier instead of the center-tapped transformer type? What is the most obvious disadvantage?

2-6 A bridge rectifier is to supply a 100-ohm resistive load at an average voltage of 150 volts. Determine the voltage and current specifications for the transformer and the diodes.

2-7 Repeat Prob. 2-2 for a bridge circuit.

2-8 Repeat Prob. 2-3 for a bridge circuit.

2-9 Repeat Prob. 2-4 for a bridge circuit.

2-10 Determine the greatest average voltage and average current output that can be supplied using four diodes having ratings of 200 volts PIV, average current of 75 ma, and recurrent peak current of 500 ma and a center-tapped transformer whose secondary is rated as 100 volts end to end, and average current of 300 ma.

3

THE CAPACITOR AS A POWER-SUPPLY FILTER

When we began our discussion of power supplies, one of the examples of where such a circuit would be needed was that of supplying power to electronic equipment. However, this is not an example of where the circuits we have so far designed might be employed. For use with electronic equipment, the amount of output voltage fluctuation must be held to a much more rigid requirement than we have so far been able to provide.

The output of the rectifier circuits studied thus far can be classified as dc voltage according to the strictest definition of the term. However, because of the large amount of fluctuation, let us call such an output a *unidirectional fluctuating voltage*. Required for use with electronic equipment is as close to a flat nonvarying output voltage as is possible. Figure 3-1 gives a comparison between the unidirectional voltage we have been able to obtain so far and the nonvarying output voltage which in theory we hope to obtain in this chapter for powering electronic equipment.

THE CAPACITOR AS A STORAGE DEVICE

Our problem now is to develop some scheme for reducing the fluctuation in the output of the half-wave- and full-wave-rectifier circuit so that it approaches the desired flat output. A device is needed which is capable of storing electric energy during one portion of the cycle and returning it during the next portion of the cycle. What about the capacitor? If you are in doubt about the

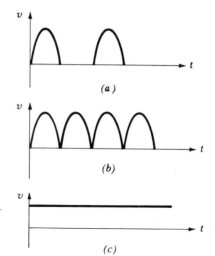

FIGURE 3-1 *The fluctuating unidirectional output obtained from (a) a half-wave rectifier and (b) a full-wave rectifier. (c) The nonvarying dc output desired.*

ability of a capacitor to store electric energy temporarily and then return it, consider the safety rule that requires all capacitors to be discharged before being handled after a circuit has been deenergized. The reason for this safety rule is that while the circuit is hot, capacitors are storing energy.

CIRCUIT ACTION

Let us investigate the effect of placing a capacitor across the output of a rectifier circuit, as shown in Fig. 3-2. For the first 90° of the positive half-cycle that the circuit is energized the capacitor is

FIGURE 3-2 *A capacitor-filtered power supply under no-load conditions.*

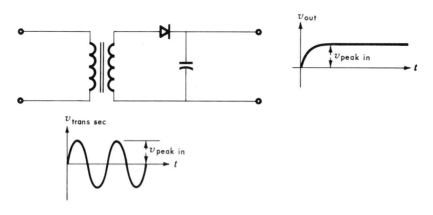

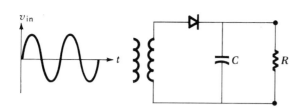

FIGURE 3-3 *A capacitor-filtered power supply with a load R attached.*

forced to charge to the peak voltage of the transformer secondary. During this time current for charging the capacitor is flowing. As the transformer-secondary voltage decreases from the peak value, the diode becomes reverse-biased and the capacitor is unable to discharge, thus maintaining the voltage which has been impressed on it. As long as no load is attached to the output terminals of the circuit of Fig. 3-2, no path exists for discharging the capacitor.

This provides the desired nonfluctuating output voltage. The magnitude of this dc voltage level is equal to the peak value of the transformer-secondary voltage. However, upon adding a resistive load in parallel with the capacitor, some variation is introduced in the output voltage waveform, as shown in Fig. 3-3. To determine how much fluctuation is introduced by adding a particular resistive load requires a short study of *RC* circuits.

CHARGING THE CAPACITOR

The circuit of Fig. 3-4 is a series combination of a battery, a switch, a resistor, and a capacitor. What happens after the switch is closed? Current will begin to flow in order to deposit negative charge on the negative plate of the capacitor and draw off negative charge from the positive plate. How much current flows? This question poses a problem for the Kirchhoff voltage law, which states that the sum of the voltage rises must equal the sum of the voltage

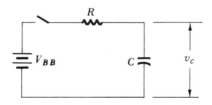

FIGURE 3-4 *A typical RC charge circuit.*

drops in a complete electric loop. Thus,

$$V_{BB} = iR + v_c \qquad \text{from Fig. 3-4}$$

To determine the amount of current flowing at any instant it is necessary to know the voltage across the capacitor at that instant. The voltage across the capacitor at any instant in time depends on how much charge has been deposited on its plates ($v_c = Q/C$), and this in turn depends on the history of the past current which flowed in the circuit. If we were to assume that there was initially no charge on the capacitor plates, and thus initially no voltage across them, we could determine the amount of current which must flow immediately after the switch has been closed in the circuit of Fig. 3-4.

$$i_0 = \frac{V_{BB}}{R}$$

As soon as this amount of current begins to flow, the situation changes, because the assumption of no charge on the capacitor becomes invalid. With charge, and thus voltage, continually building up on the capacitor plates, the current must decay. The sum total of the voltage available to accommodate the voltage drop across the resistor is decreased because of the voltage across the capacitor building up and the necessity for satisfying Kirchhoff's voltage law ($V_{BB} = iR + v_c$). What does the waveshape of the current actually look like? Does it ever get to zero? As time passes,

FIGURE 3-5 *Current-vs.-time graph for the RC circuit.*

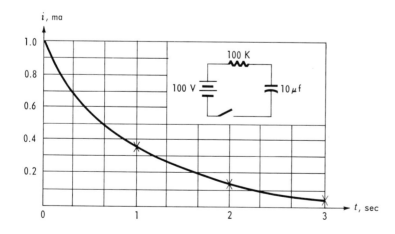

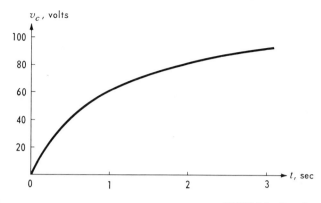

FIGURE 3-6 *Capacitor voltage vs. time for the circuit in Fig. 3-5.*

the voltage across the capacitor increases, allowing less and less voltage to be dropped across the resistor. Thus, the current-vs.-time graph for an *RC* circuit is that shown in Fig. 3-5, while the voltage-vs.-time graph is that shown in Fig. 3-6. The quantitative notations in Figs. 3-5 and 3-6 are for a circuit whose components have values specified in the figures.

The current in the circuit theoretically never gets to zero, although it approaches zero closer and closer with the passage of time. As we approach the condition of the fully charged capacitor, less and less voltage difference remains between the supply V_{BB} and the capacitor v_c. Therefore, there is less and less voltage available to provide a voltage drop across the resistor which is due to current flowing in the circuit. The current therefore gets smaller and smaller and is never large enough to deposit the last remaining charge on the capacitor plates.

DISCHARGING THE CAPACITOR

Having studied the situation existing when a capacitor which is in series with a resistor is being charged, let us investigate the conditions existing when a charged capacitor is made to discharge

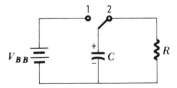

FIGURE 3-7 *Typical RC discharge circuit.*

THE CAPACITOR AS A POWER-SUPPLY FILTER 31

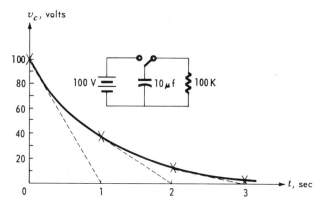

FIGURE 3-8 *Voltage-vs.-time graph for the RC discharge circuit.*

through a circuit which contains resistance. Consider the circuit shown as Fig. 3-7 and assume that prior to our appearance on the scene the switch is in position 1, whereby the capacitor is charged to voltage V_{BB}. At the instant we become interested in the circuit the switch is thrown into position 2.

We must again resort to the same basic considerations, Kirchhoff's voltage law and the equation $Q = Cv_c$. At the first instant the switch is closed a relatively large current is made to flow because we have the full initial voltage V_{BB} across the capacitor and, according to Kirchhoff's voltage law, the voltage across the resistor is equal to it. However, immediately upon current flow, the voltage across the capacitor drops off because charge Q is being drained from it. According to $v_c = Q/C$, the voltage across the capacitor must also drop off. Less voltage can now be dropped across the resistor, and since $v_r = iR$, the current decreases. This continues throughout the discharge, so that theoretically the discharge must continue forever in order to fully discharge the capacitor.

Plotting a graph of the discharge, point by point, for a situation with component values as shown in the diagram, we obtain the capacitor voltage graph shown in Fig. 3-8.

THE UNIVERSAL DESCENDING *RC* CURVE

If we reproduced the same discharge experiment, using different values of resistance and capacitance, we would arrive at a similarly shaped curve but one whose time axis differed from that of Fig. 3-8. Performing many of these experiments, we would find that the voltage decreases to 37 percent of the initial voltage V_{BB} in an amount

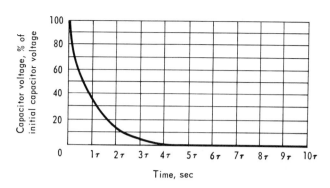

FIGURE 3-9 *Universal RC discharge curve.* $\tau = RC$.

of time which is equal to the product of the resistance and the capacitance. The resistance is measured in ohms, the capacitance in farads, and the time in seconds. Logically, the larger the capacitance, the more charge there is to be conducted off the capacitor plates for a given voltage ($Q = Cv_c$), and thus the discharge should take more time. The larger the resistance, the larger the incremental drop-off in voltage for a given incremental drop-off in current ($v_r = v_c$). Increases in the size of the resistor should also increase the discharge time.

The product of the resistance and the capacitance, called the *time constant* of the circuit, is represented by the Greek letter τ (tau). From laboratory experience it is found that in one time constant the voltage across a discharging capacitor discharges to 37 percent of the initial value of voltage across the capacitor at the start of the time constant. For example, at the end of the first time constant the voltage across a discharging capacitor is 37 percent of the voltage at the beginning of the discharge. At the end of the second time constant the voltage is down to $0.37 \times 0.37 = 0.137$, or 13.7 percent, of the voltage at the start of the discharge. At the end of the third time constant the voltage is down to $0.37 \times 0.37 \times 0.37 = 0.056$, or 5.6 percent, of the value at the start of the discharge. Thus we can develop a universal curve which can be used for the study of any descending RC curve. Such a universal curve is shown in Fig. 3-9.

THE UNIVERSAL ASCENDING RC CURVE
A universal ascending RC curve can be plotted which, like the universal curve for the descending condition, facilitates the solution of RC circuit problems.

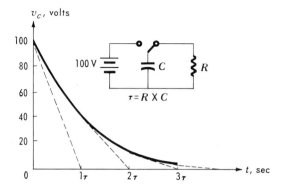

FIGURE 3-10 *Construction of an RC descending curve.*

In the ascending case the voltage across the capacitor increases by 63 percent of the remaining difference between the forcing function and the voltage across the capacitor in each time constant. The development of a universal ascending *RC* curve will be left as an exercise.

CONSTRUCTION OF *RC* CURVES

The actual plotting of a discharge curve is done in the following manner. First the voltage at the end of each time constant is determined and plotted on the graph. A line is then drawn connecting each of these points to the horizontal axis at a distance of one time constant to the right of the point. When plotting the final curve, it is laid in so that it will be tangent to each of these lines as it passes through each of the plotted points. The actual construction, with construction lines, is shown in Fig. 3-10. The reason for the tangency lines is that the curve leaves each of the plotted points as though it was going to discharge the capacitor completely in just one more time constant. We know that this is not the case, because the current immediately begins to decrease, preventing the aimed-for complete discharge.

PROBLEMS

3-1 In the problems of previous chapters we did not use power supplies intended for use with electronic equipment as examples. Why not?

3-2 A particular half-wave rectifier has no resistive load across its output terminals. A capacitor is placed across the output terminals. Sketch the voltage waveform that appears across the capacitor. If this rectifier circuit does not contain a transformer but instead plugs directly into a 120-volt-rms 60-Hz outlet, what is the magnitude of the voltage across the capacitor?

3-3 A series circuit consists of a 5-kilohm resistor, a 10-μf capacitor, a 100-volt battery, and a switch.
  (a) Using Kirchhoff's voltage law, write an equation that describes this circuit.
  (b) Determine the time constant of this circuit.
  (c) How long will it take after the switch is closed for the voltage across the capacitor to reach 63 volts?
  (d) When the voltage across the capacitor is 63 volts, what is the voltage across the resistor?
  (e) How much current flows through the resistor when the voltage across the capacitor is 63 volts?

3-4 A series circuit consists of a 150-ohm resistor, a 5-μf capacitor, a 50-volt battery, and a switch. Assuming that the capacitor is initially uncharged, how much current flows after one time constant has passed? Determine the time constant for this circuit.

3-5 How many coulombs of electric charge are on each plate of a 20-μf capacitor when it has 100 volts across it? A 5-μf capacitor?

3-6 A 10-μf capacitor which was initially charged to 100 volts is allowed to discharge through a 25-kilohm resistor.
  (a) Determine how long it takes for the capacitor voltage to fall to 25 volts.
  (b) How much time does it take for the voltage across the resistor to change from 50 to 30 volts?
  (c) Determine the value of the current flowing in the circuit after 300 msec have elapsed after the start of the discharge.

3-7 A 25-μf capacitor which has been charged to 500 volts is connected to a 2-megohm resistor.
  (a) What is the voltage across the capacitor *immediately* after making the connection?
  (b) What is the voltage across the resistor immediately after making the connection?
  (c) Determine the current which flows in this circuit immediately after making the connection.
  (d) Determine the current which flows in the circuit 100 sec after making the connection.

3-8 A capacitor initially charged to 100 volts is placed in series with a resistor. On the same set of axes make a rough sketch of the discharge curves which describe the voltage across the capacitor in each of the following cases.
  (a) $C = 10$ μf; $R = 2000$ ohms
  (b) $C = 5$ μf; $R = 1000$ ohms
  (c) $C = 5$ μf; $R = 2000$ ohms
  (d) $C = 6$ μf; $R = 2500$ ohms
  (e) $C = 3$ μf; $R = 1000$ ohms

3-9 Consider the series combination of a 10-μf capacitor, a 1200-ohm resistor, and a switch. The capacitor initially was charged to 100 volts.

(a) How many coulombs of excess charge are there on each of the capacitor plates?

(b) Determine the time constant of the circuit.

(c) Using the relationship $I = \Delta Q/\Delta t$, determine the average current that would have to flow in order to remove all the excess charge from the capacitor plates in one time constant.

(d) Calculate the amount of current that flows immediately upon initiating the discharge (closing the switch) in the circuit.

(e) Compare the answers to (c) and (d).

3-10 How long would it take to completely remove all the excess charge from the capacitor plates if the current in an RC circuit was held constant at its value immediately upon the initiation of the discharge?

POWER-SUPPLY FILTERS

Having studied the charging and discharging of RC circuits, we can now consider the case of the capacitor-filtered power supply under loaded conditions, such as that shown in Fig. 4-1.

CIRCUIT ACTION

In studying the action of this circuit it is necessary to refer to the waveshape of the transformer-secondary voltage, which is given in Fig. 4-1b. We will assume that the circuit is energized just as the voltage across the transformer secondary is going through the zero point on its way into its positive half-cycle. During the first quarter-cycle (90°) both the capacitor and the load are being fed from the transformer, thereby charging the capacitor. Note that the path through which the capacitor is charging is a very low resistance path consisting of the transformer secondary and the diode. For our purposes now, let us assume that the transformer-secondary resistance and the diode forward resistance are negligible. This then provides us with a situation in which the capacitor is being charged through an approximately zero resistance path. Because the time constant of the path is approximately zero $(R \times C \approx 0)$ the voltage across the capacitor, as it is being charged, follows immediately behind as the voltage across the transformer secondary is increased during the rising quarter cycle. At the end of this first quarter-cycle we find the capacitor charged to the peak value of the transformer-secondary voltage.

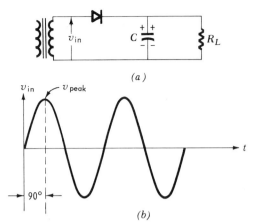

FIGURE 4-1 (a) Capacitor-filtered power supply under loaded conditions. (b) Transformer-secondary voltage.

As the peak of the transformer-secondary voltage is reached and then passed, the voltage across the capacitor remains almost at the peak value it attained while the transformer-secondary voltage begins its downward quarter-cycle. In what condition is the diode in the second quarter-cycle, in which the transformer-secondary voltage is still positive but decreasing? Applying Kirchhoff's voltage law, which states that around a complete electric loop the sum of the voltage rises must equal the sum of the voltage drops, we find that during the second quarter-cycle the voltage across the diode is in such a direction as to reverse-bias the diode and have it act as an open switch. The only component of interest at this time, as far as the output of the circuit is concerned, is the load R_L and the capacitor C, the rest of the circuit being isolated from the output by the open switch action of the diode. Thus we must now consider only the capacitor C discharging through R_L. The time constant of this portion of the circuit is $R_L C$. The capacitor will continue to discharge through resistor R_L only so long as two conditions prevail. First, of course, there must be an excess of charge on the capacitor plates. Second, the diode must be nonconducting. The diode will remain open-circuited only so long as the voltage across the transformer secondary does not exceed the voltage across the capacitor.

WAVESHAPES

In attempting to gain a more detailed understanding of the circuit operation let us examine the waveshapes and constructions of Figs. 4-2 and 4-3.

First we have plotted the transformer-secondary voltage, and

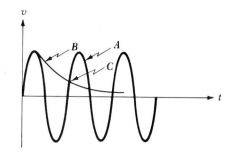

FIGURE 4-2 *Curve A: transformer-secondary voltage; curve B: RC discharge curve; point C: intersection of RC discharge curve and sine-wave transformer voltage.*

then we have constructed a capacitor-voltage-discharge curve which is beginning at the positive peak of the transformer-secondary voltage. The point at which the discharge curve intersects the next positive half of the sine wave is a point of great interest (see Fig. 4-2, point C). It is at this point of intersection that the voltage across the capacitor is equal to the voltage across the transformer secondary. Immediately after this point is reached, the voltage across the transformer secondary exceeds the voltage across the capacitor. The capacitor then begins to charge and continues to charge until the peak voltage across the transformer secondary is reached. The discharge portion of the output cycle then begins again, generating the output voltage waveshape shown in Fig. 4-3.

RIPPLE CONTENT

We can control the ripple content of the output waveshape by increasing the time constant of its discharge portion. This can be accomplished by increasing either R_L or C. In most cases, in-

FIGURE 4-3 *Output voltage waveshape from a capacitor-filtered power supply.*

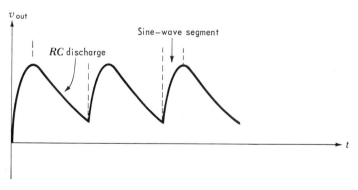

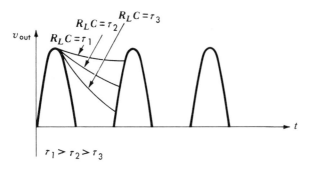

FIGURE 4-4 *The effect of time constant on ripple.*

$\tau_1 > \tau_2 > \tau_3$

creasing R_L is not a practical approach since R_L represents the load which must be fed and usually is determined by considerations external to the power supply. However, increasing the capacitance is usually a feasible solution. Figure 4-4 depicts a number of different discharge portions of the waveshape for different time constants superimposed on the rest of the wave. The discharge wave which represents the situation of greatest time constant is the one which will provide the least ripple content. In addition it will also provide the greatest average value of output voltage. In the extreme case in which the time constant is infinitely long the output voltage is equal to the peak voltage of the transformer secondary. In a good many cases this is taken as a fairly accurate approximation

$$V_{\text{dc out}} \approx V_{\text{peak in}}$$

HALF-WAVE VS. FULL-WAVE SUPPLIES

So far in our study of the capacitor-filtered power supply we have been examining the half-wave-rectified case. The important difference between the output voltage of the half-wave and the full-wave cases is that the positive peaks are occurring twice as frequently in the full-wave case. The frequency of the ripple content in the full-wave case will be twice that of the half-wave case. In addition the magnitude of the ripple content of the full-wave supply is appreciably less than that of the half-wave case with the same sized capacitor as a filter. Figure 4-5 is a comparison between the half-wave and full-wave situations.

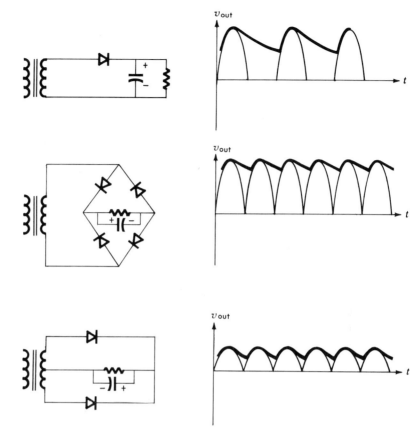

FIGURE 4-5 *Comparison between the outputs of the three different capacitor-filtered power supplies.*

A QUANTITATIVE STUDY

Let us begin our quantitative study by first considering a numerical description of the ripple content of the output waveshape.

A generally accepted figure of merit regarding ripple is the *ripple factor*, which is defined as

$$\text{Ripple factor} \equiv k_r \equiv \frac{\text{rms of ripple}}{\text{average output level}}$$

Although it is not exactly true, the ripple is assumed to be a sine wave. It is the rms value of this fictitious sine wave which is indicated in the above formula for k_r. The rms value is obtained by noting the peak-to-peak value of the ripple and then converting it into the equivalent rms that such peak-to-peak readings would indicate had the ripple been a sine wave

$$\text{rms} = \frac{\text{peak-to-peak}}{2\sqrt{2}}$$

Expressed as a percent, the ripple factor is called the *percent ripple*.

The average output level or the dc level, as it may be called, can be approximated closely by taking it as the midpoint between the upper and the lower peaks of the ripple.

Illustrative Problem 4-1
Determine the ripple factor and the percent ripple of the wave-shape shown in Fig. Prob. 4-1.

FIGURE PROB. 4-1

SOLUTION

Ripple peak-to-peak $= 100 - 70 = 30$ volts

$$\text{Ripple peak} = \frac{\text{peak-to-peak}}{2} = 15 \text{ volts}$$

$$\text{rms of sine-wave equivalent} = \frac{\text{peak}}{\sqrt{2}} = \frac{15}{\sqrt{2}} = 10.6 \text{ volts}$$

$$\text{dc level} = 70 + \frac{100-70}{2} = 70 + \frac{30}{2} = 85 \text{ volts}$$

$$k_r = \frac{\text{rms ripple}}{\text{dc level}} = \frac{10.6}{85} = 0.125$$

$$\boxed{\begin{array}{l} k_r = 0.125 \\ \% \text{ ripple} = 12.5\% \end{array}}$$

HOW TO CHOOSE THE CAPACITOR
A key question as yet unanswered is: How do we choose the proper sized capacitor to function as a filter in a power supply? Obviously

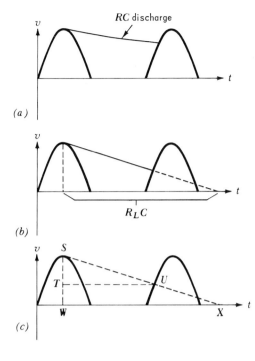

FIGURE 4-6 The wave-shapes and constructions used in the development of the formula for C_{min}.

one answer is to use the largest capacitor available. We cannot eliminate all the ripple completely, and the larger the capacitor, the more ripple removed. Then we must ask: What is the minimum sized capacitor we can get away with using, in order to limit the ripple factor to the maximum value permitted by the design requirements?

Let us begin our study of this problem by analyzing the wave-shapes shown in Fig. 4-6. We can make the approximation that the RC discharge portion of the output curve is a straight line, based on the assumption that the time constant involved is very long compared to that portion of the discharge curve which is part of the output waveshape. With this as an assumption, the extension of the discharge curve will intercept the horizontal time axis after a portion of time equal to one RC time constant has elapsed, as noted in Fig. 4-6b. Recall that the slope of the RC discharge curve, just as the discharge begins, is such as to attempt to discharge the capacitor within one time constant.

Another approximation we must make is that the time elapsed between the peak of the output wave and the point at which the discharge curve intercepts the next half-cycle of the sine wave is equal to the fraction 1 over frequency of the ripple, or the ripple period. Again, this is only an approximation because it ignores that portion of time in which the sine-wave segment of the output waveshape occurs. This does not generate too great an error because as long as we keep the ripple content small, the sine wave segment is part of the output waveshape for only a very small portion of the period. This will provide us with a reasonably close approximation to the size capacitor we are seeking. In Fig. 4-6c we can make out two similar triangles

$$\triangle STU \approx \triangle SWX$$

Using our knowledge of the relationship which exists between the corresponding sides of similar triangles, we can write

$$\frac{\text{Side } SW}{\text{Side } ST} = \frac{\text{Side } WX}{\text{Side } TU}$$

And since

$$\text{Side } SW = V_{\text{peak out}}$$
$$\text{Side } ST = V_{\text{p-p ripple}}$$
$$\text{Side } WX = R_L C$$
$$\text{Side } TU = \frac{1}{f_{\text{ripple}}}$$

we get

$$\frac{V_{\text{peak out}}}{V_{\text{p-p ripple}}} = \frac{R_L C}{1/f_{\text{ripple}}}$$

Is this equation adequate for determining the proper value of a capacitor? Let us see if we have only one unknown with this one equation. To start with, the frequency of the ripple is known once we know the frequency of the power line and whether we are using a full-wave or a half-wave rectifier. R_L is usually known since this is the resistance of the load being fed.

Once we know the ripple content and the required dc level, we can find $V_{\text{peak out}}$. Again, however, if we assume that the ripple content will be small compared to the dc level, we can approximate $V_{\text{peak out}}$ by $V_{\text{dc out}}$. This simplifies matters greatly since $V_{\text{dc out}}/V_{\text{p-p ripple}}$ can be found directly from k_r, the ripple factor. k_r is usually determined by the type of service for which the supply is intended. This equation is then adequate because we are left with just one unknown. It would be more convenient if we were to swap the ratio of peak output voltage to peak-to-peak voltage for some relationship involving the ripple factor, which we now do.

$$k_r = \frac{V_{\text{rms ripple}}}{V_{\text{dc}}} = \frac{V_{\text{p-p ripple}}/2\sqrt{2}}{V_{\text{dc}}}$$

$$V_{\text{p-p ripple}} = k_r V_{\text{dc}} \, (2\sqrt{2})$$
$$= 2\sqrt{2} k_r V_{\text{dc}}$$

$$\frac{V_{\text{peak out}}}{V_{\text{p-p ripple}}} \approx \frac{V_{\text{dc}}}{V_{\text{p-p ripple}}} \approx \frac{R_L C}{1/f_{\text{ripple}}}$$

$$\frac{V_{\text{dc}}}{2\sqrt{2} k_r V_{\text{dc}}} \approx \frac{R_L C}{1/f_{\text{ripple}}}$$

$$\frac{1}{2\sqrt{2} k_r} \approx R_L C$$

$$\boxed{C_{\min} \approx \frac{1}{2\sqrt{2} k_r R_L f_{\text{ripple}}}}$$

This value of capacitance is the *minimum* value needed in order to limit the ripple to the value set by k_r.

Illustrative Problem 4-2

A full-wave-rectified power supply is to be designed to operate directly from a 120-volt 60-Hz line and supply a 10,000-ohm load. The output voltage is to be approximately 170 volts dc. The percent ripple is to be limited to 5 percent. Determine the minimum value of capacitance which must be placed across the output of the rectifier in order to meet the requirements of the design.

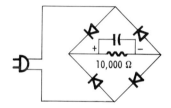

FIGURE PROB. 4-2

SOLUTION

$$C_{\min} = \frac{1}{2\sqrt{2} k_r R_L f_{\text{ripple}}}$$
$$= \frac{1}{2\sqrt{2} \times 0.05 \times 10,000 \times 120}$$

$$\boxed{C_{\min} = 5.9 \ \mu\text{f}}$$

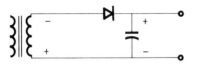

ADDITIONAL STRESSES ON THE DIODE DUE TO THE CAPACITOR FILTER

Let us examine the power-supply circuits to see if additional stresses are placed on the diodes due to the added capacitor filter. First we will study the half-wave circuit shown as Fig. 4-7.

The voltage across the capacitor is equal to the peak voltage of the transformer secondary. This voltage across the capacitor remains constant. When the voltage across the transformer secondary has the polarity as shown in Fig. 4-7 and the peak voltage occurs, we have the greatest PIV because the voltage across the transformer and the voltage across the capacitor are series-aiding, placing a PIV across the diode of $2V_{\text{peak trans sec}}$, twice the peak voltage which occurs across the transformer secondary.

In the case of full-wave rectifiers the PIV situation is the same as that which existed without the capacitor, because we already had to deal with the case of a peak voltage across the output and a peak voltage across the transformer secondary occurring simultaneously in a series-aiding combination.

What about the current-handling requirements of the diode in the capacitor-filtered situation? Obviously it will have to be greater than without the capacitor because the diode is now back-biased for a longer time, and since the average output current is the same as before, greater currents must pass through the diodes because they are conducting for a shorter time span.

Making use of the principle of conservation of electric charge, we see that the total amount of electric charge which is sent to the capacitor during the conduction portion of the cycle must equal the amount of charge the capacitor is feeding the load over the rest of the cycle. Again a few approximations will greatly simplify our analysis. Since the capacitor feeds the load for the greater amount of time, we can make the approximation that the capacitor feeds the load for the entire cycle, and thus we can write that the total amount of electric charge which the capacitor feeds to the load during the entire cycle must be fed to the capacitor during the time that the diode conducts. Since electric charge is equal to current times the amount of time the current is flowing, we can write

$$i_c t_c = I_{\text{dc}} T$$

where i_c = charging current flowing into capacitor
t_c = capacitor charging time
I_{dc} = dc load current
$T = 1/f_{ripple}$

Figure 4-8 compares the output voltage and the charging current. The ripple content has been exaggerated in order to simplify understanding.

It can be shown that the peak current that occurs during the portion of the cycle that the capacitor is charging can be determined from*

$$I_{\text{peak diode}} \approx I_{\text{dc load}} \left(1 + 2\pi \sqrt{\frac{V_{\text{peak}}}{V_{\text{ripple peak}}}}\right)$$

and since

$$\sqrt{\frac{V_{\text{peak}}}{V_{\text{ripple peak}}}} \approx \sqrt{\frac{V_{\text{dc}}}{\sqrt{2}V_{\text{rms ripple}}}} = \sqrt{\frac{1}{\sqrt{2}k_r}}$$

$$I_{\text{peak diode}} \approx I_{\text{dc load}} \left(1 + 2\pi \sqrt{\frac{1}{\sqrt{2}k_r}}\right)$$

* J. F. Gibbons, "Semiconductor Electronics," p. 252, McGraw-Hill Book Company, New York, 1966.

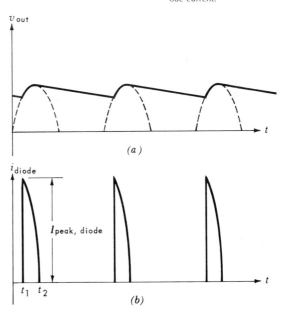

FIGURE 4-8 *Waveshapes for the half-wave-rectified supply with capacitor filter. (a) Output voltage; (b) diode current.*

Illustrative Problem 4-3

Determine the specifications required of the diodes and the capacitor which are to be used in a full-wave bridge-capacitor-filtered dc supply. The permitted ripple is 3 percent. The load is to take 2 ma dc at 150 volts dc.

SOLUTION

Given: $k_r = 0.03$; $I_{dc\ load} = 2$ ma; $V_{dc\ load} = 150$ volts

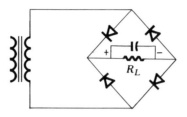

FIGURE PROB. 4-3

Find:

(a) $PIV_{min\ rating}$
(b) $I_{av\ min\ rating\ diode}$
(c) $I_{recurrent\ peak\ diode\ min\ rating}$
(d) C_{min}
(e) $V_{rating\ for\ capacitor}$

(a) $V_{dc\ out} = 150$ volts

$$k_r = \frac{V_{rms\ ripple}}{V_{dc}}$$

$$0.03 = \frac{V_{rms\ ripple}}{150}$$

$V_{rms\ ripple} = 0.03 \times 150 = 4.50$ volts
$V_{peak\ ripple} = \sqrt{2} \times 4.50 = 6.35$ volts
$V_{peak\ out} = V_{dc\ out} + V_{peak\ ripple} = 150 + 6.35 = 156$ volts

slide-rule accuracy, or three digits

$$PIV = 2V_{peak\ out} = 2 \times 156 = 312 \text{ volts}$$

$$PIV_{min\ rating} = \frac{312}{0.8} = 390 \text{ volts}$$

$$\boxed{PIV_{min\ rating} = 390 \text{ volts}}$$

(b) $I_{av\ per\ diode} = \tfrac{1}{2}I_{av\ out} = \tfrac{1}{2}(2\ ma) = 1$ ma

$$I_{av\ min\ rating\ per\ diode} = \frac{1\ ma}{0.8}$$

$$\boxed{I_{av\ min\ rating\ per\ diode} = 1.25 \text{ ma}}$$

(c) $\quad I_{\text{recurrent peak}} \approx I_{\text{dc load}} \left(1 + 2\pi \sqrt{\dfrac{1}{\sqrt{2}k_r}} \right)$

$$\approx 2 \times 10^{-3} \left(1 + 2\pi \sqrt{\dfrac{1}{\sqrt{2} \times 0.03}} \right)$$

$$\approx 2 \times 10^{-3} \left(1 + 2\pi \sqrt{\dfrac{1}{0.0425}} \right)$$

$$\approx 2 \times 10^{-3} \left(1 + 2\pi \dfrac{1}{0.206} \right)$$

$$\approx 2 \times 10^{-3}(1 + 30.5)$$

$$I_{\text{recurrent peak diode min rating}} \approx \dfrac{63 \times 10^{-3}}{0.8}$$

$$\boxed{I_{\text{recurrent peak diode min rating}} = 78.6}$$

(d) $\quad C_{\min} = \dfrac{1}{2\sqrt{2}k_r R_L f_{\text{ripple}}}$

$$R_L = \dfrac{V_{\text{dc out}}}{I_{\text{dc out}}} = \dfrac{150}{2 \times 10^{-3}} = 75 \times 10^3 \text{ ohm}$$

$$C_{\min} = \dfrac{1}{2\sqrt{2}(0.03)(75 \times 10^3)(120)}$$

$$\boxed{C_{\min} = 1.31 \ \mu\text{f}}$$

(e) $\quad V_{\text{peak cap}} = V_{\text{peak out}} = 156 \text{ volts}$

$$V_{\text{cap min rating}} = \dfrac{156}{0.8}$$

$$\boxed{V_{\text{cap min rating}} = 195 \text{ volts}}$$

VOLTAGE DOUBLERS

While we are on the topic of capacitor-filter power supplies, we will discuss a popular variation of such a circuit, known as a *voltage doubler*. The reason for this name is that the dc output voltage is equal to approximately twice the peak value of the ac input voltage. The schematic diagram for the voltage doubler is shown as Fig. 4-9. The major advantage of this circuit is that it allows us to obtain a large output voltage without having to use a transformer.

During the negative half-cycle of the input waveshape of Fig. 4-9, capacitor C_1 is charged to a voltage which is equal to the peak value of the input voltage. During the positive portion of the input voltage the voltage across C_1 is in a series-aiding condition with respect to the input. This then provides a voltage presented to

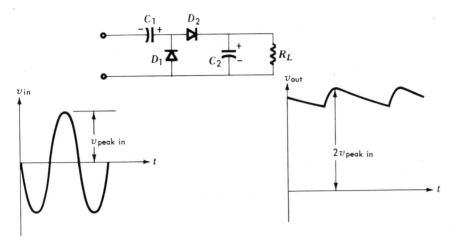

FIGURE 4-9 *The voltage doubler and its waveshapes.*

C_2 equal to the sum of the input voltage and the voltage across C_1. When the peak of the positive-going portion of the voltage is present, the voltage presented to C_2 and the load is equal to $2V_{peak\ input}$.

The PIV which the diodes D_1 and D_2 must withstand is equal to $2V_{peak\ input}$ each. Knowing how the circuit works and having studied capacitor-filtered power supplies in detail, we should not find it difficult to determine the component specifications for this circuit.

THE INDUCTOR AS A FILTER

The capacitor is used as a filter because it has the capability of temporarily storing electric energy. Is there any other device which also has this capability? The inductor has the property of storing energy in a magnetic field while current is flowing and returning this energy to the circuit when the current through it is being reduced. This property manifests itself in the sluggishness with which current changes occur in a circuit containing an inductance. This property is usually expressed by the statement that

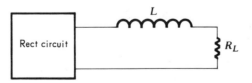

FIGURE 4-10 *An inductor used as a power-supply filter.*

current changes cannot occur instantaneously in an inductance. If such a device is incorporated into the power-supply circuit in such a way that it is in series with the load, it will tend to smooth out variations in load current. Such a circuit is shown in its simplest form in Fig. 4-10.

THE BLEEDER RESISTOR

Since the inductor depends upon current for its operation, it functions best under large current demands. For optimum functioning the inductor should have at least a certain minimum current flowing through it at all times. In order to provide this minimum current a *bleeder resistor* is usually included in circuits which use inductor filters. The function of the bleeder is to maintain the minimum current necessary for optimum inductor operation (see Fig. 4-11).

The bleeder resistor can serve a number of other functions as well. For example, it can be used as a voltage divider in providing a variable voltage output from the supply. It can also serve as a discharge path for capacitors which may be included in the circuit so that the voltage does not remain across the output terminals of the power supply for an indefinitely long period of time after the load has been disconnected and the circuit deenergized (see Fig. 4-12).

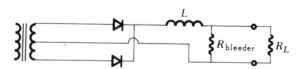

FIGURE 4-11 A full-wave rectifier with an inductor filter and a bleeder resistor.

FIGURE 4-12 A bleeder resistor being used to maintain minimum current in L, discharge C, and vary output voltage.

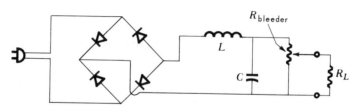

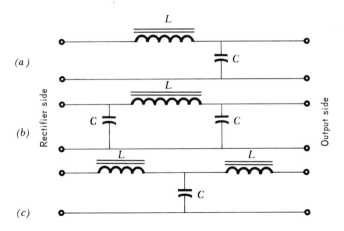

FIGURE 4-13 *Filters using both an inductor and a capacitor: (a) L-section filter; (b) π-section filter; (c) T-section filter.*

In order to be sure that enough current is being drawn by R_{bleeder}, the following inequality should be satisfied:

$$R_{\text{bleeder}} < 1000L$$

COMPARING THE INDUCTOR AND THE CAPACITOR FILTERS

The capacitor functions best as a filter under no-load conditions. Thus when the output of the power supply which is using a capacitor as a filter is open-circuited, the percent ripple is zero. As more and more load current is taken, the percent ripple increases. On the other hand, when the inductor is used as a filter, the opposite is true. As more current is drawn, the percent ripple becomes smaller. Because the capacitor and the inductor complement each other when functioning as a filter, many cases arise in which a combination of the two is used (see Fig. 4-13 for the combinations frequently employed).

PROBLEMS

4-1 What is the approximate time constant of the circuit through which the capacitor in a capacitor-filtered power supply charges?

4-2 What determines the time constant of the capacitor discharge in a capacitor-filter power supply?

4-3 How large is the approximate average output voltage from a capacitor-filtered power supply being fed directly from a 120-volt-rms 60-Hz line if the ripple content is negligible?

4-4 Sketch the output voltage waveshape for a capacitor-filtered power supply under moderate load conditions. Show at least three cycles of the waveshape.

4-5 What is the significance of the point of intersection of the *RC* discharge curve and the sine-wave segment in the output voltage waveform of a capacitor-filtered supply?

4-6 Describe the effect of appreciably reducing the value of the load resistance on the output voltage waveshape of a capacitor-filtered power supply.

4-7 Sketch and compare the output voltage waveshape of a half-wave capacitor-filtered supply and a full-wave capacitor-filtered supply. Both are to have the same peak output voltage and the same value of filter capacitor and load resistance. (Exaggerate the ripple content of both.)

4-8 Determine the ripple factor and the percent ripple of a waveshape that has a peak-to-peak ripple content of 5 volts and a dc level of 50 volts.

4-9 Calculate the approximate ripple factor and the percent ripple of a waveshape having a peak-to-peak ripple content of 2 volts and a peak voltage of 75 volts.

4-10 Find the minimum value of capacitance necessary to provide 5 percent ripple content from a half-wave-rectified capacitor-filtered supply feeding a 500-ohm load. The supply is to operate from a standard 120-volt rms 60-Hz supply line.

4-11 Determine the PIV a diode must withstand in a capacitor-filtered power supply whose peak output voltage is 500 volts. Does it matter whether we are dealing with a full-wave or a half-wave supply as far as PIV is concerned?

4-12 Specify the requirements for all the components that are to be used in a bridge-type capacitor-filtered rectifier which is to supply 1.5 ma at 250 volts dc. The ripple content is to be held below 2 percent.

4-13 Repeat Prob. 4-12 for a half-wave rectifier.

4-14 Describe how an inductor functions when used as a power-supply filter.

4-15 Calculate the maximum value of bleeder resistance required when using a 4-henry inductance for filtering a power supply.

CHAPTER

5

VOLTAGE REGULATION

We have all seen the dimming of house lights when a fairly large electric appliance is turned on, e.g., a refrigerator or air conditioner. This is due to the reduction in power-line voltage caused by voltage being dropped along the power lines when a large current is drawn. This effect is also found on an area-wide basis and results in the variation in line voltage associated with shift times at nearby factories or with the use of large appliances at neighboring establishments. This variation of line voltage with load is classified as a regulation problem. What effect does this variation in line voltage have on the output of the power supplies which we designed previously? *Of course the dc output voltage will follow power-line voltage fluctuations.* As the voltage on the power line drops, so will the dc output voltage available at the output of the supply. There are also other causes for variation of output voltage from our dc power supplies, such as internal resistance of the rectifier and filter sections. As more current is drawn from the supply, the output voltage drops because a greater part of the voltage is taken inside the supply by internal resistance.

PERCENT REGULATION AND THE VOLTAGE REGULATOR
One of the measures of the quality of a power supply is its ability to maintain a constant output voltage even though the load on the circuit may be changing. A figure of merit of the supply is its

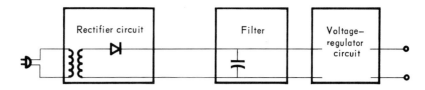

FIGURE 5-1 *Block diagram of a complete voltage-regulated power supply.*

percent regulation, defined as

$$\text{Percent regulation} = \frac{V_{\text{no load}} - V_{\text{rated full load}}}{V_{\text{rated full load}}} \times 100\%$$

Frequently design specifications require very stable and well-regulated output voltages from dc power supplies even in the face of power-line or internal regulation difficulties. In such situations it is necessary to add an additional section to the power supply to compensate for the regulation problems inherent in the power line and components of the rectifier and filter sections of the supply. This additional section is called a *voltage-regulator circuit* (see Fig. 5-1 for a block diagram of a power supply which makes use of a voltage-regulator circuit).

THE ZENER DIODE

The zener diode is a semiconductor device which can be used as the key component in a voltage-regulator circuit. The zener diode

FIGURE 5-2 *Complete semiconductor-diode characteristic.*

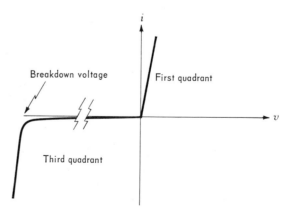

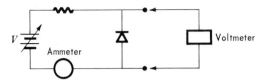

FIGURE 5-3 *Test circuit for obtaining the third-quadrant characteristic of a diode.*

does not replace the diodes used in the rectifier circuit but is an additional diode which is added on as a part of the regulator circuit.

When semiconductor diodes were studied in previous chapters, we assumed that the diode would not pass current in the reverse direction. However, remember that precautions were taken to prevent the rated PIV from being exceeded. Let us now reexamine the reverse conduction region of the semiconductor-diode characteristics in more detail. The complete semiconductor-diode characteristic is shown as Fig. 5-2.

We can actually determine the characteristic for third-quadrant operation of the diode by making use of the circuit shown in Fig. 5-3.

The voltage V of Fig. 5-3 is increased in small increments, each time noting the voltage across the diodes and the current through it. Note that until the breakdown voltage is reached, *practically* no current flows through the diode. Once the breakdown voltage is reached, the current rises by large increments for each very small increase in diode voltage. This breakdown of the diode is called *zener breakdown.* For many practical purposes it can be considered that the voltage across the diode remains practically constant once the breakdown voltage has been reached. Diodes which are designed for use in this region are called *zener diodes.*

The zener breakdown voltage of semiconductor diodes can be controlled during the manufacturing process. Zener regulating diodes are available with zener breakdown potentials varying from a few volts up to several hundred volts.

CIRCUIT ACTION

A typical zener-diode regulator circuit is shown as Fig. 5-4. How does this circuit function in its reduction of regulation problems? For proper operation of this circuit the voltage across the input of the regulator circuit must be greater than the voltage across the output. Enough current is made to flow through the zener diode so that the sum of the zener-diode current and the load current, which flows through the series resistor R_{series}, drops enough voltage for the voltage across the zener-diode and load combination to be

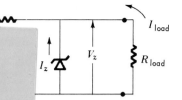

FIGURE 5-4 *Typical zener-diode voltage-regulator circuit.*

f input voltage to the
ent changes, the zener-
age across the resistor
t voltage at the desired

le, like all other electric
n rating. If this maxi-
destroyed. The simple,
approximate maximum
$_{max} = V_z I_{z,\text{max rated}}$, where

want to stay a safe dis-
g so that the design will
g a safety factor in the

FIGURE 5-5 *Character-istic curve of zener diode showing safe operating region.*

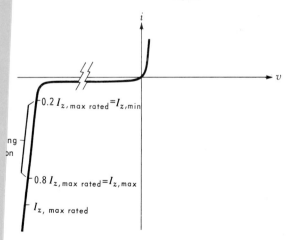

calculations. The maximum zener-diode current is therefore taken as $0.8I_{z,\text{max rated}}$.

$$I_{z,\text{max}} = 0.8I_{z,\text{max rated}}$$

A second extreme point of operation is chosen so that the rounded knee of the curve, which exists at low zener currents, is avoided. This is taken into consideration by setting a minimum allowable value for the current which is to flow through the zener diode. A reasonably good choice is to set this minimum zener current to $0.2I_{z,\text{max rated}}$ (see Fig. 5-5).

COMPONENT SPECIFICATIONS

We will assume that we know the range over which the unregulated dc input voltage varies. Let us note the extreme cases as $V_{\text{in max}}$ and $V_{\text{in min}}$. The maximum load will usually be specified as a rated maximum current drain or a minimum load resistance. The other extreme load case will be taken as the case of infinite resistance, an open-circuited output which will result when the load is disconnected. The design will revolve around the two worst-case design considerations. One worst case results with maximum input voltage and no load, while the other results from rated load resistance and minimum input voltage.

Let us consider the maximum input voltage and no-load condition first (see Fig. 5-6). The current which will flow through R_{series} in this case will be determined by $(V_{\text{in max}} - V_z)/R_{\text{series}}$. Because no load is connected, all the current will be taken by the zener diode, and thus

$$\frac{V_{\text{in max}} - V_z}{R_{\text{series}}} < 0.8I_{z,\text{ max rated}}$$

With a little algebraic manipulation we arrive at the inequality

$$R_{\text{series}} > \frac{V_{\text{in max}} - V_z}{0.8I_{z,\text{max rated}}}$$

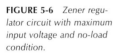

FIGURE 5-6 *Zener regulator circuit with maximum input voltage and no-load condition.*

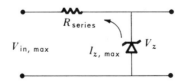

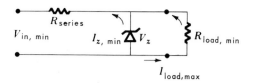

FIGURE 5-7 *Zener regulator circuit with minimum input voltage and maximum-load current condition.*

which can be written as the equation

$$R_{\text{series min}} = \frac{V_{\text{in max}} - V_z}{0.8 I_{z,\text{max rated}}}$$

Now let us consider the other worst-case situation, that of $V_{\text{in min}}$ and $R_{L,\text{min}}$ occurring simultaneously (see Fig. 5-7).

Accompanying the condition of $R_{L,\text{min}}$ is $I_{\text{load max}}$ and $I_{z,\text{min}}$. From the circuit of Fig. 5-7 we can write

$$R_{\text{series}}(I_{z,\text{min}} + I_{\text{load max}}) = V_{\text{in min}} - V_z$$

$$I_{z,\text{min}} + I_{\text{load max}} = \frac{V_{\text{in min}} - V_z}{R_{\text{series}}}$$

$$I_{z,\text{min}} = \frac{V_{\text{in min}} - V_z}{R_{\text{series}}} - I_{\text{load max}}$$

but

$$I_{z,\text{min}} > 0.2 I_{z,\text{max rated}}$$

therefore,

$$\frac{V_{\text{in min}} - V_z}{R_{\text{series}}} - I_{\text{load max}} > 0.2 I_{z,\text{max rated}}$$

With a little algebraic manipulation this can be written as

$$R_{\text{series}} < \frac{V_{\text{in min}} - V_z}{0.2 I_{z,\text{max rated}} + I_{\text{load max}}}$$

which can be replaced by the equation

$$R_{\text{series max}} = \frac{V_{\text{in min}} - V_z}{0.2 I_{z,\text{max rated}} + I_{\text{load max}}}$$

Obviously taking just any zener diode with the proper zener voltage rating will not provide proper operation of the circuit. Two additional conditions regarding the rating of the diode must be met. First, the diode maximum current rating must be such as to provide meaningful results in the formulas used in the determination of the series resistor. This requires that

$$R_{\text{series max}} > R_{\text{series min}}$$

$$\frac{V_{\text{in min}} - V_z}{0.2I_{z,\text{max rated}} + I_{\text{load max}}} > \frac{V_{\text{in max}} - V_z}{0.8I_{z,\text{max rated}}}$$

$$\frac{V_{\text{in min}} - V_z}{V_{\text{in max}} - V_z} > \frac{0.2I_{z,\text{max rated}} + I_{\text{load max}}}{0.8I_{z,\text{max rated}}}$$

$$\frac{V_{\text{in min}} - V_z}{V_{\text{in max}} - V_z} > \frac{0.2}{0.8} + \frac{I_{\text{load max}}}{0.8I_{z,\text{max rated}}}$$

$$\boxed{0.8\frac{V_{\text{in min}} - V_z}{V_{\text{in max}} - V_z} - 0.2 > \frac{I_{\text{load max}}}{I_{z,\text{max rated}}}}$$

In addition we must consider the power-handling capability of the zener diode. In the case of all load being removed from the output, the case of open circuit, all current must be taken by the diode. The current-handling capability of the diode must satisfy the inequality

$$I_{z,\text{max}} > I_{\text{load max}} + I_{z,\text{min}}$$

and since

$$I_{z,\text{max}} = 0.8I_{z,\text{max rated}}$$

and

$$I_{z,\text{min}} = 0.2I_{z,\text{max rated}}$$

we have

$$0.8I_{z,\text{max rated}} > I_{\text{load max}} + 0.2I_{z,\text{max rated}}$$

$$\boxed{0.6I_{z,\text{max rated}} > I_{\text{load max}}}$$

It is very likely that we will run into situations in which we are given the voltage extremes that are expected at the input to the regulator, the zener voltage, and the rated current expected to be drawn. This will cause the inequality generated when we considered the maximum and minimum series-resistor conditions to set a minimum current rating for the zener diode. What of the value which will be provided by the inequality just developed from power considerations? No problem at all. Since both merely set a lower limit on the current capability of the zener diode, the larger value will supercede the lower one, thus satisfying both inequalities simultaneously.

Illustrative Problem 5-1

A voltage regulator is desired which will provide an output voltage of 25 volts dc to a load whose maximum current drain will be 150 ma. The input voltage to the regulator is expected to vary from 50 to 75 volts dc. Determine the minimum power rating required of the zener diode. Determine the range of values for R_{series} if a zener diode is to be used which has a power rating of 30 watts.

SOLUTION

Given: $V_z = 25$ volts dc; $I_{load\,max} = 150$ ma; $V_{in\,max} = 75$ volts dc; $V_{in\,min} = 50$ volts dc; $P_{D,max} = 30$ watts

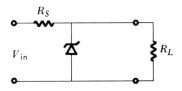

FIGURE PROB. 5-1

Find:

(a) Minimum value of $P_{D,max}$

(b) R_{series}

(a) $$0.8 \frac{V_{in\,min} - V_z}{V_{in\,max} - V_z} - 0.2 > \frac{I_{load\,max}}{I_{z,max\,rated}}$$

$$0.8 \times \frac{50 - 25}{75 - 25} - 0.2 > \frac{150 \times 10^{-3}}{I_{z,max\,rated}}$$

$$0.8 \times \frac{25}{50} - 0.2 > \frac{150 \times 10^{-3}}{I_{z,max\,rated}}$$

$$0.2 > \frac{150 \times 10^{-3}}{I_{z,max\,rated}}$$

$$I_{z,max\,rated} > \frac{150 \times 10^{-3}}{1.\ 0.2} = 750 \text{ ma}$$

$$> \frac{I_{load\,max}}{0.6} = \frac{150 \times 10^{-3}}{0.6} = 250 \text{ ma}$$

Since $750 > 250$, we go with 750 ma.

$$\boxed{I_{z,max\,rated} > 750 \text{ ma}}$$

$$P_{D,max\,rated} = V_z I_{z,max\,rated} > 25 \times 750 \times 10^{-3} = 18.8 \text{ watts}$$

$$\boxed{P_{D,max\,rated} > 18.8 \text{ watts}}$$

(b) $R_{\text{series max}} = \dfrac{V_{\text{in min}} - V_z}{0.2I_{z,\text{max rated}} + I_{\text{load max}}}$

$I_{z,\text{max rated}}V_z = P_{D,\text{max}}$

$I_{z,\text{max rated}} \times 25 = 30$

$I_{z,\text{max rated}} = {}^{30}/_{25} = 1.2 \text{ amp}$

$R_{\text{series max}} = \dfrac{50 - 25}{0.2 \times 1.2 + 0.150} = \dfrac{25}{0.24 + 0.150} = \dfrac{25}{0.390}$

$\boxed{R_{\text{series max}} = 64 \text{ ohms}}$

$R_{\text{series min}} = \dfrac{V_{\text{in max}} - V_z}{0.8I_{z,\text{max rated}}} = \dfrac{75 - 25}{0.8 \times 1.2} = \dfrac{50}{0.96}$

$\boxed{R_{\text{series min}} = 52.1 \text{ ohms}}$

PROBLEMS

5-1 Why do house lights dim when a large electric appliance is turned on?

5-2 What is meant by the term "regulation"?

5-3 Determine the percent regulation of a power supply whose no-load output voltage is 100 volts and whose output voltage drops to 92 volts under full load.

5-4 What is the function of a voltage-regulator circuit?

5-5 Sketch a *complete* characteristic curve for a semiconductor diode.

5-6 (a) Determine the maximum rated zener current for a 16-volt 10-watt zener diode.

(b) How large a current should this zener diode be called upon to pass in actual circuit operation?

(c) What should the smallest current be which the diode is called upon to pass in order to avoid the knee of the characteristic curve?

5-7 Describe the two worst-case conditions which a regulator circuit is called upon to service.

5-8 Calculate the minimum value and the maximum value which the series resistor may have in a regulator circuit whose output voltage is to be 12 volts, whose input voltage varies from 25 to 30 volts, and whose maximum load current is 50 ma. The zener diode used in this circuit has a maximum current rating of 250 ma.

5-9 Consider a regulator circuit whose output voltage is to be 20 volts dc, whose input varies from 30 to 35 volts dc, and whose rated load draws 150 ma.

(a) Determine the limitations on zener-diode current rating required to ensure that $R_{\text{series max}}$ is a larger quantity than $R_{\text{series min}}$.

(b) Calculate the minimum permitted power rating of such a diode.

5-10 Design a voltage-regulator circuit to provide a 50-volt dc output voltage to a load whose maximum current requirement is 100 ma. The voltage fed to the regulator varies from 80 to 90 volts.

(a) Determine the minimum zener-diode current rating necessary to ensure that $R_{\text{series max}}$ is greater than $R_{\text{series min}}$.

(b) Determine the current rating of the zener which results from the power-dissipation considerations.

(c) Specify the minimum power rating of the diode.

(d) Find the permitted range of R_{series} if a diode is used whose power rating is twice the minimum permitted value.

SILICON CONTROLLED RECTIFIERS

Previously, our major objective was to supply a dc, or unidirectional, output voltage and current from a supply which is provided with a sine-wave input. Let our next objective be that of providing a unidirectional output voltage whose average value is variable. Two very simple possibilities are to use a variable transformer (variac, varitran, etc.) at the input of the power supply or to use a variable resistor across the output of the power supply, as shown in Fig. 6-1.

Both these situations have disadvantages. The disadvantages of using a variable transformer are greater costs and the necessity of using a transformer when it would have been possible to feed the supply directly from the line, thus eliminating the transformer. The disadvantages of a variable resistor are the added heat dissipation and the resulting necessity of specifying greater component ratings.

What if we were able to vary the point at which the diode begins conduction instead of the situation of a half-cycle on and a half-cycle off? If we could control the amount of time during each cycle that the diode conducts, we could determine the average value of the output waveshape (see Fig. 6-2).

THE SCR
Is there a technique or a device which can provide us with this independent control of conduction angle? Yes. Such a device is

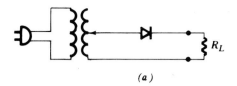

(a)

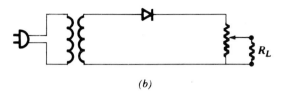

(b)

FIGURE 6-1 *Providing a variable average output voltage using (a) a variable transformer and (b) a variable resistor.*

the *controlled rectifier.* Because the overwhelming majority of solid-state controlled rectifiers are made of silicon, they are called SCRs, silicon controlled rectifiers.

Figure 6-3 shows the schematic symbol used to represent the SCR. The anode and cathode of the device serve the same function as their counterparts in the simple solid-state junction diode. The gate is the control terminal, which determines when the diode starts conducting anode current. The control signal is applied between the gate and the cathode. In Fig. 6-4 an SCR is shown in a typical circuit configuration.

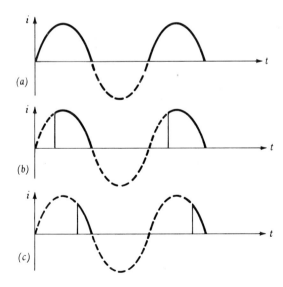

FIGURE 6-2 *Average-load current value determined by conduction angle. (a) Large average value; (b) medium average value; (c) small average value.*

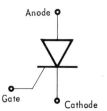

FIGURE 6-3 *Schematic symbol for the SCR.*

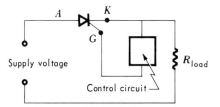

FIGURE 6-4 *Typical SCR circuit.*

A SIMPLE CIRCUIT

In an attempt to find out how the SCR functions let us investigate the operating capabilities of the SCR in a circuit in which all the sources of power are dc quantities, such as that shown in Fig. 6-5. To start our investigation open-circuit that branch of the circuit made up of V_{GG}, R_G, and the gate terminal, thus providing zero gate current. With this the case we can get a characteristic curve of the device by varying the supply voltage v_{in} and measuring the anode current and the voltage across the SCR from anode to cathode. Very little anode current flows until a certain critical voltage, called the *forward breakover voltage,* is reached, at which time the current increases greatly and the voltage across the diode from cathode to anode decreases. The characteristic curve that results from such an experiment is shown in Fig. 6-6.

Repeat this experiment a number of times, but now with the gate circuit intact, each time providing a different value of gate current I_G. This will result in a whole family of characteristic curves differing from each other only in forward breakover voltage, as shown in Fig. 6-7. Studying Fig. 6-7 in greater detail, we see that the *breakover voltage decreases with increasing gate current.*

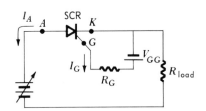

FIGURE 6-5 *Simple circuit for studying the SCR.*

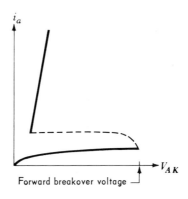

FIGURE 6-6 *The characteristic curve generated from a study of the circuit of Fig. 6-5 with zero gate current.*

AC INPUT

How can we use this device to provide a variable unidirectional output voltage with an ac power-line input? Let us start by replacing the variable battery shown in Fig. 6-5 with a transformer and line cord, as shown in Fig. 6-8. Let us now turn our attention to Fig. 6-9, showing the sine-wave output voltage available from the transformer. How does varying the amount of gate current determine the average current being passed to the load? The gate current determines the point during the positive half-cycle of the input waveshape that the SCR will fire. The earlier in the cycle the SCR fires, the greater the average current passed to the load will be. Figure 6-10 depicts two cases, each with different gate currents and thus different firing times. One very obvious shortcoming of this circuit is that we cannot control the average current

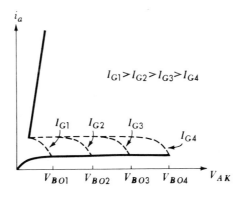

FIGURE 6-7 *Characteristic curves of an SCR for different values of gate current.*

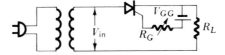

FIGURE 6-8 *A half-wave-rectifier circuit using an SCR operating from the power lines.*

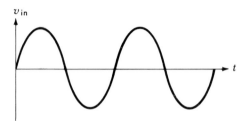

from its greatest average value to zero average value. If we set the gate current for a fixed value so that the breakdown point is between zero and $V_{peak\ in}$ this value of v_{in} will occur between 0 and 90°.

One way of providing complete control, from maximum average current to zero average current, is to switch the necessary gate current out of the circuit and then switch it back in just before it is needed. In place of such a switching we can have the gate current vary so that it is less than that required to fire the SCR until that point in the cycle at which we want the SCR to fire. Let us assume that using a particular SCR and gate resistor R_G requires a voltage of V_G to produce a large enough gate current to cause the SCR to fire. Once the SCR has been turned on, the gate loses control, and no matter what is done with the gate current, the SCR stays on until the anode current is caused to fall below a value called the *holding current* or *latching current*. In an ac circuit,

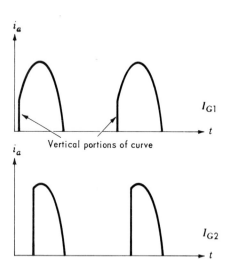

$I_{G2} > I_{G1}$

$V_{BO2} > V_{BO1}$

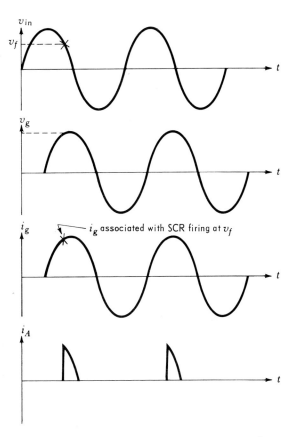

FIGURE 6-11 *Waveshapes associated with a typical SCR circuit.*

turnoff of the SCR is provided automatically because v_{in}, and thus anode current, passes through zero during the middle of each input cycle.

Refer to Fig. 6-11 and note that by varying the phase angle by which the gate circuit voltage lags the input voltage v_{in} we can control the point at which the SCR fires. Note also that the control is complete. We can control from maximum average current to zero average current.

How can the phase difference between the gate circuit and the anode-cathode circuit be provided? A reactive circuit, like that shown in Fig. 6-12, fills the need quite satisfactorily. Control of the phase angle can be provided by varying either the R or the C in the gate circuit.

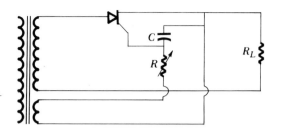

FIGURE 6-12 *An SCR circuit with an RC circuit for control of firing angle.*

DESIGN CONSIDERATIONS

Just as with the simple diodes we dealt with in previous chapters, it is necessary to list various maximum conditions which will appear in the circuit and then choose a diode which can tolerate these maximum conditions. Again we will use diodes only up to 80 percent of the manufacturer's rating. Let us examine a few of the maximum ratings which manufacturers list for the SCRs. First, of course, the manufacturers list the maximum average current permitted. This is frequently listed in their specifications as $I_{F,\text{av}}$, meaning average forward current rating. Manufacturers also list a rating for the maximum forward surge current $i_{FM}(\text{surge})$. This is the largest repetitive instantaneous value of current permitted. The maximum peak reverse voltage $V_{RM}(\text{rep})$ is analogous to what we called PIV when discussing simple diodes. It is the maximum instantaneous value of reverse voltage which can be applied repetitively across the anode-to-cathode section of the device.

Three more important ratings remain to be discussed: maximum forward breakover voltage, holding current, and maximum peak gate power. The *maximum forward breakover voltage* V_{BOO} is the voltage which when applied between the anode and the cathode will cause the SCR to fire with no gate current applied. The *holding current* is that value of anode current below which the SCR reverts to its open-circuit condition. The *maximum peak gate power* is the maximum instantaneous gate power which the SCR is permitted to handle.

DEVICES

The SCR is actually a four-layer semiconductor device, as shown in Fig. 6-13. The anode is the terminal connected to the end P layer, and the cathode is the terminal connected to the end N layer. The gate is the terminal connected to the inner P layer.

Some circuit configurations might call for a pair of SCRs in parallel, with the cathode of one attached to the anode of the other

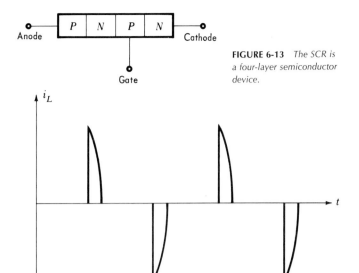

FIGURE 6-13 *The SCR is a four-layer semiconductor device.*

FIGURE 6-14 *Output signal obtained from a circuit using a pair of SCRs in parallel.*

and both gates tied together. Such a case is encountered when attempting to obtain an output signal, as shown in Fig. 6-14.

The Triac. A single device which encompasses the characteristics of two SCRs in parallel, as just described, is the triac (see Fig. 6-15). The triac and the SCR are both members of the broad family of devices called *thyristers*. Thyrister is the name which has been reserved for solid-state control rectifiers.

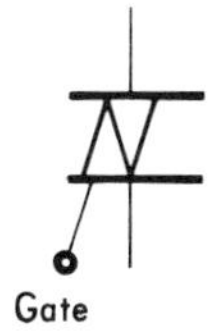

FIGURE 6-15 *Schematic symbol for a triac.*

Illustrative Problem 6-1

A power supply is desired which will be used to provide energy to a dc motor. Provision must be made for controlling the speed of the motor by making use of an SCR in the supply, so as to provide a controlled output voltage. At full speed the motor is taking 1

SILICON CONTROLLED RECTIFIERS 71

amp at 75 volts average. Determine the minimum specifications
for the following ratings of the SCR to be used in this circuit:

(a) Average forward current rating
(b) Maximum forward surge current rating
(c) Maximum peak reverse voltage rating
(d) Maximum forward breakover voltage rating

Solution

Given: $I_{L,\text{av max}} = 1$ amp; $V_{L,\text{av max}} = 75$ volts
Find: Minimum ratings for

(a) $i_{F,\text{av}}$
(b) $i_{FM}(\text{surge})$
(c) $v_{RM}(\text{rep})$
(d) V_{BOO}

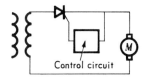

FIGURE PROB. 6-1a

(a) $I_{F,\text{av}} = \dfrac{I_{F,\text{av max}}}{0.8} = \dfrac{1}{0.8}$

$$\boxed{I_{F,\text{av min rating}} = 1.25 \text{ amp}}$$

(b) $i_{FM}(\text{surge}) = I_{\text{peak load}}$
$$= I_L \pi = 1\pi = 3.14$$

$$i_{FM}(\text{surge})_{\text{min rating}} = \dfrac{i_{FM}(\text{surge})_{\text{max}}}{0.8} = \dfrac{3.14}{0.8}$$

$$\boxed{i_{FM}(\text{surge})_{\text{min rating}} = 3.92 \text{ amp}}$$

(c) $v_{RM}(\text{rep}) = V_{\text{peak in}} = V_{L,\text{av}}\pi = 75\pi$

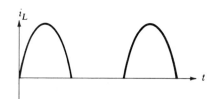

FIGURE PROB. 6-1b

$$v_{RM,\text{min rating}}(\text{rep}) = \frac{v_{RM}(\text{rep})}{0.8} = \frac{75\pi}{0.8}$$

$$\boxed{v_{RM,\text{min rating}}(\text{rep}) = 294 \text{ volts}}$$

(d) The V_{BOO} rating must be large enough so that when the gate current is zero, we do not cause anode current to flow due to exceeding V_{BOO}. Thus

$$V_{BOO} \geqslant V_{\text{peak in}}$$

Allowing the usual safety factor, we set for this problem

$$V_{BOO,\text{min rating}} = \frac{V_{L,\text{av}}\pi}{0.8} = \frac{75\pi}{0.8}$$

$$\boxed{V_{BOO,\text{min rating}} = 294 \text{ volts}}$$

PROBLEMS

6-1 Describe two techniques other than using a controlled rectifier for providing a variable output voltage. What are the disadvantages of these techniques?

6-2 What function is served by the gate of an SCR?

6-3 What effect does increasing the gate current have on the forward breakover voltage?

6-4 What effect does increasing the gate current have on the amount of time the SCR is conducting when the input voltage in the anode-cathode circuit is a sine wave?

6-5 After the SCR is conducting, what effect does reducing the gate current have?

6-6 How can conduction be stopped once the SCR is conducting?

6-7 How is the SCR turned off each cycle when the gate signal is an ac current?

6-8 Describe the physical construction of an SCR.

6-9 What is a triac? A thyristor?

6-10 Specify the minimum required ratings of $I_{F,\text{av}}$, $i_{FM}(\text{surge})$, $v_{RM}(\text{rep})$, and V_{BOO} for an SCR which is to be used in a circuit which is to provide 3 amp at 85 volts in the maximum ON condition.

6-11 A power supply is desired which can supply from zero to ½ amp average current to a 50-ohm load. Determine the following ratings for the required SCR:

(a) Average forward current rating

(b) Maximum forward surge current rating

(c) Maximum peak reverse voltage rating

(d) Maximum forward breakover voltage rating

(e) What should the transformer voltage ratio be for the required transformer?

7

BASIC AMPLIFIERS

Consider what would result if we were to connect the output leads of a phonograph cartridge directly to a loudspeaker. Practically no sound would be heard. The reason is that the electric signal emanating from the phonograph cartridge is not large enough. The signal does not contain enough power to drive the speaker to any great extent. In order to drive the speaker, an electric signal increased in both voltage and power is required. This larger signal should have a waveshape which is identical, except for magnitude, to the signal coming from the phonograph cartridge.

WHAT IS AN AMPLIFIER?

A piece of equipment is required that can increase the magnitude of the signal which comes from the phonograph cartridge. Such a piece of equipment is called an *amplifier*. By definition, *an amplifier is any device which increases the power content of a signal.* In most cases an amplifier will increase the voltage magnitude as well as the power content of the signal. Depending on the needs of the system into which the amplifier will be incorporated, it can be designed for maximum voltage gain or maximum power gain. When designed for maximum voltage gain, the amplifier is referred to as a *voltage amplifier*. When designed for maximum power gain, the amplifier is referred to as a *power amplifier*.

Note that the definition of an amplifier excludes transformers

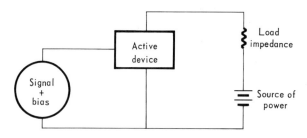

FIGURE 7-1 *Basic config-uration of an amplifier.*

because transformers do not provide an increase in power. They provide an increase in *either* voltage *or* current but never both simultaneously.

An amplifier consists of an active device, a load impedance, a source of power, and a source of bias voltage or current. Figure 7-1 shows a standard interconnection of these components in an amplifier.

ACTIVE DEVICES

An active device is one through which larger amounts of power can be controlled by the use of smaller amounts of power. The active devices in most frequent use today are the vacuum tube and the transistor.

SCHEMATICS

Figure 7-2 contains the schematic diagrams of three amplifiers. In Figure 7-2a the amplifier is using a triode vacuum tube as an active device. Figure 7-2b and 7-2c shows *NPN* and *PNP* transistors as the active devices. The amplifiers shown in Fig. 7-2 are called *common-cathode amplifier* in the case of the triode and *common-emitter amplifiers* in the case of the transistor amplifiers. The reason for these names is that the cathode and the emitter are common to both the input circuit and the output circuit. Other arrangements are possible and will be discussed in a later chapter.

BIAS CIRCUITS

The proper operation of active devices requires that the incoming signal be accompanied by a dc level, in order to prevent rectification of the input signal. This dc level is a negative voltage from grid to cathode in the case of vacuum tubes. In the case of transis-

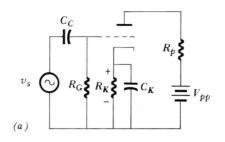

(a)

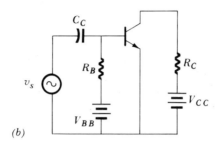

(b)

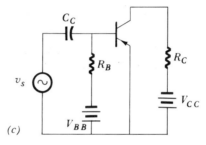

(c)

FIGURE 7-2 *Schematic diagrams of the three most frequently encountered amplifiers.* (a) *Common-cathode vacuum-tube triode amplifier;* (b) *common-emitter transistor amplifier (with NPN transistor);* (c) *common-emitter transistor amplifier (with PNP transistor).*

tors it is a base current whose proper polarity depends upon whether *NPN* or *PNP* transistors are involved.

In the case of the vacuum-tube triode amplifier of Fig. 7-2a, R_K is included to provide a bias voltage between grid and cathode. Note that the polarity of the dc voltage, which is dropped across R_K when no incoming signal is present, makes the cathode positive with respect to the grid. C_K is included in order to provide a low impedance path around R_K for the alternating signal variations, which occur when an incoming signal is applied to the amplifier ($Z = 1/2\pi fC$).

In the transistor amplifier shown in Fig. 7-2b and c, R_B and V_{BB} are included to provide for biasing the input portion of the circuit. Note that the biasing arrangement provided in the transistor amplifiers seems less sophisticated than that indicated for the vacuum-tube circuit. However, the reverse is usually true. The rather simple arrangement shown for the transistor amplifiers is not commonly used in practice. A much more sophisticated arrangement is used to eliminate the need for a separate bias supply battery. Detailed discussion of transistor amplifier biasing circuits is provided as a separate chapter.

POLARITIES

In Fig. 7-2*b* and *c* it can be seen that the polarity of all the power supplies appears to be pushing *electron current* in the direction *opposite* to the arrow on the transistor symbol. This is one way of always being correct when drawing schematics of amplifiers. The supplies should all be such that they are attempting to push electron current in the direction opposite to the arrow on the transistor symbol.

Another noteworthy point is that one can always get the arrow pointing in the proper direction on transistor symbols by recalling that for *NPN* transistors the arrow is

Not **P**ointing i**N**

and for *PNP* transistors the arrow is

Pointing i**N P**

THE REMAINING PARTS OF AN AMPLIFIER

In Fig. 7-2 both the vacuum-tube triode and the transistors act as valves, allowing small amounts of power to control larger amounts of power. V_{PP} and V_{CC} provide the larger amounts of power which are being controlled, while R_P and R_C provide a place for the output voltage to be developed.

The source of signal to be amplified is indicated in the diagrams as v_s. In practice v_s can be anything from an antenna to a sensing device implanted under the skin of an animal for medical research or the output of a phonograph cartridge.

Another component found in both vaccum-tube and transistor amplifiers which remains to be explained is the capacitor, indicated as C_C in Fig. 7-2*a* to *c*. The function which C_C is called upon to perform is that of blocking any dc level which the input signal may be riding on. If it is desired that an incoming dc level not be blocked, C_C is omitted from the circuit.

The last of the components needing explanation is the resistor, indicated as R_G in the vacuum-tube amplifier circuit of Fig. 7-2a. The function served by R_G is twofold. First, it provides a path whereby the dc voltage bias developed across R_K can appear at the grid of the tube. Note that without R_G the bias voltage is blocked by the capacitor C_C. The second function performed by the resistor R_G is that of providing a path whereby electrons which may accumulate on the grid can leak off. Because they are in the path of the electron stream between the cathode and the plate, some electrons collide with the grid and remain. If R_G were not present, these electrons would accumulate until a large enough charge built up to repel the electrons coming from the cathode, and then the tube would be *blocked*. The name given to R_G therefore is *grid leak resistor*.

CHARACTERISTIC CURVES

In describing the operating characteristics of a particular active device two approaches are available. Equations can be written describing the behavior of the device, or the behavior of the device can be described by means of graphs. Equations for describing the behavior of an active device would be too unwieldy and cumbersome for use by circuit designers. The equations are therefore relegated to use by a small group of people who design the actual active devices themselves. A set of graphs describing the behavior of each device is more precisely what is needed and is used extensively by circuit and equipment designers throughout the electronics field. Though many different sets of curves can be drawn, the most popular are the collector characteristics for the transistor and their vacuum-tube counterpart, the plate characteristics. Figure 7-3 depicts these characteristic curves.

Note that all the currents and voltages indicated on the collector-characteristic curves of the *PNP* transistor are negative quantities. This should not be a cause for alarm. The negative sign appears because of the convention which calls electron currents flowing into a transistor negative quantities and electron currents flowing out of a transistor positive quantities. The reason for the negative sign for v_{ce} on the *PNP* curves is that the collector is negative with respect to the emitter in a properly biased *PNP* common-emitter amplifier.

These characteristic curves prove to be an immense help in designing and analyzing the operation of circuits which contain active devices.

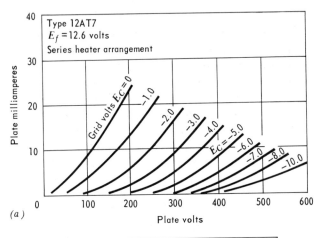

(a)

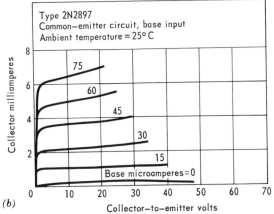

(b)

FIGURE 7-3 *Typical set of characteristic curves. (a) Plate characteristics of a triode; (b) collector characteristics of an NPN transistor; (c) collector characteristics of a PNP transistor. (RCA.)*

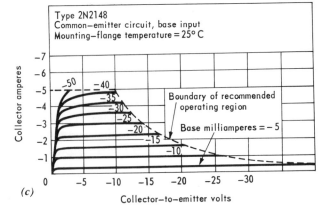

(c)

THE LOAD LINE

In analyzing any piece of equipment it is necessary to have a complete description of all its components. It is therefore necessary to have a description of all parts of the amplifier circuit when undertaking a design or analysis. Referring to Fig. 7-4, it is seen that the following are necessary for a complete description of the output section of an amplifier. First a description of the behavior of the active device is needed. This is provided by the characteristic curves discussed above, which are supplied by the manufacturer. Second, a description of the load resistance and the power supply is necessary. This is easily determined by writing the equation obtained from the Kirchhoff voltage law around the output circuit loop. (Kirchhoff's voltage law: the sum of the voltage rises is equal to the sum of the voltage drops around a complete electric loop.) Applying this law gives

$$V_{XX} = iR + v$$

(see Fig. 7-4). In the case of the vacuum tube this becomes

$$V_{PP} = i_p R_P + v_p$$

In the case of the transistor amplifier

$$V_{CC} = i_c R_C + v_{ce}$$

(see Fig. 7-5).

Note in the case of the vacuum-tube amplifier that R_K has been left out of the equation. In a rigorous analysis it should be included, but in most cases it is much smaller than R_P and therefore is left out to simplify the analysis. In the event that R_K should be more than one-tenth of R_P, it should be included. An easy way to do this is to increase the value of R_P in the above equation, making

FIGURE 7-4 A complete basic amplifier circuit.

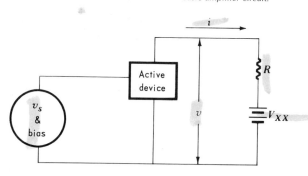

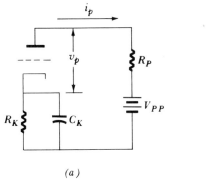
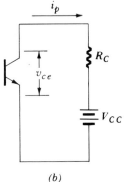

(a)

(b)

FIGURE 7-5 *The output section of an amplifier.* (a) *Triode amplifier;* (b) *transistor amplifier.*

it read

$$V_{PP} = i_p(R_P + R_K) + v_p$$

However, in most cases this is not necessary, and the simplified equation

$$V_{PP} = i_p R_P + v_p$$

is satisfactory; thus it will be used here.

Note that the output section of the amplifier is completely described by the above output circuit equation plus the active-device characteristic curves. In analyzing a circuit it is necessary to run a simultaneous solution of the characteristic curves with the output circuit equation described above. A solution of this circuit can be obtained in one of two ways. One is to write an algebraic equation for the characteristic curves and then solve it simultaneously with the output circuit equation. Obviously this is highly impractical since writing an equation for the characteristic curves involves much effort and results in an unwieldy set of equations. The other method, which proves quite easy and practical, is to describe the output circuit equation as a graph and plot it on the same set of axes as the characteristic curves. One reason for the ease with which this can be done is that the output equation results in a straight-line equation of the form $y = mx + b$.

Since the output equation is a straight line, only two points are necessary in its determination. The two easiest points to determine are the x- and y-axis intercepts.

In the equation for the vacuum-tube amplifier output circuit, v_p is set to zero and i is determined; then i is set to zero and v_p det

Let

Nov

Thu   :termined (see
Tab

Let

Let

(see

TABLE 7-2

v_{ce}	i_c
0	$\dfrac{V_{CC}}{R_C}$
V_{CC}	0

                                                                plotted on the
chara   ted represents
the c   *ad line* of the
ampl

THE
The   l line at which
the a   a zero magni-

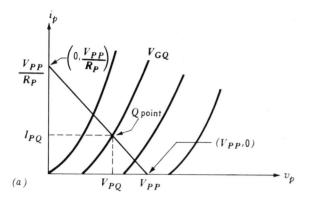

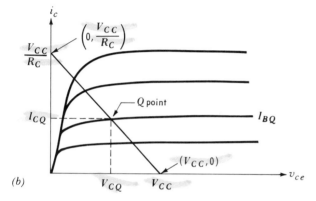

FIGURE 7-6 *Plotting a load line and determining the Q point on a set of characteristics.* (a) *Vacuum tube;* (b) *transistor.*

tude. The *Q point*, as it is frequently called, is determined by the intersection of the load line and the curve of the characteristics which corresponds to the bias on the input of the amplifier. The bias, in the case of the vacuum-tube amplifier, is a grid voltage denoted by V_{GQ} or V_{GG}, while in the case of the transistor amplifier the bias is base current and denoted by I_{BQ} (see Fig. 7-6).

The load line represents all the possible points of operation. At no time can the amplifier be operating at a point other than one which is located on the load line.

Illustrative Problem 7-1

A transistor which has the collector-characteristic curves shown below (RCA 40309) is used in the circuit shown in Fig. Prob. 7-1.

Construct the load line which represents the operation of this circuit and determine the operating point for a quiescent base current of 24 μa.

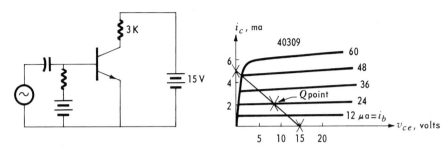

SOLUTION
Given: Curves and circuit shown in Fig. Prob. 7-1; $V_{CC} = 15$ volts; $R_C = 3$ kilohms; $I_{BQ} = 24$ μa
Find: Load line; Q point

$$V_{CC} = i_c R_C + v_{ce}$$
$$15 = i_c (3 \times 10^3) + v_{ce}$$

v_{ce}	i_c
0	$\dfrac{V_{CC}}{R_C} = \dfrac{15}{3 \times 10^3} = 5$ ma
$V_{CC} = 15$ volts	0

Illustrative Problem 7-2

A vacuum tube with the plate-characteristic curves shown in Fig. Prob. 7-2 is used in the amplifier circuit illustrated. Construct the load line and indicate the operating point which describes the operation of the circuit for a grid-to-cathode bias voltage of -10 volts.

SOLUTION
Given: Curves and circuit shown in Fig. Prob. 7-2; $R_P = 20$ kilohms; $V_{PP} = 400$ volts; $V_{GG} = -10$ volts

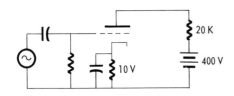

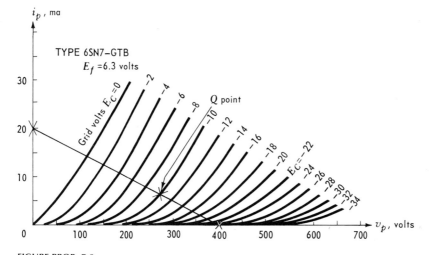

Find: Load line; Q point

$$V_{PP} = i_p R_P + v_p$$
$$400 = i_p(20 \times 10^3) + v_p$$

	i_p	v_p
	0	$V_{PP} = 400$ volts
$\dfrac{V_{PP}}{R_P} = \dfrac{400}{20 \times 10^3} = 20$ ma		0

THE POINT-SLOPE METHOD OF LOAD-LINE CONSTRUCTION

Many situations make the previously described method of load line construction impractical. In some cases the current intercept point (collector current in the case of the transistor and plate current

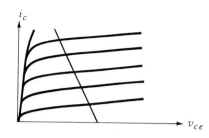

FIGURE 7-7   *The current axis intercept off the scale of the characteristic curves.*

in the case of the vacuum tube) is off the scale of the characteristic provided by the manufacturer.   Figure 7-7 depicts such a case.

An alternative to the intercept method of load-line construction is called the *point-slope method* of construction.   Load-line construction is merely the construction of a straight line from an equation.   Referring back to courses in geometry, we see that a line can be determined not only by two points but also by one point and the slope of the line.

TABLE 7-3

$V_{PP} = i_p R_P + v_p$	$V_{CC} = i_c R_C + v_{ce}$

$y = mx + b$	$i_p = \dfrac{-v_p}{R_P} + \dfrac{V_{PP}}{R_P}$	$i_c = \dfrac{-v_{ce}}{R_C} + \dfrac{V_{CC}}{R_C}$

Comparing the load-line equations with the general equation of a straight line, we obtain Table 7-3.   One finds that the slope of the load line is $-1/R_P$ for the vacuum-tube amplifier and $-1/R_C$ for the transistor amplifier.

The load line can therefore be constructed by drawing a line at a slope of $-1/R_P$ or $-1/R_C$.   It is known that this line will pass through the two intercept points if it is extended far enough.   Although this discussion began with the assumption that one of the intercept points may not be available, one of the two is usually available and is used as the point which, in conjunction with the slope, will determine the line.   The intercept point usually available is the x axis, or voltage intercept point.

Thus, to construct the load line which represents the working of a given amplifier one method is to construct a line at a slope of $-1/R_P$ or $-1/R_C$ through the V_{PP} or the V_{CC} intercept point.

Figure 7-8 is a descriptive diagram showing how a load line

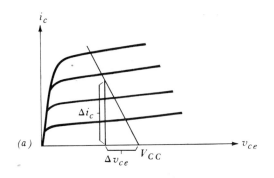

(a)

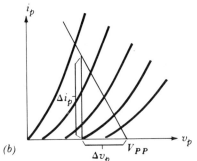

(b)

FIGURE 7-8 *Point-slope method of constructing load lines on (a) transistor characteristic and (b) triode vacuum-tube characteristic.*

is constructed by the point-slope method. First the V_{PP} or V_{CC} point is marked on the horizontal axis. Any convenient value of Δi_c or Δi_p is then taken and injected into the formula

$$\frac{-1}{R_P} = \frac{\Delta i_p}{\Delta v_p} \qquad \text{or} \qquad \frac{-1}{R_C} = \frac{\Delta i_c}{\Delta v_{ce}}$$

which in simpler and more obvious form can be written

$$R_P = \frac{\Delta v_p}{\Delta i_p} \qquad \text{or} \qquad R_C = \frac{\Delta v_{ce}}{\Delta i_c}$$

From this the appropriate value of Δv_p or Δv_{ce} is determined.

Illustrative Problem 7-3
Construct the load line which describes the circuit in Fig. Prob. 7-3, assuming that the characteristic curves represent the operation of the active device.

SOLUTION
Given: Curves and circuit shown in Fig. Prob. 7-3; $R_C = 1500$ ohms; $V_{CC} = 15$ volts

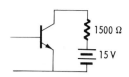

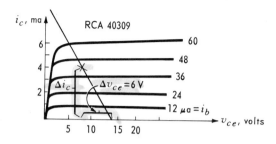

FIGURE PROB. 7-3

Find: Load line

$$R_C = \frac{\Delta v_{ce}}{\Delta i_c}$$

$$= 1500 \text{ ohms}$$

Let $\Delta i_c = 4$ ma. Then

$$1500 = \frac{\Delta v_{ce}}{4 \times 10^{-3}}$$

$$\Delta v_{ce} = 1500 \times 4 \times 10^{-3} = 6.0 \text{ volts}$$

THE MAXIMUM-POWER-DISSIPATION CURVE

As with all electric components, all active devices have a limit to the amount of power they can dissipate. The amount of power an active device is called upon to dissipate at any given instant is determined by the product of the voltage across it and the current through it at that instant. An aid in preventing the designer from exceeding the maximum power-dissipation capabilities of a device is the maximum-power-dissipation curve, which can be constructed on the set of characteristic curves for the device. The maximum-power-dissipation curve is the boundary between the permissible operating region and the forbidden region.

The rated maximum-power-dissipation capabilities of the device can be found in the literature provided by the manufacturer describing the device. This information is used to construct a maximum-power-dissipation curve by choosing values of either

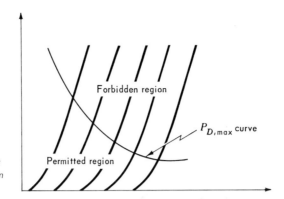

FIGURE 7-9 $P_{D,\text{max}}$ curve
separating forbidden region
from permitted region.

current or voltage which can conveniently fit on the characteristic
curves and then determining the other variable, current or voltage,
from the formula

$$\text{Power} = \text{current} \times \text{voltage}$$

A smooth curve through these points provides the required curve.
Figure 7-9 shows a typical maximum-power-dissipation curve.

Illustrative Problem 7-4

The device represented by the characteristic curves shown in Fig.
Prob. 7-4 has a maximum power-handling capability of 2.5 watts.
Construct the maximum-power-dissipation curve for the device.

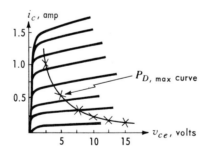

FIGURE PROB. 7-4

Solution

Given: Characteristic curve shown in Fig. Prob. 7-4; $P_{D,\text{max}} = 2.5$
watts
Find: $P_{d,\text{max}}$ curve

92   **AMPLIFIERS**

v_{ce}	i_c
2.5	1
5.0	0.5
7.5	0.33
10.0	0.25
12.5	0.2
15.0	0.167

$$v_{ce}i_c = 2.5$$
$$i_c = \frac{2.5}{v_{ce}}$$

RESTRICTIONS ON THE LOAD LINE DUE TO THE MAXIMUM-POWER-DISSIPATION CURVE

The operation of any given amplifier is limited to the load line. All points of operation must lie on the load line since the load line represents the operating restrictions placed on the amplifier by the components, other than the active device, which make up the output circuit of the amplifier.

Since all points of operation are described by the load line, it is mandatory that the load line be completely within the permissible operating region as described by the maximum-power-dissipation curve. Thus one extreme position of the load line is tangent to the maximum-power-dissipation curve. In many cases the circuit designer is limited to using a given power supply voltage which is available, and he must determine the load resistance which best suits the requirements placed on the amplifier by the function it is to perform. In this type of design problem the designer must limit his choice to a load resistance which is larger than that determined by the load line tangent to the maximum-power-dissipation curve. Thus the minimum resistance allowed for a load resistor is that which is described by the load line tangent to the maximum-power-dissipation curve.

Illustrative Problem 7-5

Determine the minimum allowable value of load resistance for an amplifier which uses the vacuum tube described by the characteristic curves in Fig. Prob. 7-5. The available plate power-supply voltage is 200 volts.

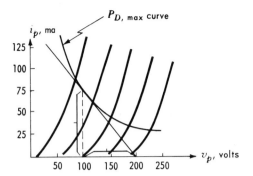

FIGURE PROB. 7-5

SOLUTION

Given: Characteristic curves shown in Fig. Prob. 7-5; $P_{D,\text{max}}$ curve as shown; $V_{PP} = 200$ volts

Find: $R_{P,\text{min}}$

$$R_{P,\text{min}} = \frac{\Delta v_p}{\Delta i_p} = \frac{200 - 100}{75 \times 10^{-3} - 0} = \frac{100}{75 \times 10^{-3}}$$

$$\boxed{R_{P,\text{min}} = 1330 \text{ ohms}}$$

THE FOUR-QUADRANT GRAPH

Use can be made of the characteristic curves and the load line in determining the output signal of an amplifier when the input signal is known. Since all points of operation must lie on the load line, a varying input signal causes the operating point to move up and down the load line. For any given operating point, the active-device output voltage is found by projecting the operating point down from the load line onto the horizontal axis. The active-device output current is determined by projecting the operating point from the load line to the vertical axis (see Fig. 7-10).

A simple way of handling an entire waveshape is to use the load line as an input axis for plotting the input signal (see Figs. 7-11 and 7-12). *The values of the various points on the load line (axis calibration) are determined by the intersection of the load line with the characteristic curves.* A time axis for the input signal is drawn perpendicular to the load line through the Q point. Thus, a set of axes is available for describing the input signal. The input signal is then plotted on this set of axes and can be projected to the load line, point by point, and then down to the voltage-output axis and across to the output-current axis of the characteristic curves. Thus a descriptive diagram of the output current and voltage waveshapes is provided. This is done using the format shown in Fig.

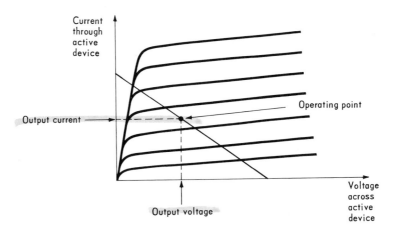

FIGURE 7-10 *Projecting the operating point to the horizontal and vertical axes in order to obtain the current and voltage values associated with the operating point.*

7-12. The page is divided into four quadrants, the first quadrant housing the original characteristic curves and input signal, the second providing a place for the output-current waveform to be drawn, and the fourth allowing for the construction of the output-voltage waveform. The third quadrant remains for use as a calculation or diagram box. This format is known as a four-quadrant construction, the graphs being referred to as a set of *four-quadrant graphs.*

FIGURE 7-11 *The load line as an input-signal axis.*

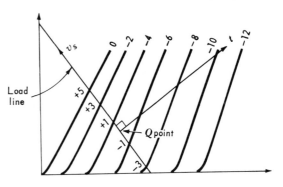

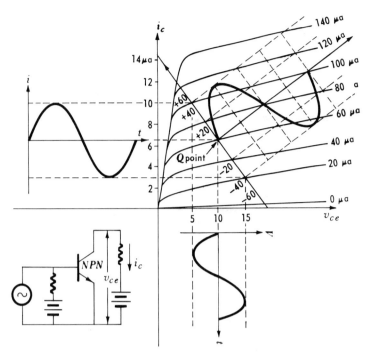

FIGURE 7-12 *Four-quadrant graph construction.*

Note that the gain of the amplifier can be obtained directly from the four-quadrant graphs, current gain in the case of the transistor amplifier and voltage gain in the case of the vacuum-tube amplifier, the peak-to-peak output signal being divided by the peak-to-peak input signal. A major advantage of using graphs rather than the gain formula is that they show how well the amplifier reproduces the waveform of the input signal and how much distortion is introduced by the amplifier.

Illustrative Problem 7-6

A 2N2613 transistor is used in an amplifier circuit with a load resistance of 1 kilohm and a collector supply of 10 volts. A common-emitter configuration is used, and the base bias current is $-30\ \mu a$. An input signal of 40 μa peak-to-peak is applied.

(a) Determine the coordinates of the Q point.
(b) Draw the four quadrant graphs for this situation.
(c) Determine the current gain for this amplifier.
(d) If the input impedance of this transistor is 800 ohms, what is the voltage gain?

SOLUTION

Given: 2N2613; $R_L = 1$ kilohm; $V_{CC} = 10$ volts; $I_{BQ} = -30$ μa; $I_{signal} = 40$ μa peak-to-peak; $R_{in} = 800$ ohms

Find:

(a) Q point
(b) Four-quadrant graph
(c) A_i
(d) A_v

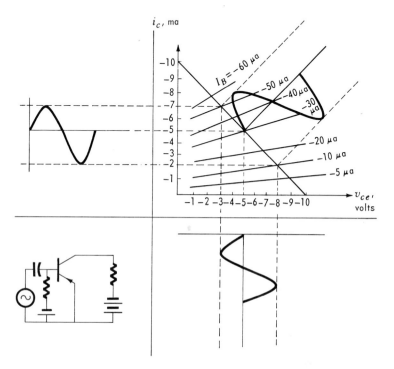

FIGURE PROB. 7-6

(a) The coordinates of the Q point are

$$
\boxed{
\begin{aligned}
I_{CQ} &= -5 \text{ ma} \\
V_{CEQ} &= 5 \text{ volts} \\
I_{BQ} &= -30 \text{ } \mu\text{a}
\end{aligned}
}
$$

(b) See Fig. Prob. 7-6.

(c) $A_i = \dfrac{\Delta i_{out}}{\Delta i_{in}} = \dfrac{7 \times 10^{-3} - 2 \times 10^{-3}}{40 \times 10^{-6}}$

$$\boxed{A_i = 125}$$

(d) $\quad \Delta v_{in} = R_{in} \Delta i_{in} = 800 \times 40 \times 10^{-6} = 32 \times 10^{-3}$

$$A_v = \frac{\Delta v_{out}}{\Delta v_{in}} = \frac{8 - 3 \quad \text{(from graph)}}{32 \times 10^{-3}}$$

$$\boxed{A_v = 158}$$

THE MOSFET

A comparatively new active device combines the advantages of both the transistor and the vacuum tube. It has the high input impedance of the vacuum tube and the small size and negligible warm-up time of the transistor. The advantage of high input resistance is that it draws practically no power from whatever is supplying the input signal. The new device is called the MOSFET, frequently referred to merely as the FET. MOSFET stands for *metal oxide silicon field effect transistor*. It is made of semiconductor material, as are the *NPN* and the *PNP* transistors. The MOSFET has two types, the *N*-channel type and the *P*-channel type.

SCHEMATIC SYMBOLS

The symbols for the two types are shown in Fig. 7-13, which also shows the terminal designations. The one terminal which is probably causing confusion at this point is the one marked SUBSTRATE. The substrate is the block of material upon which the MOSFET

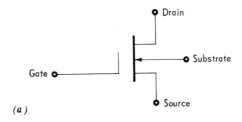

(a)

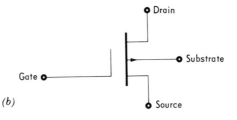

FIGURE 7-13 *Symbolic representation of MOSFETs. (a) N-channel type; (b) P-channel type.*

(b)

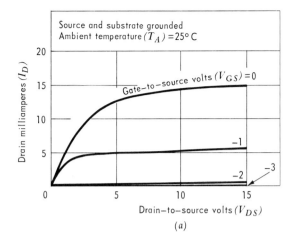

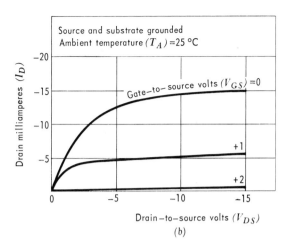

FIGURE 7-14 *Typical characteristic curves for an (a) N-channel MOSFET; (b) P-channel MOSFET. (RCA.)*

is built. In most circuit configurations the substrate is connected to the source terminal or is grounded.   As is obvious from Fig. 7-13, the indication of whether the MOSFET is of the N- or the P-channel variety is indicated by the direction of the arrow on the substrate terminal, pointing in for N-channel and pointing out for the P-channel variety.

For our present purposes we can make the following analogy between the vacuum tube, the transistor, and the MOSFET:

Vacuum Tube	Transistor	MOSFET
Cathode	Emitter	Source
Plate	Collector	Drain
Grid	Base	Gate

Typical characteristic curves for the N- and the P-channel MOSFET are shown as Fig. 7-14.

AMPLIFIER CONFIGURATIONS

Figure 7-15 shows two typical amplifier configurations for common-source amplifiers. One is for an N-channel MOSFET and the other is for a P-channel MOSFET. All the auxiliary components included in the amplifier are directly analogous in position and in function to those used in the vacuum-tube common-cathode amplifier. V_{DD} provides the large amounts of power which are needed

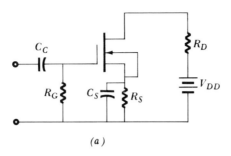

(a)

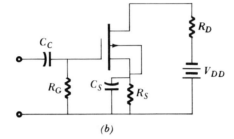

FIGURE 7-15 *Typical common-source MOSFET amplifiers.* (a) N-channel type; (b) P-channel type.

(b)

in the output section of the amplifier, R_D provides a place for the output voltage to be developed, and R_S is included in order to provide a bias voltage between the gate and the source terminals as was done by R_K in the case of the vacuum-tube amplifier. C_S is of course included to provide a low impedance path for signal currents to take, thereby avoiding passage through R_S. R_G is included to provide the necessary path to avoid having the coupling capacitor C_C block the bias which has been developed across R_S. C_C was of course included in order to block any dc level upon which the incoming signal may be riding.

Studying an amplifier circuit with the use of a set of four-quadrant graphs presents no particularly new or unusual considerations when the circuit includes a MOSFET as its active device, but to prevent any possible difficulties from arising the following illustrative problem presents a typical MOSFET design.

Illustrative Problem 7-7

An N-channel MOSFET whose characteristic curves are shown in Fig. Prob. 7-7a is to be used in a common-source amplifier. A dc supply of 20 volts is available for use as a drain supply. The drain circuit load resistor R_D is to be 2000 ohms. Plot a load line for

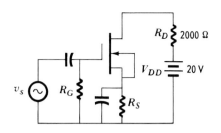

this circuit, locate the Q point for a gate-to-source bias voltage of -3 volts, and complete the set of four-quadrant graphs for an input signal voltage of 4 volts peak-to-peak. Determine the required value of R_S, the source bias resistor.

SOLUTION

Given: N-channel MOSFET with characteristics shown in Fig. Prob. 7-7b; $V_{DD} = 20$ volts; $R_D = 2000$ ohms; $V_{GG} = -3$; $V_{\text{sig}} = 4$ volts peak-to-peak

Find:

(a) Load line
(b) Q point
(c) Four-quadrant graph
(d) R_S

(a) $V_{DD} = i_d R_D + v_{ds}$
     $20 = i_d 2000 + v_{ds}$

i_d	v_{ds}
0	20
$\dfrac{20}{2000} = 10$ ma	0

(b) and (c) See Fig. Prob. 7-7b.

(d) $I_{DQ} = 4.1$ ma

$$R_S = \frac{V_{GG}}{I_{DQ}} = \frac{3}{4.1 \times 10^{-3}} = 732 \text{ ohms}$$

$$\boxed{R_S = 732 \text{ ohms}}$$

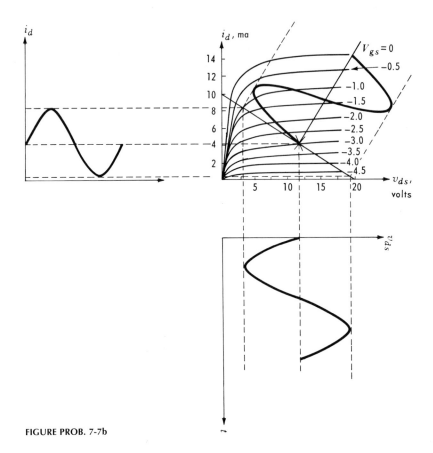

FIGURE PROB. 7-7b

PROBLEMS

7-1 What is an amplifier?

7-2 Is a transformer an amplifier? Why?

7-3 What is the only way in which the output of an amplifier should differ from its input?

7-4 What is the difference between a voltage amplifier and a power amplifier?

7-5 What is an active device?

7-6 Why is the common-emitter amplifier called by that name? The common-cathode amplifier?

7-7 Why is a bias voltage or current needed?

7-8 Refer to Fig. 7-2. What function is provided by V_{CC}, R_C, V_{BB}, R_B, C_C, V_{PP}, R_P, R_G, R_K, C_K?

7-9 Sketch the circuit of a common-emitter amplifier using an *NPN* transistor. Repeat for a *PNP* transistor.

7-10 How can the characteristics of an active device be fully described (two ways)? Which of the two ways is preferable?

7-11 (*a*) List all the parts of the output section of an amplifier which must be included in order for the operation of the circuit to be completely described.

(*b*) What is a load line? What function does it serve?

7-12 A common-emitter *PNP* transistor amplifier has the following component values: $R_B = 50$ kilohms, $V_{BB} = 9$ volts, $R_C = 2.5$ kilohms, $V_{CC} = 12$ volts, $C_C = 0.5$ μf. Sketch a schematic diagram of the circuit and write a Kirchhoff voltage equation for the output portion of the circuit.

7-13 A 2N2614 *PNP* transistor is to be used in a common-emitter configuration. The collector supply voltage is to be 10 volts, and the load register is to be 333 ohms.

(*a*) Sketch a diagram of the circuit.

(*b*) Write a Kirchhoff voltage equation describing the output section of the amplifier.

(*c*) Determine the intercept points of the load line and then plot the load line.

7-14 Repeat Prob. 7-13 for a 40317 *NPN* transistor using a 15-volt collector supply and a 3-kilohm load resistor.

7-15 A 40309 *NPN* transistor is used in a common-emitter configuration. A quiescent operating point located at a base current of 24 μa and a collector-to-emitter voltage of 7.5 volts is required. A collector supply of 15 volts is being used.

(*a*) Locate the quiescent operating point.

(*b*) Construct the load line.

(*c*) Determine the collector current at the Q point.

(*d*) At what value of collector current does the load line intercept the collector-current axis?

(*e*) Determine the required value of the collector load resistor.

7-16 The triode section of a 7199 vacuum tube is to be used in a common-cathode amplifier. The plate supply voltage is 200 volts, and the load resistor is 20 kilohms.

(*a*) Sketch the schematic diagram of the circuit.

(*b*) Write an equation describing the load line.

(*c*) Construct the load line.

(*d*) Locate the Q point for a grid bias of -4 volts.

(*e*) How much plate current flows when no varying input signal is applied (quiescent conditions)?

(*f*) Calculate the resistance of the cathode resistor R_K required to provide the necessary -4 volt grid bias.

7-17 Write an equation describing the output circuit of a triode amplifier feeding a load of 15 kilohms connected to a 300-volt plate supply. A 6SN7 triode is used as the active device. Plot the load line and indicate the quiescent point for a grid bias of -3 volts. What are the plate current and plate voltage during quiescent conditions?

7-18 Why is it necessary to know more than one method of load-line construction?

7-19 What function does the maximum-power-dissipation curve serve? How is it constructed?

7-20 An amplifier using a 2N3439 transistor is to be operated from a 60-volt supply using a collector load resistor of 300 ohms. Construct the load line. Construct a 5-watt maximum-power-dissipation curve. Is this operation reasonably safe?

7-21 A 40263 transistor is to be used with a collector supply of 9 volts. Sketch a maximum-power-dissipation curve for limiting the maximum power dissipation to 50 mw. Calculate the minimum allowable collector load resistor for these conditions.

7-22 A 2N2953 *PNP* germanium transistor-amplifier is to have a quiescent base current of 20 μa and a quiescent collector current of 5 ma. Both V_{BB} and V_{CC} are 6-volt batteries.

(a) Find the Q point and construct the load line.

(b) Calculate the resistance of the collector load resistor.

7-23 The triode section of a 7199 vacuum tube is to be operated from a plate supply of 250 volts with a plate load resistor of 20 kilohms. The grid is to be biased at −4 volts. The input is a 6-volt peak-to-peak sine wave.

(a) Draw a schematic diagram of the circuit.

(b) Plot the load line and locate the quiescent operating point.

(c) Determine the required value of the cathode resistor.

(d) What value of bypass capacitance will provide a capacitive reactance which will be one-tenth of R_K at 40 Hz?

(e) Complete the four-quadrant graph which describes the operation of this amplifier.

(f) What is the voltage gain of this amplifier?

7-24 A 2N2102 transistor is being used in a common-emitter amplifier. A collector supply of 15 volts is available, and a collector load resistance of 50 ohms is to be used. The base bias current is to be 1.5 ma. An input signal of 2.0 ma peak-to-peak is anticipated. Sketch a four-quadrant graph describing the operation of this amplifier.

7-25 The triode section of a 7199 vacuum tube is to be used in an amplifier. A 300-volt plate supply is to be used along with a 20-kilohm plate load resistor. The quiescent plate current is to be 7.5 ma. A 10-volt peak-to-peak input signal is expected.

(a) Draw a schematic diagram of the amplifier.

(b) Construct the appropriate load line and determine the quiescent operating point.

(c) What is the quiescent grid voltage?

(d) Determine the value of the cathode resistor necessary to provide the required grid bias.

(e) Complete the four-quadrant graph describing the amplifier.

7-26 A common-emitter transistor amplifier makes use of a 2N2613 as its active device. The collector supply voltage is 15 volts, and the collector load resistor is 1500 ohms. The base current is biased at 50 μa. A peak-to-peak input signal of 40 μa is applied to the circuit. Construct the four-quadrant graph for this amplifier and then determine its current gain and voltage gain.

7-27 A 2N2102 transistor is used in a common-emitter amplifier circuit. The collector supply battery is 20 volts, and the collector resistor R_C is 100 ohms. A quiescent base current of 1 ma is desired. An input signal current of 2 ma peak-to-peak is impressed on the amplifier. This input is due to a signal voltage of 0.2 volt peak-to-peak.

(a) Draw the schematic diagram of the amplifier.
(b) Draw the appropriate load line.
(c) Indicate the Q point.
(d) What is the quiescent value of the collector current and the collector-to-emitter voltage?
(e) Complete the four-quadrant graph.
(f) Determine the peak-to-peak collector current.
(g) Find the peak-to-peak collector-to-emitter voltage.
(h) Calculate the current gain.
(i) Calculate the voltage gain.
(j) Calculate the power gain.

7-28 What function is performed by the source resistor R_S in a common-source MOSFET amplifier?

7-29 What is the chief advantage of the MOSFET over the conventional transistor?

7-30 An N-channel MOSFET whose characteristics are shown in Fig. 7-16 is to be used in a common-source amplifier. A 24-volt power supply is available for use with this amplifier. The load resistor in the drain circuit is 2500 ohms. Construct the set of four-quadrant graphs and determine the necessary value of source bias resistor R_S for a quiescent gate voltage of -3 volts and an input gate signal of 4 volts peak-to-peak.

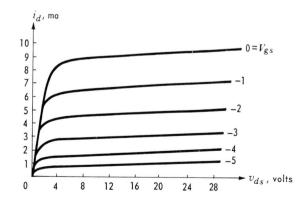

FIGURE 7-16 Characteristic curve for Prob. 7-30.

CHAPTER

BIAS AND STABILIZATION CIRCUITS

In the previous chapter the bias current required by the transistor was supplied by a source which was independent of the collector supply. Obviously, this is rather inconvenient and expensive. A much better design would make use of the collector supply already present. A number of such schemes have been developed and will be discussed in this chapter. The key feature which makes the various schemes different is the effect they have on the *stability* of the amplifier. The term stability refers to the ability of the circuit to maintain the same quiescent operating point under various adverse operating conditions or replacement of the active device.

SENSITIVITY OF TRANSISTORS

The reason for the additional concern for the stability of transistor amplifiers, over that for the vacuum-tube amplifier, is the extreme sensitivity of transistors to their environment and the greater variation in operating characteristics from one sample to another for the same transistor type. Of major concern when designing transistor amplifiers is the effect of temperature on the quiescent base and collector currents. The effect which troubles the designer is known as *thermal runaway*. A small rise in temperature causes an increase in base current. This increase in base current is amplified and causes an increase in collector current, which, in

106

turn, causes an increase in temperature. If precautions are not taken to prevent it, the process continues to repeat itself—possibly until the transistor is destroyed because it exceeded the maximum permissible temperature. Heat is the major enemy of the transistor, so much so that many transistors come with special finned mounting plates to carry away excessive heat that develops even under normal anticipated operating conditions. This special mounting hardware is known as a *heat sink*.

FIXED CURRENT BIAS

The simplest biasing arrangement which does not require a separate bias supply but makes use of the collector supply is known as the *fixed-current-bias* arrangement and is shown in Fig. 8-1. Note the path taken by the bias current and observe that the bias current in the case of both the *NPN* and the *PNP* transistor is in the proper direction for biasing the transistor.

A detailed study of this bias arrangement requires use of Kirchhoff's voltage law: in a complete electric loop the sum of the voltage rises must be equal to the sum of the voltage drops.

The loop to be used in applying Kirchhoff's voltage law is the one indicated by the current path shown in Fig. 8-1. This loop contains the collector power supply, R_1 (the biasing resistor), and the base-emitter junction of the transistor.

Applying Kirchhoff's voltage law gives

$$V_{CC} = I_{BQ}R_1 + V_{BEQ}$$

FIGURE 8-1 *Fixed-current-bias arrangement with (a) NPN transistor and (b) PNP transistor.*

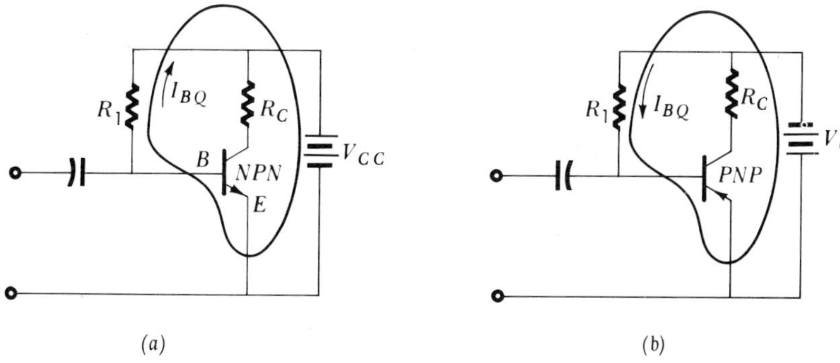

(a)   (b)

The proper signs of the terms in the above equation depend on whether a *PNP* or an *NPN* transistor is being used. The equation can be simplified to

$$V_{CC} = |I_{BQ}R_1| + |V_{BEQ}|$$

where the vertical lines indicate absolute values (sign always taken as positive). This eliminates the problem of determining the proper sign for each of the terms of the equation.

The voltage V_{BEQ} is dependent on many factors, the most significant of which is the transistor material. For germanium transistors a reasonable approximation for V_{BEQ} is considered to be 0.2 volt, while silicon transistors are taken to have a V_{BEQ} of 0.6 volt. The above equations then become

$$V_{CC} = |I_{BQ}R_1| + \begin{cases} 0.2 \\ \text{or} \\ 0.6 \end{cases}$$

Illustrative Problem 8-1

A *PNP* germanium transistor is used in a common-emitter amplifier. The quiescent base current is to be 12.5 μa. The collector supply voltage is 10 volts, and the load resistance is 5 kilohms. Determine the required value of R_1 for these conditions if a fixed-current bias arrangement is used.

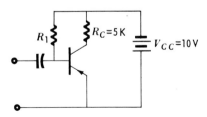

FIGURE PROB. 8-1

SOLUTION
Given: *PNP* Ge transistor; fixed-current bias; common emitter; I_{BQ} = 12.5 μa; V_{CC} = 10 volts; R_C = 5 kilohms
Find: R_1 for fixed-current bias

$$V_{CC} = |I_{BQ}R_1| + |V_{BEQ}|$$
$$10 = 12.5 \times 10^{-6}R_1 + 0.2$$

$$\boxed{R_1 = 784 \text{ kilohms}}$$

SELF-BIAS

The self-bias arrangement is similar to the fixed-bias arrangement except that rather than feeding the bias circuit directly from the collector supply V_{CC}, one end of the bias resistor R_1 is returned to the collector terminal of the transistor (see Fig. 8-2).

The advantage of self-bias over fixed bias is increased stabilization. Let us now undertake a study of this circuit to see how this increased stabilization is obtained. Assume that the base current of the transistor increases for any reason (increase in temperature, replacement of the transistor by a different transistor, etc.). This increased base current results in an increase in collector current which causes a rise in voltage drop across R_C, reducing the voltage across the collector-to-emitter terminals of the transistor. This decrease in voltage must be taken up somewhere in the bias loop. The base-emitter junction voltage will not vary appreciably, so the change must be made up by a decreased voltage across R_1. The voltage across R_1 is $I_{BQ}R_1$. R_1 is a fixed value and does not vary, so that I_{BQ} is therefore forced to decrease. The original disturbance to the amplifier was an increase in base current, which, as has been shown, brings about a reduction in the original disturbance. Thus, though a rise in base and collector currents do occur, they are *partly* compensated for.

This increased stabilization is not achieved without paying a price. Since the effect discussed reduces the desirable as well as the undesirable variations in base and collector current, it reduces the overall gain of the amplifier in order to effect an improvement in stabilization. However, stabilization of the circuit is so important that we are usually happy to pay the price.

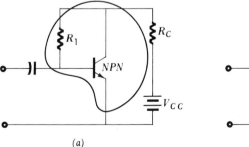

FIGURE 8-2 *The self-bias arrangement with (a) NPN transistor and (b) PNP transistor.*

(a)   (b)

The loops indicated in Fig. 8-2a and b are of interest for studying the bias circuit. The following equation is written making use of Kirchhoff's voltage law around the loops indicated in Fig. 8-2a and b. The equation for the loops is

$$V_{CEQ} = I_{BQ}R_1 + V_{BEQ}$$

which becomes

$$|V_{CEQ}| = |I_{BQ}R_1| + |V_{BEQ}|$$

when simplifying to eliminate the difficulties which might arise due to sign convention.

Illustrative Problem 8-2

An *NPN* silicon transistor is used in a common-emitter amplifier. The characteristic curves of the transistor are shown in Fig. Prob. 8-2. The base bias current is to be 10 μa, the collector supply voltage is 8 volts, and the load resistance is 4000 ohms. Construct the appropriate load line, determine the quiescent operating point, and calculate the required value of the base bias resistor R_1.

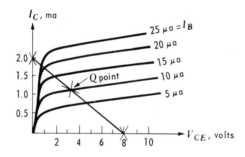

FIGURE PROB. 8-2

SOLUTION

Given: *NPN* silicon transistor; characteristic curves shown in Fig. Prob. 8-2; $I_{BQ} = 10$ μa; $V_{CC} = 8$ volts; $R_C = 4000$ ohms

Find: Load line and Q point; R_1

$$I_{C,\text{intercept}} = \frac{8 \text{ volts}}{4000} = 2 \text{ ma}$$

Q-point coordinates:

$$V_{CEQ} = 3 \text{ volts} \qquad I_{CEQ} = 1.1 \text{ ma} \qquad I_{BEQ} = 10\,\mu\text{a}$$
$$|V_{CEQ}| = |I_{BQ}R_1| + |V_{BEQ}|$$
$$3 = 10 \times 10^{-6}R_1 + 0.6 \qquad \text{for silicon}$$

110   AMPLIFIERS

$$R_1 = \frac{3 - 0.6}{10 \times 10^{-6}}$$

$$\boxed{R_1 = 240 \text{ kilohms}}$$

THE EMITTER SWAMPING RESISTOR

As previously indicated, stabilization against thermal runaway is a major problem in the design of transistor amplifiers. Another method for overcoming this tendency toward thermal runaway makes use of an emitter swamping resistor. A circuit containing such an emitter swamping resistor R_E is shown in Fig. 8-3.

As increased temperature causes a rise in base and collector currents, the emitter current, being equal to the sum of the base and collector currents, also rises. An increase in emitter current brings about an increase in voltage drop across R_E, the emitter swamping resistor. The Kirchhoff's voltage loop of interest in this study is shown in Fig. 8-4.

Note that an increase in voltage across the emitter swamping resistor R_E reduces the available voltage for a drop across R_1, the base biasing resistor. Since the voltage across the base biasing resistor R_1 is equal to $I_{BQ} \times R_1$, I_{BQ} is caused to decrease. This decrease in I_{BQ} in turn causes a reduction in collector current. Realizing that this whole cycle began with a rise in base and collector currents, it is obvious that this circuit arrangement produces increased stabilization, since the final result is a decrease in the original change.

Like the previously discussed methods of stabilization, this arrangement cannot differentiate between changes of base current and collector current due to undesirable causes and changes brought about by signal currents. In this case, however, an attempt is made to reduce this effect of gain degeneration by placing a capacitor C_E in parallel with the emitter swamping resistor R_E, as shown in Fig. 8-5. Since variations in emitter current due to undesirable causes, such as temperature or replacement of the

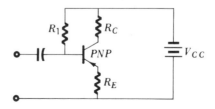

FIGURE 8-3 *Fixed-bias arrangement with swamping resistor R_E.*

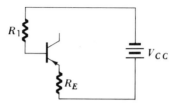

FIGURE 8-4 *Kirchhoff voltage loop involving R_E.*

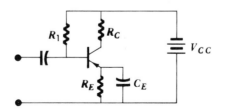

FIGURE 8-5 *C_E shunts R_E in order to reduce gain degeneration.*

transistor, are always slower than those due to signal variations, the capacitor reduces gain degeneration. The impedance of the capacitor is greater for slowly varying signals and thereby appears as practically an open circuit for these slow variations. However, for more rapid variations, such as those caused by the signal, the capacitor impedance is rather low and therefore appears as almost a short circuit, providing a bypass around the swamping resistor.

The use of the emitter swamping resistor is not limited to the fixed-bias arrangement. It is used with a self-bias arrangement as well as other schemes of bias provision (see Fig. 8-6).

VOLTAGE-DIVIDER BIAS

In previously discussed bias and stabilization methods, the stabilization provided by the emitter swamping resistor is dependent on a voltage change which appears across the bias resistor R_1 (see Fig. 8-5). This voltage change is caused by the emitter swamping resistor providing a change in voltage due to changes in current flowing in the output loop.

The voltage change across R_E causes changes in the voltage

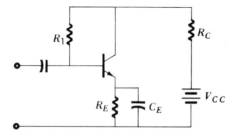

FIGURE 8-6 *A self-bias arrangement with swamping resistor and bypass capacitor.*

112   **AMPLIFIERS**

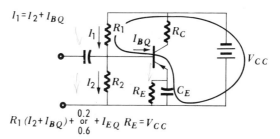

$$I_1 = I_2 + I_{BQ}$$

$$R_1(I_2 + I_{BQ}) + \begin{matrix} 0.2 \\ \text{or} \\ 0.6 \end{matrix} + I_{EQ} R_E = V_{CC}$$

FIGURE 8-7 *Voltage-divider bias with swamping.*

across R_1 because the sum of the voltage across R_1 and the voltage across R_E must equal the difference of the supply voltage V_{CC} and the voltage from the base to the emitter.

Thus it is seen that the emitter swamping resistor R_E is in both the output loop and the bias loop, and voltage changes which appear across R_E due to output current variations are reflected back into the bias loop providing compensatory bias change.

Since the stabilization provided by the emitter swamping resistor is dependent on the voltage $I_{BQ}R_1$, designing with R_1 small in magnitude forces larger changes in I_{BQ} for a given change in voltage across the swamping resistor R_E. A problem presents itself, however, since in all the circuits thus far studied R_1 is determined by the required base bias current.

Figure 8-7 shows a scheme for providing leeway in choosing R_1. A path is provided through R_2 to allow a bleeder current to flow. Thus a manipulation in the value of R_1 is allowed, and if R_2 is of proper value, the required voltage across R_1 can be provided.

A study of the loop in Fig. 8-7 provides the Kirchhoff voltage equation

$$R_1(I_{2Q} + I_{BQ}) + \begin{cases} 0.2 \\ \text{or} \\ 0.6 \end{cases} + I_{EQ}R_E = V_{CC}$$

With V_{CC}, I_{EQ}, and I_{BQ} determined by the requirements set for the design of the amplifier, R_1 is still not limited to one value but can be chosen any reasonable value providing then that R_2 is chosen so as to balance the equation above.

Equations are available for determining the various component values for given allowances in current variation. Because of the complexity of these equations and because an exact tolerance is not called for in many applications, a much simpler design method will be followed which provides for circuits which are quite stable for all but the most delicate of transistor amplifier applications.

Since there are so many variables in the design of this type of circuit, many different solutions to a design problem are feasible. However, in order to have a point of beginning, certain *design criteria* are established. The voltage across R_E presents the first problem. V_{RE} is not very critical but should be large enough to introduce adequate feedback for reasonable stability and yet not reduce the output voltage of the amplifier excessively. It is found that a reasonable compromise exists when V_{RE} is made at least five times V_{BE}, where V_{BE} can be approximated by 0.2 or 0.6 depending on whether the transistor is germanium or silicon. R_E can then be found by dividing V_{RE} by I_{EQ}

$$R_E = \frac{V_{RE}}{I_{EQ}}$$

The second difficulty which presents itself is that of determining R_2; it (Fig. 8-7) should be quite a bit larger than R_E. A reasonably good starting point is to require that R_2 be equal to $10R_E$. The typical design problem below shows an application of these design criteria.

Illustrative Problem 8-3

A silicon transistor is to be used in a common-emitter transistor amplifier. Voltage-divider bias and an emitter swamping resistor are used. The quiescent emitter current is 5 ma, and the quiescent base current is 200 μa. The emitter supply is 20 volts dc. Determine the required value of the swamping resistor and the values of both resistors of the voltage divider.

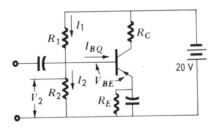

FIGURE PROB. 8-3

SOLUTION

Given: Silicon transistor; $I_{EQ} = 5$ ma; $I_{BQ} = 200$ μa; $V_{CC} = 20$ volts

Find: R_E; R_1; R_2

$$V_{RE} = 5V_{BE} = 5 \times 0.6 = 3 \text{ volts}$$
$$V_2 = V_{BE} + V_{RE} = 0.6 + 3 = 3.6 \text{ volts}$$
$$V_1 = V_{CC} - V_2 = 20 - 3.6 = 16.4 \text{ volts}$$

$$R_E = \frac{V_{RE}}{I_{EQ}}$$

$$\boxed{R_E = \frac{3}{5 \times 10^{-3}} = 600 \text{ ohms}}$$

$$R_2 = 10 R_E$$

$$\boxed{R_2 = 6 \text{ kilohms}}$$

$$I_2 = \frac{V_2}{R_2} = \frac{3.6}{6 \text{ kilohms}} = 0.6 \text{ ma}$$
$$I_1 = I_2 + I_{BQ} = 0.6 \text{ ma} + 0.2 \text{ ma} = 0.8 \text{ ma}$$
$$R_1 = \frac{V_1}{I_1} = \frac{16.4}{0.8 \text{ ma}}$$

$$\boxed{R_1 = 20.5 \text{ kilohms}}$$

PROBLEMS

8-1 Why is there more concern for the stability of transistor amplifiers than for tube amplifiers?

8-2 What is a heat sink? Why is it used?

8-3 Determine the base bias resistor required to produce a base bias current of 0.1 ma in an *NPN* germanium transistor when a collector supply voltage of 9 volts is used in a fixed-bias configuration.

8-4 A *PNP* germanium transistor is to be used as the active device in a common-emitter amplifier using fixed-bias technique. The collector supply voltage is 12 volts.   Sketch a schematic diagram of the circuit and calculate the base bias resistor which will provide a quiescent base current of 200 μa.   Determine the required power rating of the bias resistor.

8-5 A 2N2614 *PNP* germanium transistor requires 0.15 ma for base bias current.   A 9-volt supply battery is being used in the circuit with a collector load resistor of 225 ohms.   A fixed bias arrangement is used.

(*a*)   Draw the schematic diagram of the circuit.

(*b*)   Find the required base bias resistor for fixed-bias operation.

(*c*)   Construct a load line for this circuit and locate the quiescent operating point.

(*d*)   Construct a four-quadrant graph for an input of a 0.2-ma peak-to-peak sine wave.

(*e*)   Determine the current gain of the amplifier from the four-quadrant graph.

8-6 How does a self-bias arrangement differ from a fixed-bias arrangement?

8-7 Describe one advantage and one disadvantage of the self-bias over the fixed-bias arrangement.

8-8 A 40317 *NPN* silicon transistor is to function as the active device in a self-biased common-emitter amplifier. The base bias current is to be 24 μa. The collector load resistor is 2 kilohms, and the supply voltage is 15 volts.
  (*a*) Sketch a schematic diagram of the circuit.
  (*b*) Construct a load line and locate the quiescent operating point.
  (*c*) Determine the quiescent collector-to-emitter voltage.
  (*d*) Calculate the required ratings of the base bias resistor (resistance and power).
  (*e*) Sketch a four-quadrant graph for an input of 36 μa peak-to-peak.
  (*f*) What is the rms output voltage?
  (*g*) Calculate the current gain of the amplifier.

8-9 Draw a schematic diagram and determine the required base bias resistor R_1 for a *PNP* silicon transistor used in a common-emitter self-bias configuration. The quiescent base current should be 0.2 ma, and the quiescent collector current should be 25 ma. The collector load resistor is 1 kilohm, and the collector power supply is 45 volts dc.

8-10 A self-biased *NPN* silicon transistor in common-emitter configuration has a quiescent collector current of 5 ma and a quiescent base current of 0.04 ma. The circuit is supplied from a 15-volt collector supply, and the collector load resistor is 2 kilohms. Determine the quiescent collector-to-emitter voltage and the required base bias resistor.

8-11 (*a*) How does an emitter swamping resistor increase stability?
  (*b*) Why would a designer call for a bypass capacitor across the emitter swamping resistor?

8-12 A *PNP* germanium transistor is to be used in a common-emitter amplifier with voltage-divider bias and emitter swamping. A base bias current of 0.05 ma is desired. A collector supply of 18 volts dc is to be used. A quiescent emitter current of 4 ma is required.
  (*a*) Draw a schematic diagram of the circuit.
  (*b*) What should the value of the quiescent voltage across the swamping resistor be?
  (*c*) Determine the required resistance across the swamping resistor.
  (*d*) Calculate the required value of R_2 (the resistor from base to ground).
  (*e*) Determine the value of R_1 (the resistor from base to collector supply).

8-13 An *NPN* silicon transistor is to be used in a common-emitter amplifier. The amplifier uses voltage-divider bias with emitter

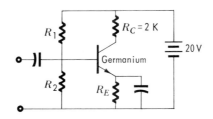

FIGURE 8-8 *Diagram for Prob. 8-15.*

swamping. It is desired that the quiescent base current be 0.1 ma while the quiescent emitter current is 12 ma. The collector power supply is 24 volts. Calculate the value of the emitter swamping resistor and the resistors which make up the voltage divider.

8-14 A *PNP* germanium transistor is used in a common-emitter amplifier with voltage-divider bias with swamping. A collector load resistor of 1200 ohms and a 15-volt power supply are in the output circuit. Sketch the circuit and determine the value of the emitter swamping and voltage-divider resistors. The required base bias current is 100 μa, and the quiescent collector current is 10 ma.

8-15 The common-emitter amplifier shown in Fig. 8-8 has the quiescent coordinates $I_{CQ} = 3.5$ ma and $I_{BQ} = 0.03$ ma. Determine the required value of R_1, R_2, R_E.

8-16 A 2N2953 *PNP* germanium transistor is to be used as the active device in a common-emitter transistor amplifier. The amplifier is to be voltage-divider biased with swamping. A bypass capacitor of 200 μf is used across the swamping resistor. A 9-volt supply is used with a collector load resistor of 500 ohms in the output circuit. It is desired that the quiescent base current be 40 μa.

(*a*) Sketch a schematic diagram of the circuit.

(*b*) Construct a load line and locate the quiescent operating point.

(*c*) Determine the quiescent collector current.

(*d*) What is the value of the quiescent emitter current?

(*e*) Using the design criteria described in this chapter, determine what the voltage drop across the emitter swamping resistor should be.

(*f*) Calculate the required value of the emitter swamping resistor.

(*g*) Find the value of the resistor to be placed in the lower leg of the voltage divider.

(*h*) Determine the voltage drop across the resistor referred to in (*g*).

(*i*) How much current passes through the resistor in (*g*)?

(*j*) Calculate the amount of current passed by the resistor in the upper leg of the voltage divider.

(*k*) What is the voltage drop across the resistor in the upper leg of the voltage divider?

BIAS AND STABILIZATION CIRCUITS   117

(*l*)   Determine the necessary resistance of the resistor in the upper leg of the voltage divider.

(*m*) Make a parts list for this amplifier.

(*n*)   Complete a four-quadrant graph for this amplifier with an input of 60 μa peak-to-peak.

(*o*)   Calculate the current gain of the amplifier.

9

ACTIVE-DEVICE PARAMETERS

In past chapters we used characteristic curves to describe the manner in which particular active devices were functioning. It was shown that active devices with different type designations (tube or transistor numbers) have different characteristic curves. It is obvious that in order to consider a particular active device for use in a circuit under design, the designer must know the operating characteristics of the particular active device. Use of the characteristic curves, however, is not always the best method of obtaining the required information. Consider the case in which the designer wishes to know the response of an amplifier to a very tiny signal. It is possible that the input signal which the designer is considering shows up as merely a pinpoint on the characteristic curves because the curves have been drawn for use with much larger input signals. Because of this consideration manufacturers usually provide additional information in the form of *small-signal parameters.*

SMALL-SIGNAL PARAMETERS
Small-signal parameters describe the functioning of the active device as long as the device is operating over a linear portion of the characteristics. By linear portion of the characteristics is meant that portion of the curves which can be considered as equally spaced straight lines. The amount by which the operating region

119

deviates from these requirements determines the amount by which the results obtained from the use of these parameters differs from those obtained from direct use of the curves themselves.

VACUUM-TUBE PARAMETERS

The three small-signal parameters used with vacuum tubes are the dynamic plate resistance r_p, the amplification factor μ (mu), and the transconductance g_m.

The *dynamic plate resistance* r_p is defined as the ratio of the *change* in plate voltage to the *change* in plate current with grid voltage held constant:

$$r_p \equiv \frac{\Delta v_{pk}}{\Delta i_p}\bigg|_{v_{gk} = \text{const}}$$

The *amplification factor* μ is defined as the ratio of the *change* in plate voltage to the *change* in grid voltage with plate current held constant:

$$\mu \equiv \frac{\Delta v_{pk}}{\Delta v_{gk}}\bigg|_{i_p = \text{const}}$$

The *transconductance* g_m is defined as the ratio of *change* in plate current to the *change* in grid voltage with plate voltage held constant:

$$g_m \equiv \frac{\Delta i_p}{\Delta v_{gk}}\bigg|_{v_{pk} = \text{const}}$$

Note that not all three of the parameters are independent:

$$\frac{\Delta v_{pk}}{\Delta i_p} \frac{\Delta i_p}{\Delta v_{gk}} = \frac{\Delta v_{pk}}{\Delta v_{gk}}$$
$$r_p g_m = \mu$$

When two of the three parameters are known, the third is predetermined.

Since r_p is defined as a change in voltage divided by a change in current, its units will be ohms. The units of transconductance will be mhos, since transconductance is defined as a change in current divided by a change in voltage. Obviously, the amplification factor μ is unitless since it is defined as a change in voltage divided by another change in voltage.

Transconductance is defined as a change in *plate* current divided by a change in *grid* voltage. It is a relationship between an output signal and an input signal. Therefore, we refer to this quantity as a *transfer conductance*; transfer conductance is then shortened to *transconductance*.

DETERMINING SMALL-SIGNAL VACUUM-TUBE PARAMETERS FROM CHARACTERISTIC CURVES

It is necessary at times to determine the small-signal parameters directly from tube characteristics. When this is required, simply

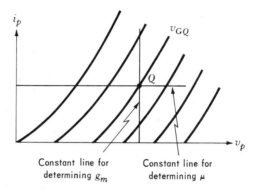

Constant line for determining g_m Constant line for determining μ

FIGURE 9-1 Constant-v_{pk} line for determining g_m and constant-i_p line for determining μ.

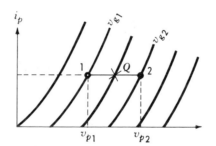

$$\mu = \left.\frac{v_{p2} - v_{p1}}{v_{g1} - v_{g2}}\right|_{i_p = \text{constant}}$$

FIGURE 9-2 Determination of amplification factor.

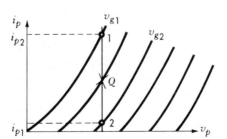

FIGURE 9-3 Determination of g_m.

$$g_m = \left.\frac{i_{p2} - i_{p1}}{v_{g2} - v_{g1}}\right|_{v_p = \text{constant}}$$

ACTIVE-DEVICE PARAMETERS   121

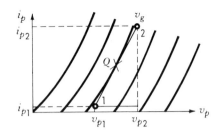

$$r_p = \frac{v_{p2} - v_{p1}}{i_{p2} - i_{p1}}\bigg|_{v_g = \text{constant}}$$

FIGURE 9-4 *Determination of r_p.*

refer to the original definitions of the parameters. In the case of the amplification factor and transconductance, the appropriate constant line is drawn through the quiescent point for which it is desired to know the parameters (see Fig. 9-1).

Two convenient points are chosen on this constant line, and the changes in the appropriate variables are recorded. The two parameters, g_m and μ, can now be determined from their defining equations (see Figs. 9-2 and 9-3).

As far as determining r_p is concerned, it is merely the slope of the characteristic at the point in question. Figure 9-4 gives instructive diagrams for determining r_p.

Illustrative Problem 9-1

Determine the amplification factor, the dynamic plate resistance, and the transconductance at the quiescent point indicated for the triode whose characteristic curves are shown in Fig. Prob. 9-1a.

SOLUTION

Given: Characteristic curves and Q point

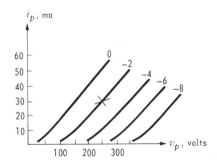

FIGURE PROB. 9-1a

Find:

(a) μ

(b) r_p

(c) g_m

(a) See Fig. Prob. 9-1b.

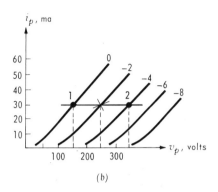

(b)

$$\mu = \frac{\Delta v_{pk}}{\Delta v_{gk}}\bigg|_{i_p = \text{const}}$$

$$= \frac{350 - 150}{4 - 0} = \frac{200}{4}$$

$$\boxed{\mu = 50}$$

(b) See Fig. Prob. 9-1c.

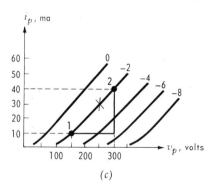

(c)

$$r_p = \frac{\Delta v_{pk}}{\Delta i_p}\bigg|_{v_{gk}\,=\,const} \quad \Delta e_b$$

$$= \frac{300 - 150}{(40 - 10) \times 10^{-3}} = \frac{150 \text{ kilohms}}{30}$$

$$\boxed{r_p = 5 \text{ kilohms}}$$

(c)   See Fig. Prob. 9-1d.

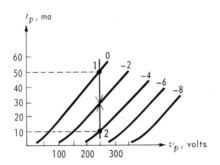

FIGURE PROB. 9-1d

$$g_m = \frac{\Delta i_p}{\Delta v_{gk}}\bigg|_{v_{pk}\,=\,const} = \frac{(50 - 10) \times 10^{-3}}{4 - 0}$$

$$\Delta e_c$$

$$\boxed{g_m = 10{,}000 \ \mu\text{mhos}}$$

(g_m is usually expressed in micromhos.)

TRANSISTOR PARAMETERS

Quite a few parameters have grown up in the study of transistor circuits. Many of them will be discussed in the chapter on equivalent circuits. For the present, the two most important ones will be discussed here, namely, the common-*base* forward-current transfer ratio α and the common-*emitter* forward-current transfer ratio β. Unlike the vacuum-tube parameters, both these have dc as well as ac values which are in common use.

Though their names refer to particular circuit configurations, α and β are characteristics of the transistor, regardless of the configuration in which it is found.

The static, or dc, common-base forward-current transfer ratio is denoted by either α_{dc} or h_{FB}, while the dynamic, or ac, common-base forward-current transfer ratio is denoted by either α_{ac} or

h_{fb}. Both α_{dc} and α_{ac} approach 1 but never equal 1, a typical value being 0.98.   The α of a transistor determines how much of the emitter current gets to the collector.

$$h_{FB} \equiv \alpha_{dc} \equiv \frac{I_C}{I_E}$$
$$h_{fb} \equiv \alpha_{ac} \equiv \frac{\Delta i_c}{\Delta i_e}\bigg|_{v_{cb} = \text{const}}$$

The static, or dc, common-emitter forward-current transfer ratio is denoted by either β_{dc} or h_{FE}, while the dynamic, or ac, common-emitter forward-current transfer ratio is denoted by either β_{ac} or h_{fe}.   The β_{ac} of a transistor is the maximum possible current gain of the unit when it is in a common-emitter configuration.

$$h_{FE} \equiv \beta_{dc} \equiv \frac{I_C}{I_B}$$
$$h_{fe} \equiv \beta_{ac} \equiv \frac{\Delta i_c}{\Delta i_b}\bigg|_{v_{ce} = \text{const}}$$

The α and β of any given transistor are not independent but are related to each other by the relationships

$$\beta_{ac} = \frac{\alpha_{ac}}{1 - \alpha_{ac}}$$
$$\beta_{dc} = \frac{\alpha_{dc}}{1 - \alpha_{dc}}$$

In an effort to be concise, manufacturers sometimes list the transistor parameters α and β instead of providing characteristic curves.   It may then be necessary to construct the characteristic curves from these parameters.   An approximation of the curves used in the study of the common-emitter circuit, the collector curves, is quite easy to construct if one remembers that they are almost horizontal. β_{dc} being equal to I_C/I_B provides the necessary relationship.   The boundaries of the area of interest are provided

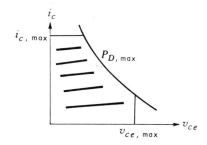

FIGURE 9-5   An approximation to characteristic curves drawn from a knowledge of β_{dc}, $P_{D,max}$, $i_{c,max}$, and $v_{ce,max}$.

by the maximum allowable V_{CE}, the maximum-power-dissipation curve and the maximum allowable i_C (see Fig. 9-5).

THE DETERMINATION OF α AND β FROM COLLECTOR CHARACTERISTICS

It is often necessary to determine the characteristic parameters of a transistor from the collector-characteristic curves. α_{dc} and β_{dc} are easily determined by merely choosing the point on the characteristic which it is desired to know about. Currents are then picked off, and a simple division produces the required result

$$\alpha_{dc} = \frac{I_C}{I_E}$$

$$\beta_{dc} = \frac{I_C}{I_B}$$

α_{ac} and β_{ac}, however, are a bit more difficult to obtain. In order to obtain β_{ac} at a particular point, a constant-v_{ce} line must be drawn through the point in question (see Fig. 9-6).

Two points equally spaced from the point in question are then chosen on the constant-v_{ce} line and Δi_c and Δi_b between these points are determined. β_{ac} is then found from

$$\beta_{ac} = \frac{\Delta i_c}{\Delta i_b}\bigg|_{v_{ce}\,=\,\mathrm{const}}$$

α_{ac} cannot be found directly from the collector characteristics since a constant v_{cb} line cannot be drawn on this set of characteristics. However, having found β_{ac}, α_{ac} can be determined from

$$\alpha_{ac} = \frac{\beta_{ac}}{1 + \beta_{ac}}$$

More will be said in the next chapter about the determination and the meaning of transistor parameters.

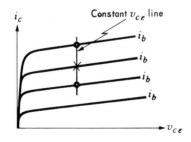

FIGURE 9-6 *Characteristic curve with constant-v_{ce} line.*

Illustrative Problem 9-2

A common-emitter transistor amplifier is required which has a V_{CC} of 10 volts and an R_C of 5000 ohms. The required quiescent base current is 30 μa. A 2N406 transistor is to be used.

(a) Find the Q point.
(b) Determine α_{dc} and β_{dc} at the Q point.
(c) Determine α_{ac} and β_{ac} at the Q point.

SOLUTION

Given: $V_{CC} = 10$ volts; $R_C = 5000$ ohms; 2N406
Find:

(a) Q point
(b) α_{dc} and β_{dc}
(c) α_{ac} and β_{ac}

(a) See Fig. Prob. 9-2.

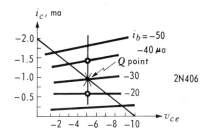

FIGURE PROB. 9-2

(b) $\alpha_{dc} = \dfrac{I_C}{I_E}$

$I_E = I_C + I_B = 1 \text{ ma} + 30 \text{ μa} = 1.03 \text{ ma}$

$\alpha_{dc} = \dfrac{1 \times 10^{-3}}{1.03 \times 10^{-3}}$

$$\boxed{\alpha_{dc} = 0.95}$$

$\beta_{dc} = \dfrac{I_C}{I_B} = \dfrac{1 \times 10^{-3}}{30 \times 10^{-6}}$

$$\boxed{\beta_{dc} = 33.3}$$

(c) $\beta_{ac} = \left. \dfrac{\Delta i_c}{\Delta i_b} \right|_{v_{ce} = \text{const}}$

$= \dfrac{(1.4 \times 10^{-3}) - (0.6 \times 10^{-3})}{(40 \times 10^{-6}) - (20 \times 10^{-6})}$

$$\boxed{\beta_{\mathrm{ac}} = 40}$$

$$\alpha_{\mathrm{ac}} = \frac{\beta_{\mathrm{ac}}}{1 + \beta_{\mathrm{ac}}} = \frac{40}{1 + 40}$$

$$\boxed{\alpha_{\mathrm{ac}} = 0.98}$$

Illustrative Problem 9-3

Draw an approximate set of collector curves for the 2N442 *PNP* transistor. Maximum $V_{CE} = -60$ volts, maximum $I_C = -15$ amp, and maximum power dissipation is 150 watts. $\beta_{\mathrm{dc}} = 20$.

SOLUTION

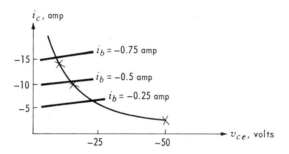

FIGURE PROB. 9-3

MOSFET PARAMETERS

The electronics industry was presented with the choice of defining MOSFET descriptive parameters either like those of vacuum tubes or those of transistors. Because it is a semiconductor device, we are tempted to define the MOSFET parameters similar to those of the transistor. This proves to be unwise because α and β are parameters which describe *current* gains. This is inappropriate for the MOSFET because the input terminal, the gate of the MOSFET, draws practically no current, as is true for the grid of the vacuum tube. We therefore define small-signal parameters of the MOSFET in a manner similar to the small-signal parameters of the vacuum tube.

$$\mu \equiv \left. \frac{\Delta v_{ds}}{\Delta v_{gs}} \right|_{i_d = \mathrm{const}} \qquad \text{amplification factor}$$

$$r_d \equiv \left. \frac{\Delta v_{ds}}{\Delta i_d} \right|_{v_{gs} = \mathrm{const}} \qquad \text{dynamic drain resistance}$$

$$g_m \equiv \left. \frac{\Delta i_d}{\Delta v_{gs}} \right|_{v_{ds} = \mathrm{const}} \qquad \text{transconductance}$$

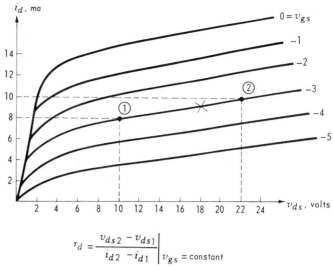

$$r_d = \frac{v_{ds2} - v_{ds1}}{i_{d2} - i_{d1}}\bigg|_{v_{gs} = \text{constant}}$$

FIGURE 9-7 *Determination of the r_d of a MOSFET.*

FIGURE 9-8 *Determination of the g_m of a MOSFET.*

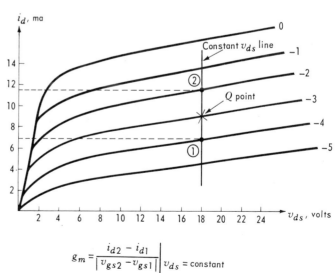

$$g_m = \frac{i_{d2} - i_{d1}}{|v_{gs2} - v_{gs1}|}\bigg|_{v_{ds} = \text{constant}}$$

ACTIVE-DEVICE PARAMETERS   129

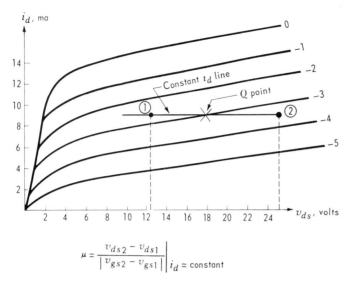

$$\mu = \frac{v_{ds2} - v_{ds1}}{\left| v_{gs2} - v_{gs1} \right|} \bigg|_{i_d = \text{constant}}$$

FIGURE 9-9 *Determination of the μ of a MOSFET.*

Figures 9-7 to 9-9 show how the determinations of these parameters from the characteristic curves can be carried out.

Illustrative Problem 9-4

Determine the small-signal parameters of the MOSFET described by the characteristic curves in Figs. 9-7 to 9-9.

SOLUTION

Given: Characteristic curves of Figs. 9-7 to 9-9

Find: r_d; g_m; μ

From Fig. 9-7

$$r_d = \frac{\Delta v_{ds}}{\Delta i_d} \bigg|_{v_{gs}=K}$$

$$= \frac{22 - 10}{(10 - 8) \times 10^{-3}} = \frac{12}{2} \times 10^{-3}$$

$$\boxed{r_d = 6 \text{ kilohms}}$$

From Fig. 9-8

$$g_m = \frac{\Delta i_d}{\Delta v_{gs}} \bigg|_{v_{ds}=K}$$

$$= \frac{(11.3 - 7) \times 10^{-3}}{4 - 2} = \frac{4.3}{2} \times 10^{-3}$$

$$\boxed{g_m = 2150 \ \mu\text{mhos}}$$

From Fig. 9-9

$$\mu = \frac{\Delta v_{ds}}{\Delta v_{gs}}\bigg|_{i_d=K}$$
$$= \frac{25 - 12.5}{3.5 - 2.5} = \frac{12.5}{1}$$

$$\boxed{\mu = 12.5}$$

PROBLEMS

9-1 Define the three small-signal parameters used with vacuum tubes.

9-2 A vacuum tube has a dynamic plate resistance of 5 kilohms and an amplification factor of 20. Determine its transconductance.

9-3 Complete the following table.

	μ	r_p, ohms	g_m, μmhos
Tube 1	40	5,000	
Tube 2	70		2,500
Tube 3	50	7,000	
Tube 4		8,500	2,350
Tube 5		60,000	11,500
Tube 6	65		70,000
Tube 7	55	8,000	
Tube 8	21		10,000
Tube 9	17	5,500	

9-4 A 12AU7A triode is to be the active device in a common-cathode amplifier. A 250-volt power supply is to be used, and a load resistor of 10 kilohms is in the plate circuit.
   (a) Sketch a schematic diagram of this circuit.
   (b) Construct the load line for this circuit.
   (c) Locate the quiescent operating point for a grid voltage of −4 volts and determine the small-signal parameters at that point.

9-5 An amplifier uses a 7199 triode section with a plate supply of 150 volts and a plate load resistor of 10 kilohms. The quiescent grid voltage is to be −3 volts. Construct the load line and determine the appropriate small-signal parameters at the quiescent point.

9-6 A 40317 transistor is being operated at a quiescent base current of 24 μa and a collector-to-emitter voltage of 10 volts. Locate the quiescent point of the collector characteristics and determine the ac and the dc α's and β's of the transistor at that point. Repeat for a 2N3439 having a quiescent base current of 0.2 ma and a quiescent collector to emitter voltage of 60 volts.

9-7 A 2N2953 transistor is to be operated from a supply voltage of 6 volts. It is to have a quiescent collector-to-emitter voltage drop of 3 volts and a quiescent base current of 30 μa.

(a) Locate the Q point.

(b) Construct the load line.

(c) Determine the value of the collector load resistor.

(d) Find the value of the ac and the dc α's and β's at the quiescent point.

9-8 Why do we speak of the μ, r_d, and g_m of a MOSFET rather than of an α and β?

9-9 Determine r_d and g_m from the MOSFET characteristic curves in Fig. 9-10. Using these values of r_d and g_m, calculate the value of μ. The point for which these determinations should be made is located at a drain-to-source voltage of 15 volts and a grid-to-source voltage of -2 volts.

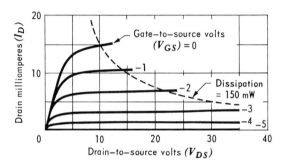

FIGURE 9-10 MOSFET characteristic for Prob. 9-9. (RCA)

10

EQUIVALENT CIRCUITS
OF ACTIVE DEVICES

In order to describe or specify the capabilities of an amplifier we must be able to compare its output and input signals. One method is to compare the output voltage with the input voltage, the output current with the input current, and the output signal power with the input signal power. These comparisons are called the *gains* of an amplifier.

CURRENT GAIN, VOLTAGE GAIN, AND POWER GAIN

Current gain is defined as output signal current divided by input signal current, *voltage gain* as output signal voltage divided by input signal voltage, and *power gain* as output signal power divided by input signal power.

To determine the gains of a particular amplifier we can construct the four-quadrant graph and use it in the determination. However, there are times when this technique is undesirable either because the signal is so small that construction on a given set of characteristics is impossible or because so many possible designs are being considered that an undue amount of work would be necessary. In such situations, gain formulas which make use of small-signal parameters prove very useful. The gain formulas play a very important role in amplifier design, especially in the preliminary stages, when it would be unduly cumbersome to construct a four-quadrant graph for each active device considered for use in a particular design.

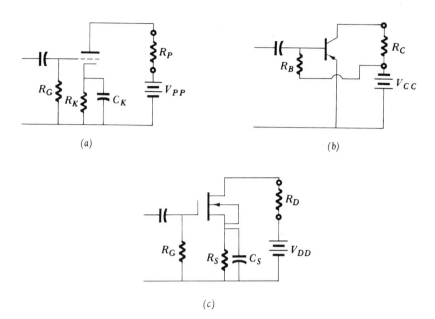

(a)

(b)

(c)

FIGURE 10-1 (a) Complete vacuum-tube amplifier. (b) Complete transistor amplifier. (c) Complete MOSFET amplifier.

Let us now attempt to develop gain formulas for the amplifiers shown in Fig. 10-1. In doing so, we find two major complications. First, the circuit contains both dc and ac quantities, and, second, we do not know how to write complete Kirchhoff voltage-loop equations for circuits containing active devices.

SUPERPOSITION THEOREM AND AC ANALYSIS

A theorem which will prove very helpful at this stage of operation is the *superposition theorem*. It allows an ac analysis to be made of a network while disregarding dc quantities if the circuit being studied is linear over the area of interest. This is done during the ac analysis by treating all dc voltage sources as short circuits.

In Fig. 10-2, the superposition theorem is used to prepare three amplifier circuits for ac analysis. It is obvious that V_{PP}, V_{CC}, and V_{DD} can be removed and replaced by a short circuit according to the superposition theorem. What may not seem as obvious, however, is the removal of R_K and C_K in the case of the vacuum-tube amplifier. Recall the purpose of adding C_K: its function is to

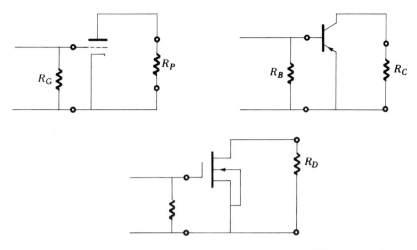

FIGURE 10-2 *Amplifiers prepared for ac analysis.*

serve as a low-impedance bypass of R_K for the varying portion of the current in the output loop. Since we are interested now only in the circuit response to the ac signal portion of the currents and voltages, the cathode resistor R_K and the capacitor C_K can be replaced by a short circuit. Similarly, R_S and C_S can be replaced by a short circuit in the MOSFET amplifiers.

THÉVENIN'S THEOREM AND NORTON'S THEOREM

Now that we have been able to limit the circuit analysis to ac, let us pursue our second problem, that of replacing the schematic symbols of the active devices, which we do not know how to handle analytically, by more familiar components. Two theorems which will prove very helpful in doing this are Thévenin's theorem and Norton's theorem.

Thévenin's theorem states: *Any two-terminal linear network may be replaced by a voltage generator in series with an impedance.*

Norton's theorem states: *Any two-terminal linear network may be replaced by a current generator in parallel with an impedance.*

See Fig. 10-3.

Even though the vacuum tube, the transistor and the MOSFET contain more than two terminals, we can consider each of these units in two portions, the input portion and the output portion, and apply Thévenin's theorem and Norton's theorem to each portion separately. First, let us investigate the output loop of an amplifier (see Fig. 10-4). Considering the output section of the am-

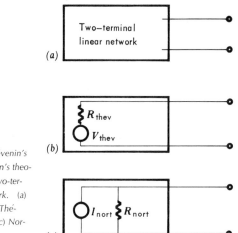

FIGURE 10-3 *Thévenin's theorem and Norton's theorem applied to a two-terminal linear network. (a) The black box; (b) Thévenin equivalent; (c) Norton equivalent.*

FIGURE 10-4 *The output portion of amplifiers being considered for ac analysis.*

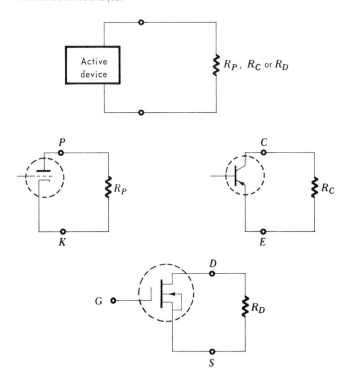

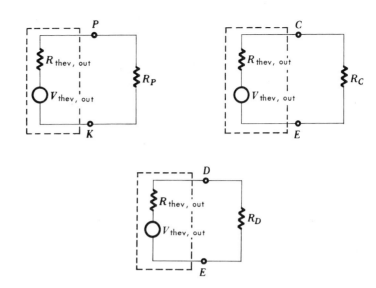

FIGURE 10-5 *Thévenin equivalents.*

plifier by itself, the active device appears as a two-terminal device, and Thévenin's theorem and Norton's theorem can be applied. In Fig. 10-5, the active devices as seen through their output terminals have been replaced by their Thévenin equivalent, and in Fig. 10-6 they have been replaced by their Norton equivalent.

Investigating the Thévenin equivalents in Fig. 10-5, we see that each of the active devices has an internal resistance and an equivalent internal voltage source.

Not all the voltage generated by the equivalent internal voltage source appears as an output voltage across R_P, R_C, and R_D, some being lost inside the active device itself across its internal resistance. Likewise, in studying the Norton equivalents of Fig. 10-6, it is obvious that a portion of the current which is generated by the internal equivalent current source is not appearing in the output but instead is bled through the internal resistance of the active device. This is understandable in both cases since it represents power which is being dissipated by the active device. It should be expected that some dissipation by the active device will occur.

Let us now attempt to match up the Thévenin and Norton equivalent components shown in Figs. 10-5 and 10-6 with the active-device parameters studied in the last chapter.

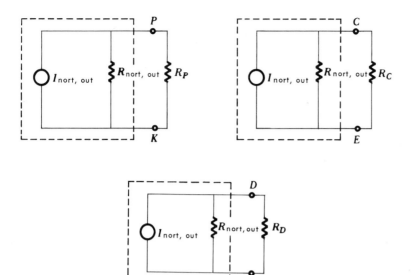

FIGURE 10-6 *Norton equivalents.*

THE THÉVENIN EQUIVALENT OF A VACUUM-TUBE AMPLIFIER

To begin with, let us first try to identify the resistance indicated in Fig. 10-5 as $R_{\text{thev out}}$ for the vacuum tube. Since we eliminated all dc quantities from the circuit and are doing strictly an ac analysis, the output resistance will be a dynamic resistance. Dynamic, or ac, resistances are defined as $\Delta v/\Delta i$, a change in voltage over a change in current. In the case of the output section of the vacuum tube, this becomes $\Delta v_{pk}/\Delta i_p$. When we consider that the bias point has been fixed and that the ac swing around that point is taken as being small, we are really seeking a resistance which is defined as

$$ r_p = \frac{\Delta v_{pk}}{\Delta i_p} \bigg|_{v_{gk}=\text{const}} $$

This we recognize immediately as the dynamic plate resistance discussed in the previous chapter. Thus, $R_{\text{thev out}}$ for the vacuum tube is r_p, the dynamic plate resistance of the tube.

Next let us attempt to identify the Thévenin voltage source of Fig. 10-5. Obviously the equivalent voltage source in the output portion of an amplifier should be related to the input signal which is applied to the input terminals of the device. We can, therefore, assume that the Thévenin voltage source for the vacuum tube of

138   AMPLIFIERS

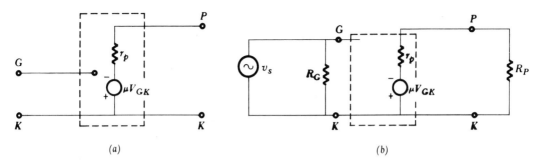

FIGURE 10-7 *Thévenin equivalent of (a) vacuum tube and (b) vacuum-tube amplifier.*

Fig. 10-5 will be some constant times the input signal, the input signal being Δv_{gk}.

The constant should relate Δv_{gk}, the input signal voltage, to Δv_{pk}, the output signal voltage. Again since the analysis is being done strictly for ac quantities and the variation around the quiescent operating point is considered to be small, we can use a parameter which is defined as

$$\mu = \frac{\Delta v_{pk}}{\Delta v_{gk}} \bigg|_{i_p = \text{const}}$$

This is at once recognizable as the amplification factor of the tube. The Thévenin voltage source for the tube of Fig. 10-5 can therefore be replaced by a voltage source equal to μV_{GK}. We now have available a Thévenin equivalent for the output section of a vacuum tube, the Thévenin resistance being r_p and the voltage source being μV_{GK}.

Let us now consider the input portion of the vacuum tube. It should be obvious that the input to the vacuum tube is an open circuit, the input being across the vacuum between the grid and the cathode. Figure 10-7a is a complete representation of the vacuum tube showing both the input and output portions. Figure 10-7b is a diagram of the complete vacuum-tube amplifier ready for ac analysis with the tube replaced by its Thévenin equivalent.

Note the polarity indicated on the voltage source of Fig. 10-7. The reason for this polarity is the 180° shift introduced by the amplifier. This phase shift can be observed whenever a four-quadrant graph is constructed.

THE NORTON EQUIVALENT OF A VACUUM-TUBE AMPLIFIER

You might expect to get as involved in determining the relationships for the Norton equivalent circuit components as for the Thévenin equivalent. We are in luck, however, because there is a relationship between the Thévenin components and the Norton components. This is to be expected since both are representing the same device. The Norton-Thévenin relationship states that the Thévenin impedance and the Norton impedance are equal $(R_{\text{thev}} = R_{\text{nort}})$ and that the Thévenin voltage source and the Norton current source are related by

$$V_{\text{thev}} = I_{\text{nort}} R_{\text{nort}}$$

Thus, we can, in Fig. 10-8, immediately draw the Norton equivalent circuit as shown for the vacuum tube and the vacuum-tube amplifier.

VOLTAGE-GAIN FORMULA FOR A VACUUM-TUBE AMPLIFIER

We now have two circuits we can use to develop gain formulas for the vacuum-tube amplifiers, Figs. 10-7b and 10-8b. For no other reason than that it is the author's preference we will develop the gain formulas using Fig. 10-7b. To begin with, let us write a formula for the output voltage which is taken across the plate load resistor R_P. Using the voltage-divider theorem, we get

$$V_{\text{out}} = \mu V_{GK} \frac{R_P}{r_p + R_P}$$

FIGURE 10-8 *Norton equivalent of (a) vacuum tube and (b) vacuum-tube amplifier.*

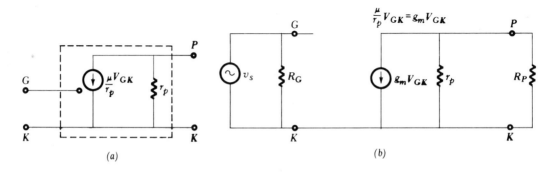

The voltage gain of an amplifier being defined as the output voltage divided by the input voltage, the following derivation is self-explanatory:

$$V_{\text{out}} = \frac{\mu V_{GK} R_P}{r_p + R_P}$$

$$V_{\text{in}} = V_{GK}$$

$$\text{Voltage gain} \equiv A_v = \frac{V_{\text{out}}}{V_{\text{in}}}$$

$$A_v = \frac{\mu V_{GK} R_P / (r_p + R_P)}{V_{GK}}$$

$$\boxed{A_v = \frac{\mu R_P}{r_p + R_P}}$$

To keep sign conventions in proper order, it is necessary to place a negative sign in front of the formula for the gain of an amplifier since the amplifier introduces a 180° phase shift. Thus, the formula for the gain of a vacuum-tube amplifier becomes

$$A_v = \frac{-\mu R_P}{r_p + R_P}$$

The equivalent circuits and the voltage formula just developed hold equally well for the pentode amplifier and the triode amplifier. An interesting point is that the pentode vacuum tube usually has a very high value for its dynamic plate resistance r_p. With this as the case, the denominator of the gain formula becomes approximately r_p, because R_P appears as negligible. Since μ / r_p is equal to g_m, the gain for a pentode amplifier whose dynamic plate resistance is much greater than the load resistance becomes

$$A_v = -g_m R_P$$

Note that this equation holds only if the dynamic plate resistance is much greater than the load resistance. For this equation to be used, a good rule of thumb is that r_p should be at least 10 times as great as R_P.

CURRENT AND POWER GAIN

An interesting but trivial point of discussion is the question of the current gain and the power gain of the vacuum-tube amplifier. Considering that the input section of the vacuum tube draws no current and the grid leak resistor R_G is very large (on the order of major fractions of a megohm), we can consider that the input current to the vacuum-tube amplifier is practically zero. Therefore, the current gain of the vacuum-tube amplifier is infinite. Likewise, the power gain of the vacuum-tube amplifier can be considered infinite, since the input power to the vacuum-tube amplifier is negligible because of the exceedingly small amount of current drawn.

Illustrative Problem 10-1
The amplifier shown in Fig. Prob. 10-1 is to be used in the control system of an automated machine. The tube has a μ of 20 and a dynamic plate resistance r_p of 4000 ohms.

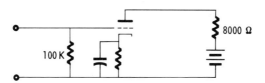

FIGURE PROB. 10-1

(a) Determine the voltage gain of the amplifier.
(b) Determine the output voltage of the amplifier if the input is a 0.3-volt-rms signal.

SOLUTION
Given: Circuit shown in Fig. Prob. 10-1; $\mu = 20$; $r_p = 4000$ ohms; $V_{in} = 0.3$ volt rms
Find:
(a) A_v
(b) V_{out}

(a) $A_v = -\dfrac{\mu R_P}{r_p + R_P}$

$A_v = \dfrac{-20 \times 8000}{4000 + 8000} = \dfrac{-160,000}{12,000}$

$$\boxed{A_v = -13.3}$$

(b) $V_{out} = A_v V_{in} = -13.3(0.3)$

$$\boxed{V_{out} = -4 \text{ volts rms}}$$

THE EQUIVALENT CIRCUIT OF A MOSFET AMPLIFIER
Since a direct analogy can be made between a vacuum tube and a MOSFET, it is not necessary to repeat the entire analysis we

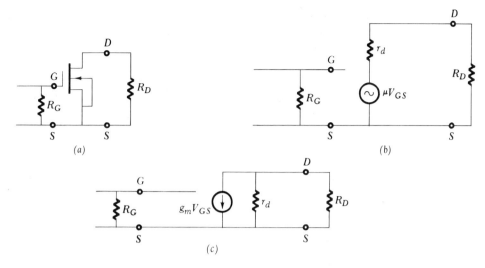

FIGURE 10-9 (a) Sche-
matic of MOSFET amplifier
prepared for ac analysis.
(b) Thévenin equivalent of
MOSFET amplifier. (c)
Norton equivalent of
MOSFET amplifier.

made for the vacuum tube. Instead we can sketch the Thévenin and Norton equivalent circuits directly, as shown in Fig. 10-9.

VOLTAGE GAIN OF A MOSFET AMPLIFIER

Again making use of the direct analogy between the MOSFET and the vacuum tube, we can write the following equation for the voltage gain of a common-source MOSFET amplifier:

$$A_v = \frac{-\mu R_D}{r_d + R_D}$$

THE EQUIVALENT CIRCUIT OF A TRANSISTOR AMPLIFIER

As we did previously, we will attempt to study the input section and the output section of the amplifier separately. Figure 10-10b and c shows the input and output sections of the amplifier drawn separately. You may have a feeling that this is not wholly legitimate and that the output section has some effect on the input section and vice versa. This is true; however, by choosing values of the Thévenin and Norton equivalent components wisely, this

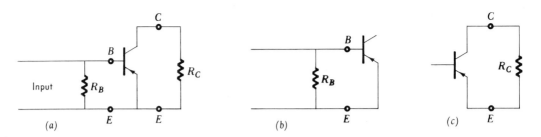

FIGURE 10-10 *Common-emitter transistor amplifier (a) prepared for ac analysis; (b) input section; (c) output section.*

interplay between the input and output sections will be taken into account.

Theoretically both the Thévenin and the Norton equivalents can be used in the input and output portions of the circuit. For reasons we omit now in order to avoid unnecessary complication, an equivalent circuit has been agreed upon which uses the Thévenin equivalent in the input portion and the Norton equivalent in the output portion.

The Input Section. In Fig. 10-11, a first attempt has been made at developing the desired equivalent circuit. Notice in this case that the input circuit requires a much more elaborate consideration then the input circuit of the vacuum tube. In the case of the vacuum tube, the input was actually an open circuit which existed between the grid and the cathode, and therefore there was no input current. In this case, the input section of the transistor must be considered because it definitely is not an open circuit, and input current will be drawn.

The voltage source indicated as $V_{\text{thev in}}$ in the input section of the equivalent circuit is included to take into account any signal which may be presented to the input terminals from *inside* the transistor. Such a signal actually does exist. Though it is small and can usually be considered negligible, this voltage source does satisfy that feeling we had about the interplay between the output circuit and the input circuit.

The input impedance of the amplifier, noted as $R_{\text{thev in}}$ in Fig. 10-11, is a parameter frequently supplied by the manufacturer of the transistor. In many cases it is referred to simply as the input resistance of the transistor in common-emitter configuration, while

144   AMPLIFIERS

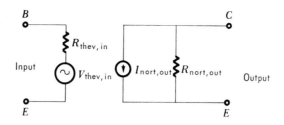

FIGURE 10-11 *Equivalent circuit of a transistor.*

at other times it is referred to as h_{ie}. It may appear strange to see an input resistance referred to as h. However, in the study of transistor equivalent circuits, a whole series of h parameters has grown up, each describing different types of quantities, from voltage gains and current gains to resistances and conductances. The only way we can tell the difference between them is by their subscripts. There are always two subscripts accompanying h parameters. The second subscript refers to the configuration to which the parameter applies, such as the common emitter. This is indicated by a lower case e for the common-emitter configuration. The first subscript indicates which parameter of the configuration is being referred to, i signifying input resistance. Thus, h_{ie} indicates the input resistance of the transistor when used in the common-emitter configuration.

Let us now turn our attention to the Thévenin equivalent voltage source of Fig. 10-11 and develop the Thévenin voltage source in such a way that it will indicate the effect that the output signal has on the input. $V_{\text{thev in}}$ of Fig. 10-11 will be made to be directly proportional to the output voltage of the amplifier. The factor of proportionality will depend upon the construction of the particular transistor being used. Again h will be used to indicate a transistor parameter. This time the subscripts will be re. The e representing the configuration, common emitter, and the r representing reverse voltage gain. Thus, the Thévenin voltage source in the input section of the transistor equivalent of Fig. 10-11 will be

$$V_{\text{thev in}} = h_{re}V_{CE}$$

The Output Section. Let us now turn our attention to the output section of the transistor equivalent of Fig. 10-11. The output resistance of the transistor in common-emitter configuration, noted in Fig. 10-11 as $R_{\text{nort out}}$, is usually provided by the transistor manufacturer when necessary and is called either R_{out} for common emitter or $1/h_{oe}$. It may appear strange that the output resistance of transistors should be specified as a conductance requiring the designer to invert the number in order to obtain the output resistance.

EQUIVALENT CIRCUITS OF ACTIVE DEVICES   145

Though strange, this is perfectly valid and appears this way because of some of the equations in use during the early days of transistors. It will be found that in many cases $1/h_{oe}$ is missing from the transistor specification sheet. In such cases it is assumed to be large enough to be ignored and replaced by an open circuit.

The last component needing discussion in Fig. 10-11 is the current source indicated as $I_{nort\ out}$. In order to obtain more information about this source, let us consider a short circuit placed across the collector-to-emitter terminals. If this were to happen, all the current from the current source would flow through the short and none through the output resistance $R_{nort\ out}$. Recall the exact name given to β, the common-emitter short-circuit gain. Obviously then

$$I_{nort\ out} = \beta_{ac}I_B = h_{fe}I_B$$

In words, then, the Norton equivalent current source in the output section of the common-emitter transistor amplifier of Fig. 10-11 is β times the ac signal current which enters the base of the transistor.

A summary of what we have developed as the equivalent circuit for the transistor amplifier in common-emitter configuration is shown as Fig. 10-12.

h_{ie} represents the input impedance of the transistor.
h_{re} represents that number which when multiplied by the output voltage gives the voltage fed back through the transistor to the input.
h_{fe} represents the short-circuit current gain of the transistor.
h_{oe} represents the output conductance of the transistor.

Use of the letter h comes from the word *hybrid*, meaning "of mixed origin." Since two of the h parameters refer to voltage gains, another to current gain, and the others to resistance and conductance, it seems reasonable to call them *hybrid parameters*.

FIGURE 10-12 *Equivalent circuit of a common-emitter transistor amplifier with h parameters indicated.*

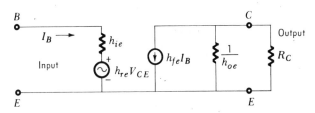

Because they are easier to obtain experimentally, some manufacturers publish *common-base h* parameters. In such a case the following approximations* can be used for making the conversion:

* J. Millman and C. C. Halkias, "Electronic Devices and Circuits," p. 304, McGraw-Hill Book Company, New York, 1967.

$$h_{ie} \approx \frac{h_{ib}}{1 + h_{fb}}$$

$$h_{fe} \approx \frac{-h_{fb}}{1 + h_{fb}}$$

$$h_{oe} \approx \frac{h_{ob}}{1 + h_{fb}}$$

$$h_{re} \approx \frac{h_{ib}\,h_{ob}}{1 + h_{fb}} - h_{rb}$$

GAIN FORMULAS FOR THE TRANSISTOR AMPLIFIER

Now that we have developed an equivalent circuit for the transistor, we can continue in our search for the gain formulas. To avoid having to backtrack each time to take into account additional components, let us develop the gain formulas for the common-emitter circuit which has all the auxiliary components already tied on. Such a circuit is the common-emitter amplifier with voltage-divider bias and swamping, as shown in Fig. 10-13.

In analyzing this circuit it is assumed that capacitor C_E is chosen so that it has a small enough impedance to be considered as a short circuit for the frequencies of interest.

For an ac analysis, which this is, all dc voltage sources can be considered as short circuits, according to the superposition theorem. Point A of Fig. 10-13 therefore can be considered identical with point M, and the amplifier can then be drawn as shown in Fig. 10-14.

Figure 10-15 can now be drawn to represent the circuit with the transistor replaced by its small-signal equivalent.

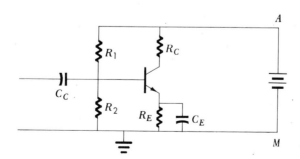

FIGURE 10-13 *Complete common-emitter transistor amplifier showing voltage-divider bias with swamping.*

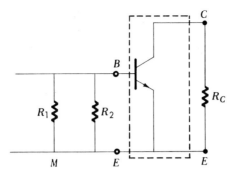

FIGURE 10-14 *Common-emitter transistor amplifier prepared for ac analysis.*

When R_C is relatively small (5 kilohms or less), $h_{re}V_{CE}$ becomes small enough to be considered negligible and therefore ignored. This is usually the case with most common-emitter amplifiers. The equivalent circuit for the transistor can be drawn as shown in Fig. 10-16a, and the entire circuit can be redrawn as Fig. 10-16b.

Since $1/h_{oe}$ is usually much greater than R_C, the output voltage can be written as

$$V_{\text{out}} = -h_{fe}I_B R_C$$

With $I_B = V_{\text{in}}/h_{ie}$ replacing I_B in the first equation, we get

$$V_{\text{out}} = -h_{fe}\frac{V_{\text{in}}}{h_{ie}}R_C$$

Dividing both sides of the equation by V_{in}, we get

$$\frac{V_{\text{out}}}{V_{\text{in}}} = -h_{fe}\frac{R_C}{h_{ie}}$$

$V_{\text{out}}/V_{\text{in}}$ is the definition of voltage gain.

FIGURE 10-15 *Equivalent circuit of the transistor amplifier of Figs. 10-13 and 10-14.*

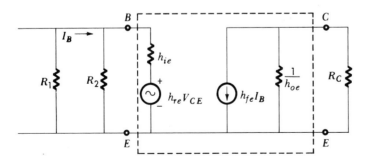

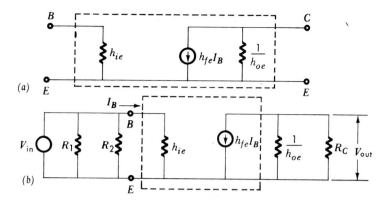

$$\boxed{A_v = -h_{fe}\frac{R_C}{h_{ie}}} \quad \text{or} \quad \boxed{A_v = -\beta\frac{R_C}{h_{ie}}}$$

Thus we see that the voltage gain of the amplifier is equal to the ac β of the transistor multiplied by the ratio of the load resistance to the input resistance of the transistor.

The current gain of the amplifier is easy to determine, provided the simplifying assumption is made that the bias resistors R_1 and R_2 are large enough, compared to h_{ie}, not to draw appreciable current. When this assumption is made, the current gain is simply h_{fe}, the ac β of the transistor. If, however, R_1 and R_2 are not large enough to be ignored, the current gain of the complete amplifier is

$$\frac{R_1 \| R_2 \| h_{ie}}{h_{ie}} h_{fe}$$

The power gain of an amplifier is defined as P_{out}/P_{in}. It can then be determined:

$$A_p = \frac{P_{out}}{P_{in}}$$
$$P_{out} = V_{out}I_{out}$$
$$P_{in} = V_{in}I_{in}$$
$$A_p = \frac{V_{out}I_{out}}{V_{in}I_{in}}$$

$$\boxed{A_p = A_v A_i}$$

EQUIVALENT CIRCUITS OF ACTIVE DEVICES   149

Illustrative Problem 10-2

Determine the voltage gain, the current gain, and the power gain of the amplifier shown in Fig. Prob. 10-2. $h_{ie} = 800$ ohms, and $h_{fe} = 90$. Calculate the output current and output voltage if the input base current is 0.1 ma peak-to-peak.

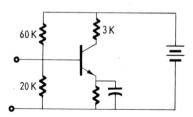

Solution

Given: $h_{ie} = 800$ ohms; $h_{fe} = 90$; $R_C = 3$ kilohms; $I_B = 0.1$ ma peak-to-peak

Find: A_v; A_i; A_p; I_{out}; V_{out}

$$A_v = -h_{fe}\frac{R_C}{h_{ie}} = -90\,\frac{3 \times 10^3}{800}$$

$$\boxed{A_v = -338}$$

$$A_i = h_{fe}$$

$$\boxed{A_i = 90}$$

$$A_p = A_v A_i = 338 \times 90$$

$$\boxed{A_p = 30.4 \times 10^3}$$

$$\frac{I_{out}}{I_{in}} = A_i$$

$$I_{out} = A_i I_{in} = 90 \times 0.1 \times 10^{-3}$$

$$\boxed{I_{out} = 9 \text{ ma peak-to-peak}}$$

$$V_{out} = I_{out}R_C = 9 \times 10^{-3} \times 3 \times 10^3$$

$$\boxed{V_{out} = 27 \text{ volts peak-to-peak}}$$

DETERMINATION OF HYBRID PARAMETERS

It is sometimes found that the hybrid parameters are not listed in manufacturer's data. If this happens, the designer has to get the information from the characteristic curves. Figure 10-17 is a typical set of curves provided by the transistor manufacturer.

The collector characteristics have been discussed previously and need no further discussion at this point. The input characteristics, however, have not been discussed.

When we were discussing bias schemes, we assumed that the voltage across the base-to-emitter junction was either 0.2 or 0.6 volt. From the input characteristics of Fig. 10-17, we can see that though the base-to-emitter voltage is not 0.2 volt for all values of base current, the variation away from this figure is small.

Since h_{ie} is the input impedance of the transistor in the common-emitter configuration, it should be equal to $\Delta v_{be}/\Delta i_b$. From the input characteristic curve of the transistor we see that this is the slope of that curve at the quiescent operating point. In order to determine h_{ie} it is necessary first to locate the quiescent operating point on the input characteristic curve and then find the slope of the curve using

$$h_{ie} = \frac{\Delta v_{be}}{\Delta i_b}$$

The output impedance of the transistor in the common-emitter configuration, $1/h_{oe}$, can be interpreted as the reciprocal slope of the

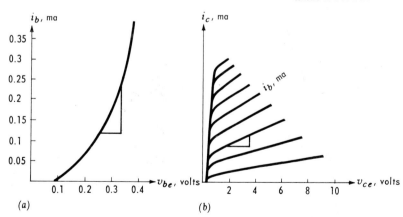

FIGURE 10-17 (a) Input characteristic of a transistor. (b) Collector characteristic of a transistor.

(a)

(b)

collector-characteristic curves at the quiescent operating point, since the reciprocal of its slope is $\Delta v_{ce}/\Delta i_c$. Obviously, this is the output impedance of the transistor in this configuration. Therefore, in order to find $1/h_{oe}$ of a given transistor, all that is required is to determine the slope of the collector-characteristic curve at the quiescent operating point. Thus, the $1/h_{oe}$ parameter is determined from

$$\frac{1}{h_{oe}} = \frac{\Delta v_{ce}}{\Delta i_c}$$

h_{fe} is the ac β of the transistor, determined as described in the previous chapter.

Since, in most cases, $h_{re}V_{CE}$ is neglected, we will not discuss the determination of h_{re}.

At times it will be found that a manufacturer will provide a transfer curve instead of an input curve. The transfer curve is a plot of collector current on the vertical axis and base-to-emitter voltage on the horizontal axis. A fair approximation to an input curve can then be had by dividing the currents on the vertical axis by h_{FE}, because $i_c = i_b h_{FE}$.

Illustrative Problem 10-3
A transistor whose characteristic curves are shown in Fig. Prob. 10-3 is being used in an amplifier such that its quiescent operating point is located at $I_{BQ} = -15\ \mu\text{a}$ and $V_{CEQ} = -30$ volts. Determine h_{ie}, $1/h_{oe}$, and h_{fe} at the quiescent point.

FIGURE PROB. 10-3

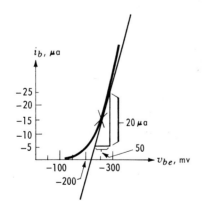

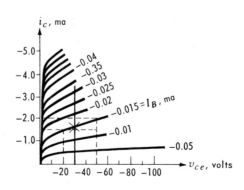

SOLUTION

Given: $I_{BQ} = -15 \ \mu a; \ V_{CEQ} = -30$ volts

Find:

(a) h_{ie}

(b) $1/h_{oe}$

(c) h_{fe}

(a) $\quad h_{ie} = \dfrac{\Delta v_{be}}{\Delta i_b} = \dfrac{50 \times 10^{-3}}{20 \times 10^{-6}}$

$$\boxed{h_{ie} = 2500 \text{ ohms}}$$

(b) $\quad \dfrac{1}{h_{oe}} = \dfrac{\Delta v_{ce}}{\Delta i_c} = \dfrac{50 - 20}{(2.0 - 1.5) \times 10^{-3}}$

$$= \dfrac{30}{0.5} \times 10^3 = 60,000 \text{ ohms}$$

$$\boxed{\dfrac{1}{h_{oe}} = 60,000 \text{ ohms}}$$

(c) $\quad h_{fe} = \dfrac{\Delta i_c}{\Delta i_b} \bigg|_{\Delta v_{ce}=0}$

$$= \dfrac{(2.0 - 1.1) \times 10^{-3}}{(20 - 10) \times 10^{-6}} = \dfrac{0.9}{0.1}$$

$$\boxed{h_{fe} = 90}$$

THE EFFECT OF SIGNAL SOURCE RESISTANCE

A number of simplifying assumptions have been carried through this chapter. The first was to consider the output resistance of the transistor as being large enough to ignore. The second simplifying assumption was to consider the voltage-divider biasing arrangement as having a large enough impedance to permit us to disregard the signal current which it bypasses. Third, we have disregarded the output impedance of the signal source providing the input signal.

The following illustrative problem is done without these simplifying assumptions.

Illustrative Problem 10-4

Determine the output voltage, the voltage gain, and the current gain of the amplifier shown in Fig. Prob. 10-4a and b without using

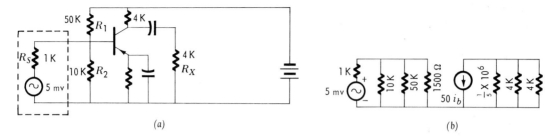

FIGURE PROB. 10-4a and b

the gain formula. The parameters of the transistor used are $h_{ie} = 1500$ ohms, $h_{fe} = 50$, and $h_{oe} = 5$ μmhos. Next, find the gain using the formula. Make no simplifying assumptions.

SOLUTION
Given: $h_{ie} = 1500$ ohms; $h_{fe} = 50$; $h_{oe} = 5$ μmhos
Find: V_{out}; A_v; A_i

See Fig. Prob. 10-4c.

$$R_{12} = R_1 \| R_2$$
$$= 10 \text{ kilohms} \| 50 \text{ kilohms} = \frac{50 \times 10^3 \times 10 \times 10^3}{50 \times 10^3 + 10 \times 10^3}$$

$$\boxed{R_{12} = 8330 \text{ ohms}}$$

FIGURE PROB. 10-4c to f

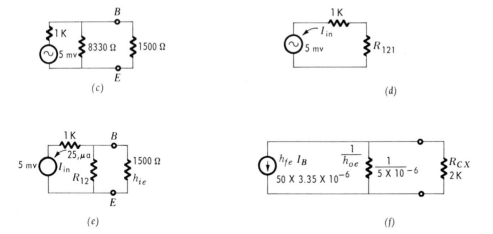

See Fig. Prob. 10-4*d*.

$$R_{121} = R_{12} \| h_{ie}$$
$$= 8330 \| 1500 \text{ ohms}$$
$$= \frac{8330 \times 1500}{8330 + 1500}$$

$$\boxed{R_{121} = 1270 \text{ ohms}}$$

$$I_{\text{in}} = \frac{V_S}{R_{121} + R_S}$$
$$= \frac{5 \times 10^{-3}}{2270} = 2.20 \times 10^{-6} \text{ amp}$$

See Fig. Prob. 10-4*e*.

$$I_B h_{ie} = I_{\text{in}} R_{121}$$
$$I_B = \frac{2.20 \times 10^{-6} \times 1270}{1500}$$

$$\boxed{I_B = 1.86 \times 10^{-6} \text{ amp}}$$

See Fig. Prob. 10-4*f*.

$$\frac{1}{5 \times 10^{-6}} = 200 \times 10^3$$

$$R_{\text{eq}} = \frac{1}{h_{oe}} \| R_C \| R_X$$
$$\approx 2 \text{ kilohms}$$
$$V_{\text{out}} = -h_{fe} I_B R_{\text{eq}}$$
$$= -50 \times 3.35 \times 10^{-6} \times 2 \times 10^3$$

$$\boxed{V_{\text{out}} = -0.335 \text{ volt}}$$

$$A_v = \frac{V_{\text{out}}}{V_{\text{in}}} = \frac{-0.335}{5 \times 10^{-3}} = -67$$

$$\boxed{A_v = -67}$$

$$I_{\text{out}} = \frac{V_{\text{out}}}{R_X} = \frac{0.335}{4 \times 10^3} = -84 \ \mu\text{a}$$
$$A_i = \frac{I_{\text{out}}}{I_{\text{in}}} = \frac{84 \times 10^{-6}}{3.95 \times 10^{-6}}$$

$$\boxed{A_i = 21}$$

PROBLEMS

10-1 What is meant by (a) current gain, (b) voltage gain, (c) power gain?

10-2 Sketch a Thévenin equivalent circuit for a complete vacuum-tube amplifier.

10-3 Sketch a Norton equivalent circuit for a complete vacuum-tube amplifier.

10-4 A common-cathode vacuum-tube amplifier makes use of a triode which has a μ of 40 and an r_p of 12 kilohms. The plate load resistor R_P is 25 kilohms.

(a) Draw a schematic diagram of the circuit.

(b) Draw a Thévenin equivalent of the amplifier.

(c) Determine the voltage gain of the amplifier.

(d) Calculate the output voltage of the amplifier if the input is 2 volts rms.

(e) How much ac signal current is flowing in R_P?

10-5 A circuit has the following parts: tube—12AX7 triode: $\mu = 100$, $r_p = 70$ kilohms; $R_P = 100$ kilohms, $V_{PP} = 180$ volts, $R_G = 100$ kilohms, $R_K = 1000$ ohms, $C_K = 4$ μf, $C_C = 25$ pf.

(a) Draw a schematic diagram of the circuit.

(b) Draw a Thévenin equivalent of the circuit.

(c) Draw a Norton equivalent of the circuit.

(d) Determine the voltage gain of the amplifier.

(e) Calculate the output voltage for an input of 10 mv rms.

10-6 Determine the output voltage of an amplifier using a vacuum tube with an r_p of 20 kilohms and a μ of 50 if the input voltage is 0.001 volt rms and the plate load resistor is 40 kilohms.

10-7 Two pentode amplifiers are being considered for use in a particular system. The first has a dynamic plate resistance of 25,000 ohms and a plate load resistor of 20,000 ohms. The second has a dynamic plate resistance of 180,000 ohms and a plate load resistor of 20,000 ohms. Both tubes have a transconductance of 8000 μmhos. Calculate the gain of each of the amplifiers. *Note:* Check to see if the formula is valid before using it.

10-8 Find the voltage gain of a common-source MOSFET amplifier which uses a MOSFET having a μ of 50 and an r_d of 25 kilohms. The drain circuit load resistor is 10 kilohms.

10-9 Draw a complete h-parameter equivalent circuit for a fixed-bias common-emitter amplifier.

10-10 A fixed-bias transistor amplifier in common-emitter configuration is feeding a 2.5-kilohm load. The base bias resistor is 90 kilohms. The h parameters for the transistor being used are $h_{fe} = 100$, $h_{ie} = 1$ kilohm, $1/h_{oe} = 100$ kilohms, and h_{re} is negligible.

(a) Draw an equivalent circuit of the amplifier.

(b) What is the current gain of the amplifier?

(c) Calculate the voltage gain of the amplifier.

(d) Determine the power gain obtained using this amplifier.

(e) Calculate the output signal current and voltage for an input signal of 20 μa rms.

10-11 An *NPN* silicon transistor is used in a common-emitter amplifier with fixed bias. The transistor has a β of 90 and an h_{ie} (input resistance) of 1200 ohms. A base bias current of 60 μa is desired. A collector load resistor of 3 kilohms is used, and a collector supply of 21 volts is available. An input signal of 40 μa is provided. The output resistance $1/h_{oe}$ of the transistor is 100 kilohms.
(a) Draw a schematic diagram of the amplifier.
(b) Draw the equivalent (*h*-parameter) circuit of the amplifier.
(c) Determine the required value of the base bias resistor R_1.
(d) Find the voltage gain of the amplifier.
(e) What is the current gain of the amplifier?
(f) Calculate the power gain of the amplifier.
(g) Determine the required peak-to-peak signal input voltage to the amplifier.
(h) Calculate the peak-to-peak output voltage of the amplifier.
(i) What is the peak-to-peak output current of the amplifier?
(j) Determine the signal power drawn from the input source.

10-12 A voltage-divider biased common-emitter amplifier is described as follows: $h_{fe} = 110$, $h_{ie} = 1200$ ohms, $1/h_{oe} = 75$ kilohms, h_{re} is negligible, $R_C = 4$ kilohms, $R_1 = 75$ kilohms, $R_2 = 15$ kilohms. A 0.04-ma-rms signal current enters the base terminal of the transistor.
(a) Draw a schematic diagram of the circuit.
(b) Sketch an *h*-parameter equivalent diagram of this circuit.
(c) Determine the current gain of the amplifier.
(d) Calculate the voltage gain.
(e) Find the applied signal voltage.
(f) How much signal current flows in the load?
(g) Calculate the output signal voltage.
(h) Determine the power gain provided by this amplifier.

10-13 Construct a load line, find the quiescent operating point, and find h_{ie}, $1/h_{oe}$, and h_{fe} for a transistor whose characteristic curves are shown in Fig. 10-18. The amplifier is operating from a collector supply of 15 volts with a collector load resistor of 15 kilohms. The base bias current is to be 60 μa.

10-14 A common-emitter amplifier uses a *PNP* transistor with the following parameters: $h_{ie} = 1.5$ kilohms, $h_{re} = 0.0003$, $h_{fe} = 80$, $h_{oe} = 200$ μmhos. The amplifier has a voltage-divider bias network consisting of an 8- and an 80-kilohm resistor. The collector load resistor R_C is 3 kilohms. The signal source supplying the input signal is generating a 10-mv peak-to-peak voltage when no current is drawn from it and has an internal resistance of 700 ohms.
(a) Sketch a schematic diagram of the circuit.
(b) Draw an *h*-parameter equivalent circuit of the amplifier and the input signal source.

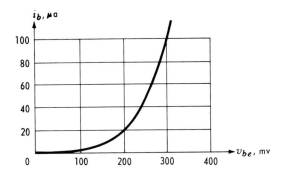

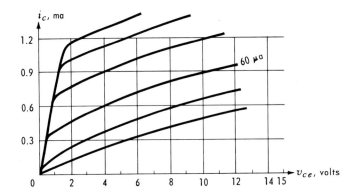

FIGURE 10-18 *Curves for Prob. 10-13.*

(c) Determine the peak-to-peak current flowing from the input signal source.

(d) Find the peak-to-peak terminal voltage of the input signal source.

(e) Calculate the peak-to-peak signal current entering the base of the transistor.

(f) What is the current gain of the amplifier?

(g) Calculate the voltage gain and power gain of the amplifier.

(h) Determine the peak-to-peak output current and output voltage.

11

CAPACITOR COUPLING

The output voltage of an amplifier contains two distinct components, a dc level and a variation which fluctuates around this dc level. It is this fluctuation around the dc level which contains the information part of the output. The dc, or quiescent, portion of the output voltage is a necessary evil that has to be tolerated in order to make the amplifier function properly. The dc, or quiescent, level of the output voltage not only does not carry any information, in many cases it also proves to be a definite disadvantage. For example, consider a situation in which the load to be connected to an amplifier is a second amplifier. This would be the situation if we were dealing with a signal that was so small originally that the gain of one stage of amplification was not enough to increase the signal to the required size. The effect of the dc component of the output of the stage is to throw an undesired bias voltage on the input of the second stage. The bias level is not necessarily the desired one for the second stage.

BLOCKING THE DC LEVEL

Consider the situation we encounter in dealing with vacuum-tube amplifiers. The quiescent plate voltage of the first stage is usually over 100 volts positive. If this were applied directly to the grid of the second stage, the second-stage tube would be ruined. In other applications, the large dc level of the output is also disad-

159

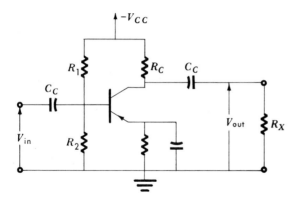

FIGURE 11-1 *Transistor amplifier with coupling capacitors.*

vantageous. We must therefore provide some means of blocking the dc component of the output from reaching the final load of the stage. One way of eliminating this problem is to provide a coupling capacitor C_C between the amplifier and its final load R_X. Figures 11-1 to 11-3 show coupling capacitors in place. Coupling capacitors are usually also included between the signal source and the amplifier to block any dc level which may be accompanying the signal.

The value of capacitance is chosen so as to cause C_C to appear as a very low impedance for ac. It will be considered as a short circuit during ac analyses in this chapter.

FIGURE 11-2 *Vacuum-tube amplifier with coupling capacitors.*

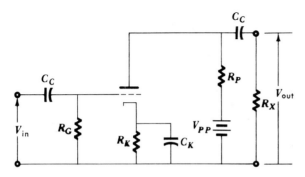

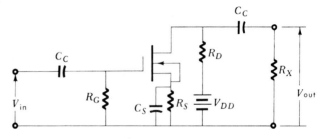

FIGURE 11-3 *MOSFET amplifier with coupling capacitors.*

THE EFFECT OF CAPACITOR COUPLING ON AMPLIFIER GAIN

Figures 11-1 to 11-3 show that as far as the ac component of the output signal is concerned, R_X, the final load on the stage of amplification, appears in parallel with the output load resistor, R_P, R_C, or R_D. It therefore seems reasonable to take another look at the gain formulas developed in the last chapter.

Recall that in deriving the voltage-gain formulas

$$A_v = \frac{-h_{fe}R_C}{h_{ie}} \qquad A_v = \frac{-\mu R_P}{r_p + R_P} \qquad A_v = \frac{-\mu R_D}{r_d + R_D}$$

circuits similar to that of Fig. 11-4 were used, except that the external load R_X was not present. The presence of the external load

FIGURE 11-4 *Equivalent circuits used in the development of gain formulas for (a) transistor, (b) vacuum tube, and (c) MOSFET.*

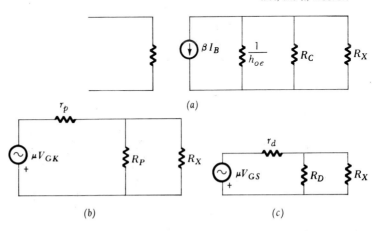

may now be taken into account by replacing R_P, R_C, and R_D in the above formulas by R_{PX}, R_{CX}, or R_{DX}, which will signify either R_P, R_C, or R_D in parallel with R_X.

Thus, the voltage-gain formulas may be written as

$$A_v = \frac{-h_{fe}R_{CX}}{h_{ie}} \qquad A_v = \frac{-\mu R_{PX}}{r_p + R_{PX}} \qquad A_v = \frac{-\mu R_{DX}}{r_d + R_{DX}}$$

where

$$R_{CX} = \frac{R_C R_X}{R_C + R_X} \qquad R_{PX} = \frac{R_P R_X}{R_P + R_X} \qquad R_{DX} = \frac{R_D R_X}{R_D + R_X}$$

We must also consider the effect capacitor coupling has on the current gain of the transistor amplifier. Since the purpose of the amplifier is to supply R_X with signal current, the gain of the amplifier becomes

$$A_i = \beta_{ac} \frac{R_{CX}}{R_X}$$

when the bias resistors are large enough to be ignored. If this is not the case, then

$$A_i = \frac{R_1 \| R_2 \| h_{ie}}{h_{ie}} \beta_{ac} \frac{R_{CX}}{R_X}$$

When the load on the amplifier is another amplifier stage, R_X is the input resistance of the second stage.

Illustrative Problem 11-1

Determine the voltage gain for each stage of the amplifier shown in Fig. Prob. 11-1. What is the overall voltage gain of the amplifier?

SOLUTION

Given: Fig. Prob. 11-1; stage I: $h_{fe} = 100$, $h_{ie} = 1500$ ohms; stage II: $h_{fe} = 75$, $h_{ie} = 750$ ohms

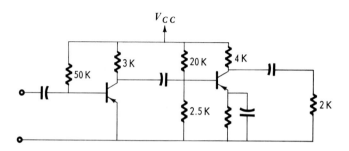

FIGURE PROB. 11-1

Find: A_{v1} ; A_{v2} ; $A_{v,\,\text{total}}$

$$A_v = \frac{-h_{fe}R_{CX}}{h_{ie}} \qquad R_{CX} = \frac{R_C R_X}{R_C + R_X}$$

Stage II:

$$R_{CX} = \frac{4 \times 2}{4 + 2} \text{ kilohms} = \frac{8}{6} \text{ kilohms} = 1350 \text{ ohms}$$

$$A_{v2} = \frac{75 \times 1330}{750} = -133$$

$$\boxed{A_{v2} = -133}$$

$R_{in2} = 20 \text{ kilohms} \| 2.5 \text{ kilohms} \| 750 \text{ ohms}$

$$20 \text{ kilohms} \| 2.5 \text{ kilohms} = \frac{20 \times 2.5}{20 + 2.5} \text{ kilohms} = \frac{50}{22.5} \text{ kilohms}$$
$$= 2220 \text{ ohms}$$

$R_{in2} = 2220 \| 750$
$$= \frac{2220 \times 750}{2220 + 750} = \frac{2220 \times 750}{2970} = 560 \text{ ohms}$$

$$\boxed{R_{in2} = 560 \text{ ohms}}$$

Stage I:

$$R_{X1} = R_{in2} = 560 \text{ ohms}$$
$$R_{CX1} = 3 \text{ kilohms} \| 560 \text{ ohms} = \frac{3000 \times 560}{3560}$$
$$= 472 \text{ ohms}$$
$$A_{v1} = \frac{-h_{fe}R_{CX}}{h_{ie}} = \frac{-100 \times 472}{1500} = -31.5$$

$$\boxed{A_{v1} = -31.5}$$

Overall:

$$A_{v,\,\text{total}} = A_{v1}A_{v2} = -31.5 \times -133 = +4180$$

$$\boxed{A_{v,\,\text{total}} = 4180}$$

Illustrative Problem 11-2

A two-stage *RC* coupled amplifier uses two 6J5's. The *B* supply is 300 volts dc. The dynamic plate resistance for the 6J5 is 7 kilohms. R_P for both stages is 20 kilohms, while R_G on the input to stage II is 80 kilohms. The amplification factor for the 6J5 is 20. The input to the amplifier is a 1-volt rms signal.

(*a*) Determine the gain of stage I.
(*b*) Find the ac output of stage I.
(*c*) Determine the gain of stage II.
(*d*) What is the overall gain for the amplifier?
(*e*) Find the output voltage for the total amplifier.

SOLUTION

Given: Two 6J5's; $V_{PP} = 300$ volts dc; $r_p = 7$ kilohms; $R_P = 20$ kilohms; $R_G = 80$ kilohms; $\mu = 20$; $V_{in} = 1$ volt rms

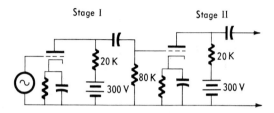

FIGURE PROB. 11-2

Find:
(*a*) A_{v1}
(*b*) $V_{out\,I}$
(*c*) A_{v2}
(*d*) $A_{v,total}$
(*e*) $V_{out\,II}$

(*a*) $$A_v = \frac{-\mu R_{PX}}{r_p + R_{PX}}$$

$$R_{PX} = \frac{R_P R_{G2}}{R_P + R_{G2}}$$

$$= \frac{(20 \times 10^3)(80 \times 10^3)}{(20 \times 10^3 + 80 \times 10^3)}$$

$$= 16 \times 10^3 \text{ ohms}$$

$$A_{v1} = \frac{-20(16 \times 10^3)}{(7 \times 10^3) + (16 \times 10^3)}$$

$$= \frac{-320 \times 10^3}{23 \times 10^3}$$

$$\boxed{A_{v1} = -13.9}$$

(*b*) $V_{out\,I} = A_{v1}\,V_{in\,I} = 13.9 \times 1$

$$\boxed{V_{out\,I} = 13.9 \text{ volts}}$$

(c) Since the second stage has only R_P and no R_G hanging onto its
output,

$$A_{v2} = \frac{-\mu R_P}{r_p + R_P}$$

$$= \frac{-20(20 \times 10^3)}{(7 \times 10^3) + (20 \times 10^3)}$$

$$\boxed{A_{v2} = -14.8}$$

(d) $A_{v,\text{total}} = A_{v1}A_{v2} = -13.9 \times -14.8$

$$\boxed{A_{v,\text{total}} = 206}$$

(e) $V_{\text{out II}} = A_{v,\text{total}}V_{\text{in}} = 206 \times 1$

$$\boxed{V_{\text{out II}} = 206 \text{ volts}}$$

or

$$V_{\text{out II}} = A_{v2}V_{\text{in II}} = -14.8 \times -13.9$$

$$\boxed{V_{\text{out II}} = 206 \text{ volts}}$$

THE EFFECT OF CAPACITOR COUPLING ON THE LOAD LINE

In the construction of the four-quadrant graph, the load line served
two purposes. First, it served to determine the quiescent operating point, and, second, it was used in the determination of the output signal. In determining the quiescent operating point, it is the
dc currents and voltages which are of concern. For this reason,
when the quiescent point is being determined, only the dc response
of the amplifier is considered. However, when analyzing the circuit for the determination of the ac output signal, we are determining the response of the circuit to an ac stimulus.

The load line when used in quiescent-point determination
must represent the dc considerations of the circuit, while the load
line when used in the ac analysis must represent the ac response
of the circuit. Observe in Fig. 11-5a that for dc considerations the
impedance of the output circuit consists of R_P in series with R_K.
The coupling capacitor isolating R_X for dc and the bypass capacitor
C_K appear as an open circuit for dc. When ac conditions must be
considered, R_K appears shorted by the bypass capacitor and the
power supply can be considered as a short, according to the superposition theorem. The coupling capacitor can also be considered

as a short, thus putting R_X in parallel with R_P. A similar argument holds true for the vacuum-tube and MOSFET amplifiers. Thus, two load lines are required to describe the complete functioning of the amplifier. One load line is required to describe the functioning of the circuit under quiescent (dc or static) conditions, and another is required to describe the functioning of the circuit under dynamic (ac) conditions. The dc load line is used in determining the quiescent operating point, while the ac load line is required in the construction of the output waveshape, which is the response of the circuit to the input signal.

The dc load line is sometimes referred to as the *static load line*, while the ac load line is referred to as the *dynamic load line*. The reason for the name static load line is that this load line describes the circuit under static, or nonvarying, conditions. The term dynamic load line is used because it describes the circuit while it is being excited and varying under the influence of a varying input signal, the dynamic conditions of operating.

The construction of the dc, or static, load line, the same as that described in previous chapters when the four-quadrant graphs were discussed, is a straight line through the intercept points, V_{CC} and V_{CC}/R_C, V_{PP} and V_{PP}/R_P, or V_{DD} and V_{DD}/R_D, having a slope of $-1/R_C$, $-1/R_P$, or $-1/R_D$.

THE CONSTRUCTION OF THE DYNAMIC LOAD LINE (AC LOAD LINE)

The construction of the dynamic load line (ac load line) requires more thought than the static load line. Recall the significance of the operating point. It is the point which describes the operation of the amplifier while it is at rest, with no varying signal applied. When a varying input signal is applied, it causes the operating point to shift away from the quiescent point. Thus, if a sine wave were presented as the input, the point of operation should return to the quiescent operating point every 180° (each half-cycle) because once every 180° the input sine wave returns to a zero level. Since the dynamic load line (ac load line) describes the operation of the circuit under the influence of a varying input, it must pass through the quiescent operating point. Thus, the operating point, which cannot leave the load line, is able to return to the quiescent point every 180°.

The load line describing the operation of the amplifier must have a slope which is $-1/R$, where R is the resistance of the load. Thus, the dynamic load line is that line which is to pass through the quiescent operating point and have a slope of $-1/R_{PX}$, $-1/R_{CX}$, or $-1/R_{DX}$ since R_{PX}, R_{CX}, or R_{DX} is the total resistance seen when the output has a varying component

$$R_{PX} = R_C\|R_X \qquad R_{CX} = R_C\|R_X \qquad R_{DX} = R_D\|R_X$$

$$R_{PX} = \frac{R_P R_X}{R_P + R_X} \qquad R_{CX} = \frac{R_C R_X}{R_C + R_X} \qquad R_{DX} = \frac{R_D R_X}{R_D + R_X}$$

(see Fig. 11-5).

From geometry we know that one point and a slope determine a line. The dynamic load line can therefore be drawn provided the quiescent point is known.

The ac load line therefore has a slope of $-1/R_{PX}$, $-1/R_{CX}$, or $-1/R_{DX}$ and passes through the quiescent operating point.

The quiescent operating point can be determined from the dc load line, which is constructed as described previously by the two-intercept method or by the point-slope method. Once the quiescent operating point is known, the dynamic load line can be constructed at a slope of $-1/R_{PX}$, $-1/R_{CX}$, or $-1/R_{DX}$ and passing through the quiescent point using the point-slope method of load-line construction. It should now be obvious why two load lines

FIGURE 11-5 *The output sections of (a) vacuum-tube triode amplifier, (b) PNP transistor amplifier, and (c) MOSFET amplifier.*

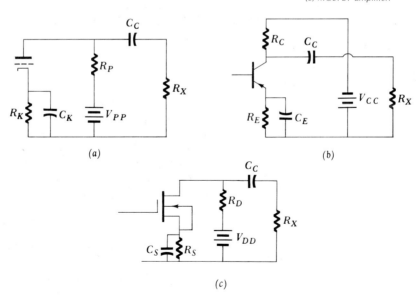

(a)

(b)

(c)

must be constructed in the determination of the four-quadrant graphs for capacitor-coupled amplifiers.

The following illustrative problem describes the construction for the four-quadrant graphs.

Illustrative Problem 11-3

A 6SL7-GT twin triode is to be used as a capacitance-coupled amplifier. All component values are as given in Fig. Prob. 11-3a, with a grid bias of 2 volts negative. The input is a 1.5-volt peak signal.

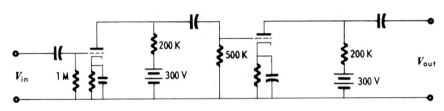

FIGURE PROB. 11-3a

(a) Draw the dc load line for the first stage.
(b) Find the Q point for the first stage.
(c) Draw the ac load line for the first stage.
(d) Draw the input waveshape on the plate characteristic.
(e) Draw the waveshape of the voltage that appears across the plate of the first stage.
(f) Draw the waveshape of the plate current for the first stage.
(g) Determine the gain of the first stage graphically.

SOLUTION
Given: Circuit shown in Fig. Prob. 11-3a
Find:
(a) dc (static) load line
(b) Q point
(c) ac (dynamic) load line
(d) Draw the input waveshape
(e) Draw the plate voltage of the first stage
(f) Plate current waveshape of first stage
(g) Gain of first stage

(a) $\dfrac{V_{PP}}{R_P} = \dfrac{300}{200 \times 10^3} = 1.5 \times 10^{-3}$

$$\boxed{\begin{aligned} y \text{ intercept} &= 1.5 \times 10^{-3} \\ x \text{ intercept} &= V_{PP} = 300 \end{aligned}}$$

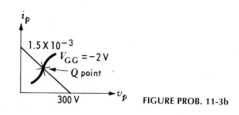

FIGURE PROB. 11-3b

(b) See Fig. Prob. 11-3*b*.
(c) See Fig. Prob. 11-3*c*.

$$R_{PX} = R_{PG} = \frac{R_P R_G}{R_P + R_G}$$

$$R_{PG} = \frac{(200 \times 10^3)(500 \times 10^3)}{(200 \times 10^3) + (500 \times 10^3)}$$

$$= \frac{10 \times 10^{10}}{700 \times 10^3}$$

$$\boxed{R_{PX} = R_{PG} = 143 \times 10^3 \text{ ohms}}$$

$$\frac{\Delta v_{pk}}{\Delta i_p} = R_{PX}$$

Allow Δv_{pk} to equal 50. Any convenient allowance for Δv_{pk} may be made.

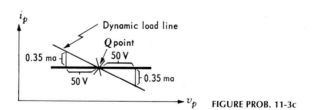

FIGURE PROB. 11-3c

$$\frac{\Delta v_{pk}}{\Delta i_p} = 143 \times 10^3$$

$$\Delta i_p = \frac{50}{143 \times 10^3}$$

$$\boxed{\Delta i_p = 0.35 \text{ ma}}$$

(d) The input voltage waveshape is drawn on the plate characteristic using the dynamic (ac) load line as a voltage axis (see Fig. Prob. 11-3*d*). Calibration of this axis comes from the

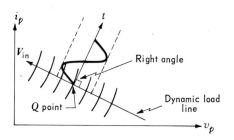

FIGURE PROB. 11-3d

points of intersection of the constant-grid-voltage curves with the dynamic load line. The time axis is obtained by drawing a perpendicular to the dynamic load line.

(e) The plate current waveshape is obtained by projecting the input voltage waveshape off the dynamic (ac) load line onto the plate current axis (see Fig. Prob. 11-3e).

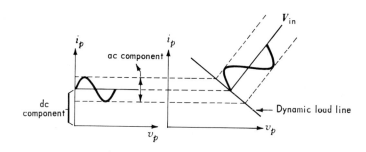

FIGURE PROB. 11-3e

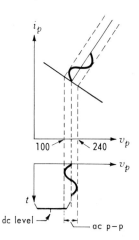

FIGURE PROB. 11-3f

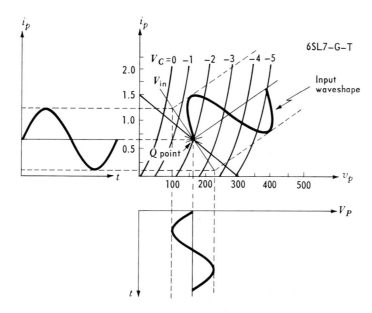

(f)   The plate voltage waveshape is obtained by projecting the input voltage waveshape off the dynamic load line onto the plate voltage axis.

(g) $A_v = \dfrac{V_{\text{out}}}{V_{\text{in}}} = \dfrac{240-100}{2 \times 1.5} = \dfrac{140}{3.0}$

$$\boxed{A_v = 46.7}$$

Illustrative Problem 11-4

A 40311 transistor is used as the active device in the first stage of the circuit shown in Fig. Prob. 11-4a.   The second stage makes use of a transistor which has an input resistance of 800 ohms.   The quiescent base current of the first stage is 24 μa.   For an input current of 20 μa peak into the base terminal of the first transistor determine:

(a)   The dc load line for the first stage
(b)   The quiescent operating point of the first stage
(c)   The ac load line for the first stage
(d)   The four-quadrant graph of the first stage

SOLUTION
Given: Circuit shown in Fig. Prob. 11-4a

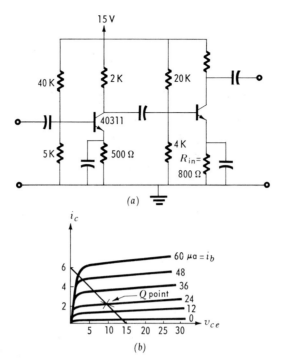

FIGURE PROB. 11-4a and b

Find:

(a) The dc load line
(b) Q point
(c) The ac load line
(d) Four-quadrant graph

(a) $\quad I_{c,\text{int}} = \dfrac{V_{CC}}{R_C + R_E} = \dfrac{15}{2 \text{ kilohms} + 500} = \dfrac{15}{2.5 \times 10^3} = 6 \times 10^{-3}$

$$\boxed{I_{c,\text{int}} = 6 \text{ ma}}$$

(b) See Fig. Prob. 11-4b

(c) $R_{CX} = 2 \text{ kilohms} \| 4 \text{ kilohms} \| 20 \text{ kilohms} \| 800$

$\dfrac{1}{R_{CX}} = \dfrac{1}{2 \text{ kilohms}} + \dfrac{1}{4 \text{ kilohms}} + \dfrac{1}{20 \text{ kilohms}} + \dfrac{1}{800}$

$\qquad = 0.5 \times 10^{-3} + 0.25 \times 10^{-3} + 0.05 \times 10^{-3} + 1.25 \times 10^{-3}$

$\qquad = 2.05 \times 10^{-3} \text{ ohms}$

$$\boxed{R_{CX} = 486 \text{ ohms}}$$

(d) For the ac load line (see Fig. Prob. 11-4c):

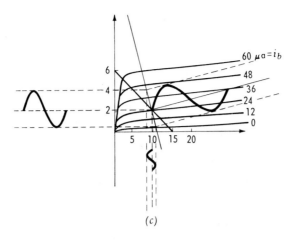

(c)

$$\frac{\Delta v}{\Delta i} = R_{CX}$$

Let $\Delta v = 2.5$ volts; then

$$\frac{2.5}{\Delta i} = 486$$

$$= \frac{2.5}{486}$$

$$\boxed{\Delta i = 5.15 \text{ ma}}$$

PROBLEMS

11-1 Why would you include coupling capacitors in the design of an amplifier?

11-2 Determine the current gain, voltage gain, and power gain of the amplifier shown in Fig. 11-6.

11-3 Draw a schematic diagram and determine the voltage gain of a

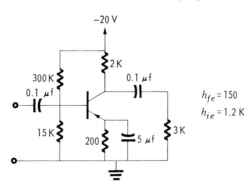

FIGURE 11-6 *Diagram for Probs. 11-2 and 11-9.*

CAPACITOR COUPLING   173

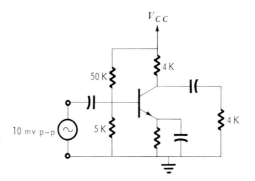

FIGURE 11-7 *Diagram for Prob. 11-6.*

vacuum-tube amplifier which has a plate circuit load resistor R_P of 10 kilohms and a capacitor-coupled external load of 50 kilohms. The tube parameters are $\mu = 50$ and $r_p = 15$ kilohms.

11-4 Determine the current gain, voltage gain, and power gain of an amplifier that uses a transistor with a β of 85 and an h_{ie} of 1800 ohms as its active device. An R_C of 3 kilohms is used with an external capacitance-coupled load of 800 ohms.

11-5 Determine the current gain, voltage gain, and power gain of an amplifier described as follows: voltage-divider bias resistors of 8 and 50 kilohms; collector load resistor of 5 kilohms; capacitor-coupled external load of 3 kilohms; transistor parameters: $h_{ie} = 1200$ ohms, $h_{fe} = 110$.

11-6 The amplifier shown in Fig. 11-7 uses a transistor having the following h parameters: $h_{ie} = 1000$ ohms, $h_{re} = 0.0004$, $1/h_{oe} = 90$ kilohms, $h_{fe} = 100$. Determine the current gain, voltage gain, and power gain of the amplifier with its external load connected.

11-7 A 2N2613 transistor is to be connected in a common-emitter fixed-bias configuration. The collector supply voltage is 15 volts. The collector load resistor is 1500 ohms, while the external capacitor-coupled load to the amplifier is a 3000-ohm resistive device. The quiescent base current is to be 50 μa.
(a) Sketch a schematic diagram of the circuit.
(b) Construct the static and dynamic load lines.
(c) Calculate R_B, the base bias resistor.
(d) Complete a four-quadrant graph for an input of 50 μa peak-to-peak.
(e) What voltage is required to provide the input signal specified in (d)?

11-8 Two identical stages of a multistage capacitance-coupled amplifier use a 40314 silicon transistor. Both stages are voltage-divider biased with swamping. The h_{ie} of each transistor is 200 ohms. A collector load resistor R_C of 2.5 kilohms is used with a collector supply of 15 volts. A 24 μa quiescent base current is desired for each stage.

(a) Sketch a schematic diagram of the circuit.

(b) Plot the static load line.

(c) Indicate the Q point.

(d) Determine the resistance of the emitter swamping resistor and both voltage-divider resistors.

(e) Draw the ac load line for stage 1.

11-9 The transistor amplifier shown in Fig. 11-6 contains a 40263 transistor. The input signal base current is 60 μa peak-to-peak while the base bias current is 40 μa.

(a) Construct a static load line for the circuit.

(b) Construct a dynamic load line for the circuit.

(c) Draw the four-quadrant graph which describes the operation of the amplifier and signal input.

(d) Find the current gain of the amplifier from the four-quadrant graph.

(e) Calculate the input signal voltage necessary to produce the desired base signal current.

(f) Determine the voltage gain of the amplifier from (e) and the four-quadrant graph.

11-10 A 2N2613 transistor is to be used as an amplifier in a common-emitter configuration. The quiescent collector-to-emitter voltage should be 3 volts, while the collector supply voltage is 7 volts dc. A 50 μa base bias current is desired.

(a) Determine the base bias resistor required to provide fixed bias.

(b) Locate the Q point and draw the dc load line.

(c) Determine the required collector load resistor.

(d) Find the h_{fe} of the transistor at the Q point.

(e) The external load which is capacitor-coupled to the amplifier is 4 kilohms. Construct the ac load line and complete a four-quadrant graph for a base current input signal of 60 μa peak-to-peak.

(f) Find the current gain and voltage gain by formula and compare it with what you obtained from the four-quadrant graph.

11-11 One triode section of a 12AU7A vacuum tube is to be used in the design of an amplifier whose function is to feed a 20 kilohm external load which is capacitor-coupled to the amplifier. The desired quiescent operating point is at a grid voltage of -4 volts and a plate voltage of 150 volts. A 300-volt plate supply is to be used with this amplifier. The parameters for the 12AU7A are $\mu = 17$ and $r_p = 7700$ ohms.

(a) Sketch the schematic diagram of the circuit.

(b) Locate the quiescent operating point on the plate characteristics of the tube.

(c) Construct the static load line.

(d) Calculate the required resistance and power-dissipation rating of the plate load resistor R_p.

(e) Construct the dynamic load line for this amplifier.

(f) Complete the four-quadrant graph which describes this amplifier for an input of 6 volts peak-to-peak.

(g) Determine the voltage gain of the amplifier first by formula and then from the construction in part (f).

11-12 Two 2N2613 transistors are to be used as the active devices in a two-stage capacitor-coupled amplifier. The pertinent information for each stage is listed below.

First Stage	Second Stage
$V_{CC} = 15$ volts	Voltage divider bias resistors $= 12$ and 2
$R_C = 1000$ ohms	kilohms
$I_{BQ} = 50$ μa	$h_{ie} = 4000$ ohms

Construct the static and dynamic load lines which describe the operation of the first stage.

12

FREQUENCY RESPONSE OF CAPACITOR-COUPLED AMPLIFIERS

An interesting and important effect is noticed if an *RC*-coupled amplifier is presented with an input sine-wave signal whose amplitude is kept constant but whose frequency is varied. It will be found that the output signal remains constant over a wide range of frequencies but falls off in amplitude at high frequencies and at low frequencies. A plot of amplitude vs. frequency looks like the curve shown in Fig. 12-1. Note that the horizontal axis is plotted as the log of frequency rather than just frequency. This is done in order to get a large span of frequency on the paper without losing the details present in the lower portion of the curve. This curve of Fig. 12-1 is known as the frequency-response curve of the amplifier. The reason the amplifier does not have a straight horizontal line as a frequency-response curve is discussed below.

EFFECT OF CAPACITANCES

Up until this point whenever a capacitor was encountered in the circuit, some reason was found for disregarding it and considering it as either a short or an open circuit, depending on whether we were discussing ac or dc conditions. In so doing, the impedance of the capacitor was disregarded. The frequency-varying impedance of the coupling capacitors is the cause of the unexpected roll-off at the low end of the frequency spectrum, as will be explained shortly. The roll-off at high frequencies is also due to capacitor

FIGURE 12-1 *Plot of voltage gain vs. frequency for an amplifier.*

impedance varying with frequency, but these capacitances are of a different variety than the coupling capacitor. As a matter of fact, the capacitances which cause the high-frequency roll-off are invisible to the human eye. It is impossible to physically remove these capacitances which cause the high frequency roll-off because they are inherent in the physical makeup of the active devices and the hook-up wire which is used.

By definition, capacitance is said to exist anywhere there are two electric conductors separated by a nonconductor or anywhere equal and opposite charge can build up and remain separated. According to this description, capacitance should exist between sections of hook-up wire, between the electrodes of a vacuum tube, across the junctions of a transistor, and between the different sections of the MOSFET. This is actually the case. The capacitance introduced between sections of hook-up wire is known as *stray wiring capacitance* and can be reduced by keeping leads as short as possible, by properly routing the leads, and by using proper soldering technique. This process of properly handling the hook-up wire is known as *dressing the leads.*

ACTIVE-DEVICE INTERNAL CAPACITANCES

Attempting to reduce the effect of internal capacitances of active devices requires techniques which are more sophisticated than merely reducing the stray wiring capacitance. However, there are compensation circuits which the designer may use to reduce the effect of these capacitances to a minimum. A discussion of design compensation techniques will not be undertaken at this point.

Figure 12-2 shows where the internal capacitances appear to

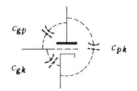

FIGURE 12-2 *Vacuum-tube triode showing interelectrode capacitances.*

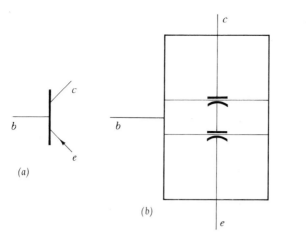

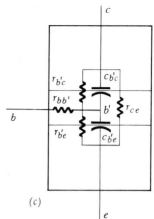

FIGURE 12-3 (a) Schematic symbol of a transistor. (b) Location of capacitances in a transistor. (c) Internal resistances and capacitances of a transistor.

have their effect within a triode vacuum tube. For obvious reasons these capacitances are called *interelectrode capacitances*. A similar diagram can be drawn for the pentode vacuum tube.

Figure 12-3 depicts the transistor and indicates where the inherent capacitances appear. Figure 12-3*b* shows only the capacitances, while Fig. 12-3*c* indicates the resistance of paths in the vicinity of these capacitances. As will be seen, these resistive paths play a rather important role in the functioning of the transistor at high frequencies. As an example, note that in order to reach the capacitances across the junction, current must pass $r_{bb'}$, the resistance of the base material. It is usually quite appreciable since the base is very narrow, and even though the analogous resistances of the emitter and collector regions are not taken into account, $r_{bb'}$ is, because of its appreciable size. $r_{bb'}$ is referred to many times in the literature as the *base spreading resistance*. $r_{b'c}$ and $r_{b'e}$ are the equivalent junction resistances of the base-collector junction and the base-emitter junction, respectively, while r_{ce} is the equivalent resistance between collector and emitter through the transistor.

Figure 12-4 is a pictorial diagram of a MOSFET. Note the many interfaces between its sections. It is along these interfaces that internal capacitances develop in the MOSFET.

Before getting too deeply involved in the frequency response of the active devices it will be wise to lay the groundwork by first studying the various possible combinations of resistance and capacitances.

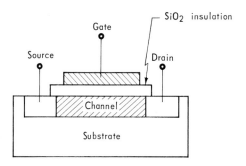

FIGURE 12-4 *Pictorial diagram of a MOSFET.*

HIGH-PASS AND LOW-PASS FILTERS

Figure 12-5 shows two possible combinations of a resistor and capacitance. One is called a *high-pass filter,* and the other is called a *low-pass filter.*

Let us investigate why these circuits were given such names. First, refer to the circuit in Fig. 12-5*a* and assume that a very high-frequency signal is applied to its input. What will be the result? At high frequency the impedance of the capacitor is very low, so that most of the applied voltage appears across the resistor. Since the output is being taken across the resistor, almost the entire input signal appears across the output.

What is the situation when a low-frequency signal is applied? The impedance of the capacitor becomes relatively high. That portion of the applied voltage which is dropped across the capacitor becomes relatively large, leaving only a small portion of the applied voltage to appear across the output. So we see that this circuit is called a high-pass filter because it allows high-frequency signals to pass through with less attenuation than low-frequency signals. A similar study can be made for the low-pass filter shown in Fig. 12-5*b*.

A more exact study of the filter circuits of Fig. 12-5 results in the curves shown in Fig. 12-6. Because there is no exact frequency beyond which it can be said that the filter passes or eliminates all traces of the input, the term *cutoff frequency* has been coined. The cutoff frequency has been chosen as the frequency at which $X_C = R$.

FIGURE 12-5 (a) *High-pass filter.* (b) *Low-pass filter.*

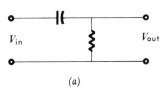

(a)

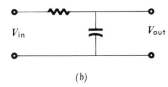

(b)

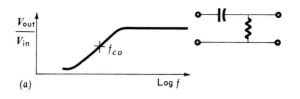

(a)

Log f

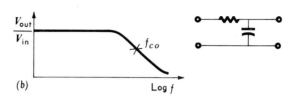

(b)

Log f

FIGURE 12-6 *Response curve of (a) high-pass filter and (b) low-pass filter.*

Let us now determine the relationship that exists between the output and the input voltages at the cutoff frequency of the high-pass filter of Fig. 12-7 and the low-pass filter of Fig. 12-8.

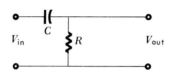

FIGURE 12-7 *High-pass filter.*

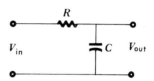

FIGURE 12-8 *Low-pass filter.*

$$V_{out} = \frac{R}{Z} V_{in}$$

$$Z = \sqrt{R^2 + X_C^2}$$

The cutoff frequency has been defined as the frequency at which $X_c = R$.

$$Z = \sqrt{R^2 + R^2} = \sqrt{2R^2}$$
$$= \sqrt{2}R$$

$$V_{out} = \frac{R}{\sqrt{2}R} V_{in}$$

$$= \frac{1}{\sqrt{2}} V_{in}$$

$$= 0.707 V_{in}$$

$$\boxed{V_{out} = 0.707 V_{in} \qquad \text{at } f_{co}}$$

$$V_{out} = \frac{X_C}{Z} V_{in}$$

$$Z = \sqrt{R^2 + X_C^2}$$

The cutoff frequency has been defined as the frequency at which $X_C = R$.

$$Z = \sqrt{2X_C^2}$$
$$= \sqrt{2}X_C$$

$$V_{out} = \frac{X_C}{\sqrt{2}X_C} V_{in}$$

$$= \frac{1}{\sqrt{2}} V_{in}$$

$$= 0.707 V_{in}$$

$$\boxed{V_{out} = 0.707 V_{in} \qquad \text{at } f_{co}}$$

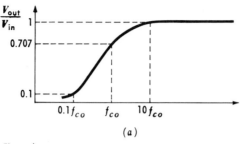

(a)

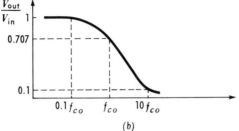

(b)

The cutoff frequency for both the high- and the low-pass filter can be found from

$$f_{co} = \frac{1}{2\pi RC}$$

This equation stems from

$$X_C = R \quad \text{and} \quad 1/2\pi f_{co}C = R$$

Therefore

$$f_{co} = \frac{1}{2\pi RC}$$

An estimated response curve can be drawn without having to go through the work of plotting the response at each point. Using the universal response curve of Fig. 12-9, V_{out}-vs.-frequency curves can be drawn for particular situations without too much effort.

A FEW REAPPEARING CIRCUITS

It will be found that in the frequency analysis of amplifiers a number of circuits keep reappearing. It will prove advantageous to do a preliminary study of a few of these in their most general form before going on to specific circuits.

The frequency analysis of an amplifier is usually made in three parts, the low-frequency analysis, the mid-frequency analysis, and the high-frequency analysis.

A COMMON LOW-FREQUENCY CIRCUIT

One circuit which will be found a number of times in the low-frequency analysis of amplifiers is shown as Fig. 12-10, where R_1 and R_2 may be the total combination of several resistances. To begin with we will find the voltage gain of the circuit at frequencies low enough for the impedance due to C to be appreciable. Note that the impedance due to C will not always be appreciable since it is a function of frequency and as frequency is increased, it will have a smaller and smaller effect. From Fig. 12-10, we see that

$$V_0 = \frac{VR_2}{\sqrt{(R_1 + R_2)^2 + X_C^2}} \qquad \text{voltage-divider theorem}$$

Let $R = R_1 + R_2$; then

$$\frac{V_0}{V} = \frac{R_2}{\sqrt{R^2 + X_C^2}}$$

$$\boxed{A_{Vlf} = \frac{R_2}{\sqrt{R^2 + X_C^2}} \qquad \text{voltage gain at low frequencies}}$$

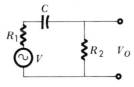

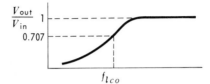

FIGURE 12-10 *A common high-pass filter and its frequency-response curve.*

Now assume that the frequency of the signal source is changed so that it is putting out a signal whose frequency is high enough to make the reactance, and thereby the impedance, of the capacitor negligible in comparison to the resistance values in the circuit. In this case, the voltage gain of the circuit is found to be

$$V_o = \frac{R_2 V}{R_1 + R_2}$$

$$A_V = \frac{V_o}{V} = \frac{R_2}{R_1 + R_2} = \frac{R_2}{R}$$

This is called the *mid-frequency voltage gain* of the circuit A_{Vmf}.

$$A_{Vmf} = \frac{R_2}{R}$$

Let us now try to find the frequency at which the gain obtained for the low-frequency situation is 0.707 of the gain obtained when the frequency was relatively high.

It will prove to be instructive to divide the voltage gain for the low-frequency case by the gain for the case in which the capacitance plays no role.

$$\frac{A_{Vlf}}{A_{Vmf}} = \frac{R_2/\sqrt{R^2 + X_c^2}}{R_2/R}$$

$$= \frac{R}{\sqrt{R^2 + X_c^2}}$$

$$= \frac{1}{(1/R)\sqrt{R^2 + X_c^2}}$$

$$= \frac{1}{\sqrt{1/R^2}\sqrt{R^2 + X_c^2}}$$

$$= \frac{1}{\sqrt{1 + X_c^2/R^2}}$$

$$= \frac{1}{\sqrt{1 + 1/(2\pi f RC)^2}}$$

Let us find the frequency at which the gain decreases by 0.707. This is a significant frequency since it is the frequency at which the power transfer to the output is down by one-half of its value when the capacitances can be ignored.

$$\frac{A_{Vlf}}{A_{Vmf}} = 0.707 = \frac{1}{\sqrt{1 + (1/2\pi f RC)^2}}$$

$$= 0.707 = \frac{1}{\sqrt{2}} = \frac{1}{\sqrt{1 + (1/2\pi RC)^2}}$$

$$\frac{1}{2} = \frac{1}{1 + (2\pi fRC)^2}$$
$$2 = 1 + (2\pi fRC)^2$$
$$1 = (2\pi fRC)^2$$
$$1 = 2\pi fRC$$

$$\boxed{f_{lco} = \frac{1}{2\pi RC} \qquad \text{where } R = R_1 + R_2}$$

Thus it is seen that when determining the low-frequency cutoff point for the circuit in Fig. 12-10 all the series resistances must be included in the calculation. The response curve is plotted in the same manner as for the high-pass filter (see Fig. 12-9).

Illustrative Problem 12-1

Determine the low-frequency cutoff point for the circuit shown in Fig. Prob. 12-1a. Sketch a curve of output voltage (rms) vs. frequency.

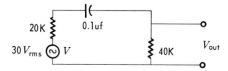

FIGURE PROB. 12-1a

SOLUTION
Given: Circuit in Fig. Prob. 12-1a
Find: f_{lco}; $V_{\text{out rms}}$ vs. frequency

$$f_{lco} = \frac{1}{2\pi RC}$$
$$R = 20 \text{ kilohms} + 40 \text{ kilohms} = 60 \text{ kilohms}$$
$$f_{lco} = \frac{1}{2\pi (60 \times 10^3)(0.1 \times 10^{-6})}$$

$$\boxed{f_{lco} = 26.6 \text{ Hz}}$$

$$\frac{V_{\text{out}}}{V_{\text{in}}} = \frac{R_2}{R_1 + R_2} \qquad \text{voltage-divider theorem}$$
$$V_{\text{out},mf} = \frac{40 \text{ kilohms}}{20 \text{ kilohms} + 40 \text{ kilohms}} \times 30 = 20 \text{ volts}$$

FREQUENCY RESPONSE OF CAPACITOR-COUPLED AMPLIFIERS   185

	f	$V_{\text{out rms}}$
$0.1f_{co}$	2.66 Hz	2 volts
f_{co}	26.6 Hz	$0.707 \times 20 = 14.14$ volts
10_{fco}	266 Hz	20 volts

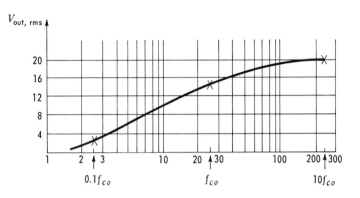

FIGURE PROB. 12-1b

A COMMON CIRCUIT AT HIGH FREQUENCIES

Just as there was a circuit we expect will appear often during low-frequency analysis of amplifiers, there is a circuit we expect will appear often during high-frequency analysis. This circuit is shown in Fig. 12-11a. An analysis similar to the one just completed for the low-frequency circuit can be performed on this circuit.

To begin with, however, some manipulation of the circuit into a more workable form is necessary. This will be done by using the relationship which is known to exist between the Thévenin and the Norton equivalent circuits. Note that the impedances of the Thévenin and the Norton equivalent circuits are equal and that the voltage source of the Thévenin and the current source of the Norton equivalent circuits are related by

$$V_{\text{thev}} = V_{\text{nort}}R_{\text{eq}}$$

On the basis of this relationship the circuit of Fig. 12-11a can be broken at the X's and the portion of the circuit to the left of the X's replaced by the Norton equivalent, as shown in Fig. 12-11b. The two resistances R_1 and R_2 of Fig. 12-11b can be combined as shown in Fig. 12-11c and the circuit broken at the Y points, followed by a replacement of the circuit to the left of the Y's by the Thévenin equivalent, as shown in Fig. 12-11d. The rest of the analysis can now be made as in the low-frequency situation.

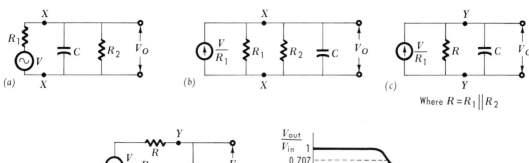

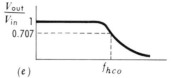

(d)

(e)

FIGURE 12-11 *Thévenin-Norton manipulation of a common high-frequency circuit.*

$$V_0 = \frac{VR}{R_1} \frac{X_c}{\sqrt{X_c^2 + R^2}}$$

$$A_{Vhf} = \frac{R}{R_1} \frac{X_c}{\sqrt{X_c^2 + R^2}}$$

$$A_{Vmf} = \frac{R}{R_1}$$

$$\frac{A_{Vhf}}{A_{Vmf}} = \frac{X_c}{\sqrt{X_c^2 + R^2}}$$

$$= \frac{1}{\sqrt{1 + R^2/X_c^2}} = \frac{1}{\sqrt{1 + 4\pi^2 f^2 R^2 C^2}}$$

$$0.707 = \frac{1}{\sqrt{1 + 4\pi^2 f^2 R^2 C^2}}$$

$$\frac{1}{\sqrt{2}} = \frac{1}{\sqrt{1 + 4\pi^2 f^2 R^2 C^2}}$$

$$2 = 1 + 4\pi^2 f^2 R^2 C^2$$

$$f^2 = \frac{1}{4\pi^2 R^2 C^2}$$

$$\boxed{f_{hco} = \frac{1}{2\pi RC} \qquad \text{where } R = R_1 \| R_2}$$

Again we have a case in which the circuit response curve looks like the filter response curve. The response curve for this circuit is drawn in the manner similar to the low-pass filter with the high-frequency cutoff point determined by R_1 in parallel with R_2 and the capacitor C.

Illustrative Problem 12-2
Determine the high-frequency cutoff point for the circuit shown in Fig. Prob. 12-2a. Sketch a curve of output voltage vs. frequency.

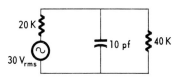

SOLUTION
Given: Circuit shown in Fig. Prob. 12-2a
Find: f_{hco}; V_{out}-vs.-f curve

$$f_{hco} = \frac{1}{2\pi RC}$$
$$R = 20 \text{ kilohms} \| 40 \text{ kilohms}$$
$$= \frac{20 \times 40}{20 + 40} \text{ kilohms} = 13.3 \text{ kilohms}$$
$$= 13,300 \text{ ohms}$$
$$f_{hco} = \frac{1}{2\pi (13.3 \times 10^3)(10 \times 10^{-12})}$$

$$\boxed{f_{hco} = 1.2 \text{ MHz}}$$

$$V_{out,mf} = \frac{R_2}{R_1 + R_2} V$$
$$= \frac{40 \text{ kilohms}}{60 \text{ kilohms}} \times 30 = 20 \text{ volts}$$

	f, MHz	V_{out}
$0.1f_{co}$	0.12	20
f_{co}	1.2	$0.707 \times 20 = 14.14$
$10f_{co}$	12	2

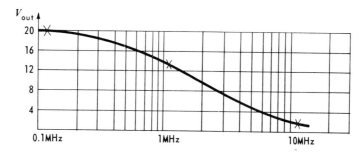

FIGURE PROB. 12-2b

PROBLEMS

12-1 Why is a log scale used on the horizontal axis of a frequency-response curve?

12-2 Why isn't the frequency-response curve of an amplifier a straight horizontal line?

12-3 What is meant by the terms "stray wiring capacitance," "interelectrode capacitance," and "junction capacitance"?

12-4 Why are "low-pass filters" referred to by that name? "High-pass filters"?

12-5 Sketch the response curve of a low-pass filter and a high-pass filter.

12-6 What is meant by the expression "cutoff frequency"?

12-7 A 0.01-μf capacitor and a 50-kilohm resistor are connected, first as a high-pass filter and then as a low-pass filter. Determine the cutoff frequency and construct a response curve for each of the two cases.

12-8 Determine the low-frequency cutoff point of the circuit shown in Fig. 12-10 if the components have the following values:

$$R_1 = 800 \text{ ohms} \qquad R_2 = 1200 \text{ ohms} \qquad C = 50 \ \mu\text{f}$$

Construct the frequency-response curve for this circuit and determine the output voltage if V is a 100-volt-rms signal whose frequency is equal to the cutoff frequency of the circuit.

12-9 Assume that the components in the circuit shown in Fig. 12-11a have the following values:

$$R_1 = 1000 \text{ ohms} \qquad R_2 = 10 \text{ kilohms} \qquad C = 200 \text{ pf}$$

(a) Find the high-frequency cutoff point.

(b) Construct a response curve for this circuit.

(c) Determine the output voltage for a signal voltage V of 150 volts rms at a frequency equal to the cutoff frequency.

(d) Calculate the amount of power that would be taken by a 150-kilohm load resistor attached across the output terminals for V as described in (c).

(e) How much power would be drawn by the 150-kilohm load of part (d) if the source frequency were much lower than the cutoff frequency?

FREQUENCY RESPONSE OF CAPACITOR-COUPLED AMPLIFIERS   189

13 THE CAPACITOR-COUPLED VACUUM-TUBE AMPLIFIER

When choosing an amplifier to do a particular job, it is important to know the frequencies at which the gain is no longer independent of frequency. For example, for use in a phonograph system, an amplifier having a frequency-response curve whose gain rolls off drastically below 1 kHz and above 5 kHz is quite inadequate. The human hearing range is 20 Hz to 20 kHz, so the frequencies at which gain roll-off occurs should be above 20 kHz and below 20 Hz.

CONSIDERING ALL CAPACITANCES

A study of the capacitor-coupled vacuum-tube amplifier with all capacitances shown is necessary in order to determine its frequency-response curve. Figure 13-1 is a diagram of a triode amplifier with all capacitances shown. The only two points of interest which have not already been fully explained are the connections to the input signal source and the connection to the load. To begin with, it must be recognized that, according to Thévenin's theorem, any two-terminal linear device can be represented by an ideal voltage source in series with an impedance, which in the simple case is a resistance. The signal input is therefore shown as originating in a source represented by the voltage generator V_s in series with a resistance R_s, which represents the output impedance of the source generator. Since an attempt will be made to find all low-pass and high-pass circuits in the amplifier, care must be taken to include all resistances and all capacitances. Second, a capacitance C_x has been included in the output circuit to represent any capacitance which the external load may have. In Fig. 13-1b the bias arrangement, R_K and C_K, has been omitted to avoid confusion. The designer can choose a value of C_K which will eliminate the effect the bias arrangement would have on frequency response. Such a value of C_K is that value whose reactance is no greater than one-tenth R_K at the low-frequency cutoff point.

Note in the input portion of the circuit of Fig. 13-1b, the small-signal equivalent representation, that the capacitances C_{GK} and C_{GP} have been replaced by the capacitance C_{in}. C_{in} depends not only upon C_{GK} but also upon C_{GP} because the input section of the amplifier is coupled to the output section through C_{GP} (see Fig. 13-1a). The formula for the determination of C_{in} is

$$C_{\text{in}} = C_{GK} + (1 + |A|)C_{GP}$$

That portion of the input capacitance which is represented by $(1 + |A|)C_{GP}$ is known as the *Miller effect capacitance*.

FIGURE 13-1 (a) *Triode amplifier with all capacitances shown.* (b) *Equivalent circuit of (a).*

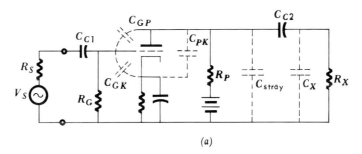

(a)

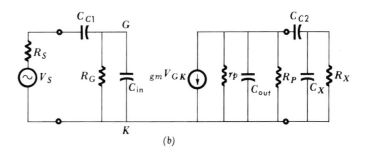

(b)

It will prove fruitful to study the circuit under three separate conditions. The circuit of Fig. 13-1b will be analyzed for low-frequency operation, high-frequency operation, and then for mid-frequency operation.

THE LOW-FREQUENCY EQUIVALENT CIRCUIT

When the input signal to the amplifier is of low frequency, the impedance of all the capacitors becomes relatively high because

$$Z_c = X_c = \frac{1}{2\pi f C}$$

FIGURE 13-2 (a) Low-frequency equivalent circuit of the vacuum-tube amplifier of Fig. 13-1. (b) Low-frequency equivalent of the output section with r_p and R_P combined. (c) Low-frequency equivalent of the output section after the Norton-Thévenin manipulation.

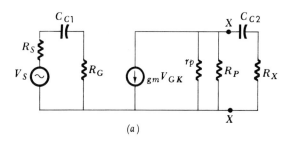

(a)

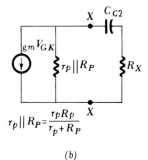

(b)

(c)

Under these conditions all *shunting* capacitors (C_{in}, C_x, and C_{out}) can be ignored, leaving the circuit as shown in Fig. 13-2a for further analysis.

Do you recognize the input section of Fig. 13-2a? It is one of the circuits we studied in the last chapter. The output section of the amplifier does not look as familiar, but with a little manipulation it too will become more recognizable. To begin, let us first make use of the Thévenin-Norton equivalency in the output section. Break the output circuit at the points marked X of Fig. 13-2a and b and replace the parallel combination of the current source and resistance ($r_p \| R_P$) by the series combination of Thévenin voltage source and resistance shown in Fig. 13-2c. Now the output and the input sections of the amplifier are recognizable. Both are high-pass filters and account for the observed roll-off of the gain at low frequencies.

To determine the quantitative effect on the gain we construct the frequency-response curves for the two high-pass circuits under discussion. However, in some cases only one curve is necessary. If the low-frequency cutoff point of one of the two high-pass filters is at least 10 times greater than the other, the circuit having the highest low-frequency cutoff point can be taken as the determining circuit for low-frequency cutoff of the whole amplifier. If, however, this is not the case, but instead the low-frequency cutoff point for both high-pass circuits is of the same order of magnitude, a graphical determination of the total low-frequency cutoff point must be made. This is done by constructing the response curve for each circuit, and then a graphical multiplication of the two curves determines the composite curve.

From the equations developed in the last chapter and from Fig. 13-2c, the low-frequency cutoff point for each of the filter circuits is

$$f_{lco,\text{in}} = \frac{1}{2\pi R_{GS}C_{c1}} \qquad \text{where } R_{GS} = R_G + R_S$$

$$f_{lco,\text{out}} = \frac{1}{2\pi R_{\text{eq}}C_{c2}} \qquad \text{where } R_{\text{eq}} = R_X + (r_p \| R_P)$$

Components which are considered in determining the frequency response of an amplifier should be taken into account only once in the analysis. For example, in cascaded amplifier stages the input section of the second stage of amplification is the load on the first stage and is taken into account when finding the low-frequency cutoff point for the first stage. It should not be taken into account again in low-frequency cutoff-point determination.

Illustrative Problem 13-1

The circuit shown in Fig. Prob. 13-1a is being used as an amplifier in an automated control system. Determine the low-frequency cutoff point due to the input circuit and the low-frequency cutoff point of the output circuit. The dynamic plate resistance of the tube being used is 12 kilohms.

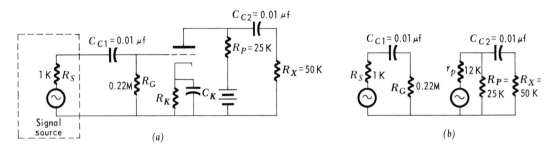

FIGURE PROB. 13-1

SOLUTION

Given: Circuit shown in Fig. Prob. 13-1a

Find:

(a) $f_{lco,in}$ (b) $f_{lco,out}$

(a) $f_{lco,in} = \dfrac{1}{2\pi R_{GS}C_{c1}}$

$R_{GS} = R_G + R_S$

$\quad\quad = 0.22 \times 10^6 + 1 \times 10^3 = 221 \times 10^3$

$f_{lco,in} = \dfrac{1}{2\pi (221 \times 10^3)(0.01 \times 10^{-6})}$

$\boxed{f_{lco,in} = 72 \text{ Hz}}$

(b) $f_{lco,out} = \dfrac{1}{2\pi R_{eq}C_{c2}}$

$R_{eq} = R_X + (r_p \| R_P)$

$\quad\quad = 50 \text{ kilohms} + (12 \text{ kilohms} \| 25 \text{ kilohms})$

$12 \text{ kilohms} \| 25 \text{ kilohms} = \dfrac{12 \times 25}{12 + 25} \text{ kilohms} = 8.1 \text{ kilohms}$

$R_{eq} = 50 \text{ kilohms} + 8.1 \text{ kilohms} = 58.1 \text{ kilohms}$

$\quad\quad = 58.1 \text{ kilohms}$

$f_{lco,out} = \dfrac{1}{2\pi (58.1 \times 10^3)(0.01 \times 10^{-6})}$

$\boxed{f_{lco,out} = 273 \text{ Hz}}$

THE HIGH-FREQUENCY EQUIVALENT CIRCUIT OF AN
RC-COUPLED VACUUM-TUBE AMPLIFIER

Refer again to Fig. 13-1 and consider the effect high frequencies will have on the impedance presented by each of the capacitances. All the capacitances will take on a relatively low impedance because

$$Z_c = X_c = \frac{1}{2\pi fC}$$

As the frequency is increased, the impedance decreases. Because of this effect we can make the approximation that the coupling capacitors are of negligible importance for the high-frequency analysis, since they present a series path to the output and are of very low impedance. However, now the shunting capacitances are of extreme importance since they are also of a relatively low impedance and present a low impedance bypass to the currents attempting to get to the load and to the input of the amplifier. The current therefore will split up, and a relatively large portion will tend to flow through the capacitors, bypassing the load and bypassing the amplifier. Figure 13-3a can therefore be drawn for use in the high-frequency analysis, replacing the coupling capacitors with shorts.

A bit of manipulation of Fig. 13-3a must be done in order to put the circuit into a form which will be more amenable to analysis. First, let us attempt a manipulation of the output section of the amplifier. In Fig. 13-3b all the parallel capacitances and all the

FIGURE 13-3 *High-frequency equivalent circuit of the triode amplifier of Fig. 13-1. (a) Total high-frequency equivalent; (b) output section only.*

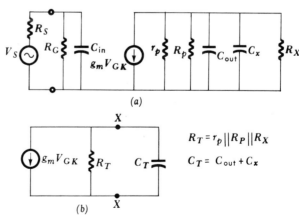

THE CAPACITOR-COUPLED VACUUM-TUBE AMPLIFIER   195

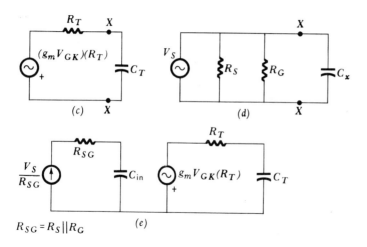

$$R_{SG} = R_S \| R_G \qquad (e)$$

FIGURE 13-3 (continued)
(c) Output section after Norton-Thévenin manipulation; (d) input section; (e) total equivalent after Norton-Thévenin manipulation of both the input and output sections.

parallel resistances have been combined. In Fig. 13-3c use has been made of the Norton-Thévenin relationship: a two-terminal linear network can be represented by either the Thévenin or the Norton equivalent circuits. The Thévenin voltage source is related to the Norton current source by the relationship $V_{\text{thev}} = I_{\text{nort}}R$, where R is the resistance in series with the Thévenin voltage source or the shunt resistance of the Norton current source. The circuit is broken at the points labeled X in Fig. 13-3b and the replacement made as shown in Fig. 13-3c.

A similar manipulation has been made in the input circuit and is shown in Figs. 13-3d and e.

Figure 13-3e shows the total circuit which will be analyzed for high-frequency operation, including both the input and the output portions of the circuit.

Note in Fig. 13-3e that there are two low-pass filters. The cutoff frequencies for each of the circuits are

$$
\begin{aligned}
f_{hco,\text{in}} &= \frac{1}{2\pi R_{SG}C_{\text{in}}} & R_{SG} &= R_S \| R_G \\
f_{hco,\text{out}} &= \frac{1}{2\pi R_T C_T} & R_T &= r_p \| R_P \| R_X \\
& & C_T &= C_{\text{out}} + C_{\text{stray}} + C_x
\end{aligned}
$$

Again, as in the low-frequency analysis, if the two cutoff frequencies are of the same order of magnitude, a graphical multiplication of the two response curves is necessary to determine the total cutoff frequency. However, if one of the cutoff frequencies is at least 10 times the other, the lowest cutoff frequency determines the response of the amplifier.

As was discussed for the low-frequency analysis, each portion of the circuit should be taken into account only once. In the event that cascade amplifier stages are being analyzed, the input section of the second stage is considered as a portion of the output section of the first stage and is not analyzed separately.

THE MID-FREQUENCY EQUIVALENT CIRCUIT OF THE CAPACITOR-COUPLED VACUUM-TUBE AMPLIFIER

The mid-frequency range of an amplifier is defined as that range of frequencies for which all the capacitances can be ignored. Such a range exists because the shunting capacitances are usually many orders of magnitude smaller than the coupling capacitances. Therefore a range of frequencies exists which is high enough so that the shunting capacitances have a high enough impedance to be disregarded and the coupling capacitances have not yet developed an appreciable impedance.

Within the mid-frequency range of frequencies the amplifier circuit can be represented as shown in Fig. 13-4, and the gain of the amplifier is given by

$$A_v = \frac{-\mu R_{PX}}{r_p + R_{PX}} \qquad \text{where } R_{PX} = \frac{R_P R_X}{R_P + R_X}$$

Because the equivalent circuit for this region contains no reactive elements, the gain remains constant over the entire mid-frequency range.

THE TOTAL RESPONSE CURVE OF THE CAPACITANCE-COUPLED VACUUM-TUBE AMPLIFIER

Combining the response curves of the three regions discussed in this chapter gives the curve shown as Fig. 13-5. The high- and

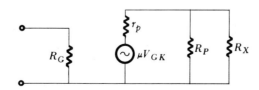

FIGURE 13-4 *Mid-frequency equivalent circuit for a complete triode amplifier, e.g., Fig. 13-1.*

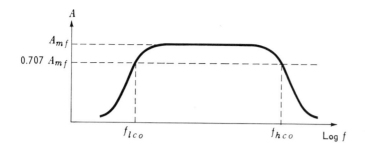

FIGURE 13-5 *Response curve for a triode amplifier.*

low-frequency cutoff points of the amplifier are those frequencies at which the gain of the amplifier is down to 0.707 of the mid-frequency gain.

Illustrative Problem 13-2

The amplifier in the circuit shown in Fig. Prob. 13-2a is receiving a signal from a microphone whose impedance is 250 ohms.

The vacuum tube being used as the active device in the amplifier has the following characteristics:

$$C_{GK} = 2 \text{ pf} \qquad \mu = 50$$
$$C_{PK} = 0.6 \text{ pf} \qquad r_p = 10 \text{ kilohms}$$
$$C_{GP} = 2.3 \text{ pf}$$

The stray wiring capacitance can be considered as 0.4 pf hanging across the output. Determine:

(a) The mid-frequency gain of the amplifier.
(b) The input capacitance of the amplifier.
(c) The high-frequency cutoff point of the amplifier.

FIGURE PROB. 13-2

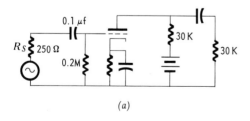

(a)

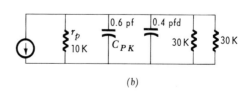

(b)

SOLUTION

Given: Circuit shown in Fig. Prob. 13-2a; $C_{GK} = 2$ pf; $\mu = 50$; $C_{PK} = 0.6$ pf; $r_p = 10$ kilohms; $C_{GP} = 2.3$ pf; $C_{\text{stray}} = 0.4$ pf

Find:

(a) A_{Vmf}

(b) C_{in}

(c) $f_{hco,\text{in}}$

(d) $f_{hco,\text{out}}$

(a) $\quad A_{Vmf} = \dfrac{-\mu R_{PX}}{r_p + R_{PX}} \qquad R_{PX} = {}^{30}/_2 \text{ kilohms} = 15 \text{ kilohms}$

$$A_{Vmf} = \frac{-50(15 \times 10^3)}{10 \times 10^3 + 15 \times 10^3}$$

$$= -\frac{750 \times 10^3}{25 \times 10^3}$$

$$\boxed{A_{Vmf} = -30}$$

(b) $\quad C_{\text{in}} = C_{GK} + (1 + |A|)\, C_{GP}$

$\qquad\quad = 2 \text{ pf} + (1+30)\, 2.3 \text{ pf}$

$\qquad\quad = 2 + 31 \times 2.3 \text{ pf}$

$\qquad\quad = 2 + 71 \text{ pf}$

$$\boxed{C_{\text{in}} = 73 \text{ pf}}$$

(c) $\quad f_{hco} = \dfrac{1}{2\pi R_{SG} C_{\text{in}}}$

$\qquad R_{SG} = R_S \| R_G$

$\qquad\quad = 250 \| 0.2 \text{ megohms} \approx 250 \text{ ohms}$

$\qquad f_{hco} = \dfrac{1}{2\pi (250)(73 \times 10^{-12})}$

$$\boxed{f_{hco,\text{in}} = 8.73 \text{ MHz}}$$

(d) $\quad f_{hco} = \dfrac{1}{2\pi R_T C_T}$

$\qquad R_T = r_p \| R_P \| R_X = 10 \text{ kilohms} \| 15 \text{ kilohms} = \dfrac{10 \times 15}{25} \text{ kilohms}$

$\qquad\quad = 6 \text{ kilohms}$

$\qquad C_T = 0.6 \text{ pf} + 0.4 \text{ pf} = 1 \text{ pf}$

$\qquad f_{hco} = \dfrac{1}{2\pi (6 \times 10^3)(1 \times 10^{-12})} = \dfrac{1}{2\pi (6 \times 10^{-9})}$

$$\boxed{f_{hco,\text{out}} = 26.7 \text{ MHz}}$$

Illustrative Problem 13-3

The tubes in the circuit shown in Fig. Prob. 13-3a have the following values of interelectrode capacitance, amplification factor, and plate resistance. The stray wiring capacitance can be accounted for by considering that an additional capacitance appears across grid and cathode of both tubes. Take this capacitance to be 10 pf per stage.

	Tube I	Tube II
C_{GK}	1.6 pf	2.8 pf
C_{GP}	1.7 pf	2.6 pf
C_{PK}	0.4 pf	0.31 pf
μ	100	20
r_p	70,000 ohms	5,000 ohms

(a) What is the mid-frequency gain of stage 1?
(b) Determine the mid-frequency gain of stage 2.
(c) Calculate the input capacitance of stage 1.
(d) What is the input capacitance of the stage 2 vacuum tube?
(e) Sketch the Norton equivalent of the first stage of the amplifier.
(f) What is the low-frequency cutoff point of the input section of stage 1?
(g) What is the low-frequency cutoff point of the coupling section between the stages?
(h) Determine the high-frequency cutoff point of the coupling section between stages.
(i) Calculate the high-frequency cutoff point of the output section of the second stage.

FIGURE PROB. 13-3a

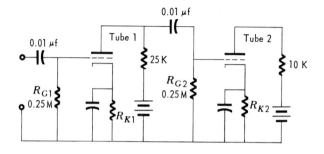

SOLUTION

Given: Tube parameters as listed above; circuit shown in Fig. Prob. 13-3a

Find:

(a) A_{Vmf1} (b) A_{Vmf2}
(c) C_{in1} (d) C_{in2}
(e) Norton equivalent   (f) $f_{lco,in1}$
(g) $f_{lco,coupling}$ (h) $f_{hco,coupling}$
(i) $f_{hco,out2}$

(a) $A_{Vmf} = - \dfrac{\mu R_{PG}}{r_p + R_{PG}}$

$$R_{PG} = 25 \text{ kilohms} \| 250 \text{ kilohms} = \frac{25 \times 10^3 \times 250 \times 10^3}{25 \times 10^3 + 250 \times 10^3}$$

$$= 22.6 \text{ kilohms}$$

$$A_{Vmf1} = - \frac{100 \times 22.6 \times 10^3}{70,000 + 22,600}$$

$$\boxed{A_{Vmf1} = -24.5}$$

(b) $A_{Vmf2} = \dfrac{-20 \,(10 \times 10^3)}{5000 + 10,000}$

$$= \frac{-200 \times 10^3}{15,000}$$

$$\boxed{A_{Vmf2} = -13.3}$$

(c) $C_{in1} = C_{GK} + (1 + |A|)\, C_{GP}$
       $= 1.6 \text{ pf} + (1+24.5)(1.7 \text{ pf})$
       $= 1.6 + 43.5 \text{ pf}$

$$\boxed{C_{in1} = 45.1 \text{ pf}}$$

(d) $C_{in2} = C_{GK} + (1 + |A|)\, C_{GP}$
       $= 2.8 \text{ pf} + (1 + 13.3)\, 2.6 \text{ pf}$
       $= 2.8 + 37 \text{ pf}$

$$\boxed{C_{in2} = 39.8 \text{ pf}}$$

(e) See Fig. Prob. 13-3b
(f) See Fig. Prob. 13-3c

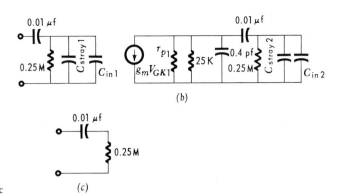

(b)

(c)

FIGURE PROB. 13-3b and c

$$f_{lco,\text{in}1} = \frac{1}{2\pi RC}$$

$$= \frac{1}{2\pi (0.25 \times 10^6)(0.01 \times 10^{-6})}$$

$$= \frac{1}{2\pi (0.0025)}$$

$$\boxed{f_{lco,\text{in}} = 63.9 \text{ Hz}}$$

(g) $R_{G2} + (r_{p1}\|R_{P1}) = R_{\text{eq}}$
$.25 \times 10^6 + (70,000\|25,000) = R_{\text{eq}}$

$$r_{p1}\|R_{P1} = \frac{70,000 \times 25,000}{95,000} = 18,400$$

$$R_{\text{eq}} = 0.268 \text{ megohm} = 268 \text{ kilohms}$$

$$f_{lco} = \frac{1}{2\pi R_{\text{eq}}C_c}$$

$$= \frac{1}{2\pi (268 \times 10^3)(0.01 \times 10^{-6})}$$

$$\boxed{f_{lco} = 60 \text{ Hz}}$$

(h) $R_T = r_{p1}\|R_{P1}\|R_{G2}$
$R_T = \underbrace{70,000\|25,000\|250,000}_{22.6 \text{ kilohms}}$

$$= \frac{70,000 \times 22,600}{92,600}$$

$$= 17,200$$

$$f_{hco} = \frac{1}{2\pi R_T C_T}$$

$$C_T = C_{GP1} + C_{in2} + C_{stray2}$$
$$= 1.7 \text{ pf} + 39.8 \text{ pf} + 10 \text{ pf}$$
$$= 51.5 \text{ pf}$$
$$f_{hco} = \frac{1}{2\pi R_T C_T}$$
$$= \frac{1}{2\pi (17.2 \times 10^3)(5.15 \times 10^{-9})}$$

$$\boxed{f_{hco} = 1.8 \text{ kHz}}$$

(i) See Fig. Prob. 13-3d.

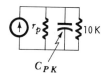

C_{PK}

FIGURE PROB. 13-3d

$$r_{p2} = 5 \text{ kilohms}$$
$$r_{p2} \| R_{P2} = \frac{5 \text{ kilohms} \times 10 \text{ kilohms}}{5 \text{ kilohms} + 10 \text{ kilohms}} = \frac{50 \times 10^6}{15 \times 10^3}$$
$$R_T = 3340 \text{ ohms}$$
$$C_T = C_{PK2} = 0.31 \text{ pf}$$
$$f_{hco,out2} = \frac{1}{2\pi R_T C_T}$$
$$= \frac{1}{2\pi (3340)(0.31 \times 10^{-9})}$$

$$\boxed{f_{hco} = 155 \text{ kHz}}$$

PROBLEMS

13-1 Draw an equivalent circuit of a vacuum-tube amplifier showing all capacitances.

13-2 Determine the input capacitance of a vacuum-tube amplifier stage whose voltage gain is 40 and whose vacuum-tube interelectrode capacitances are $C_{GK} = 3$ pf and $C_{GP} = 0.5$ pf. Find the impedance of this input capacitance at 10, 100, 1000, 10,000, and 100,000 Hz.

13-3 Calculate the impedance of a 0.01 μf coupling capacitor at 10, 100, 1000, 10,000, and 100,000.

13-4 For the circuit shown in Fig. 13-6:

  (*a*) Sketch an equivalent circuit for low frequencies.
  (*b*) Find the low-frequency cutoff point for the input section.
  (*c*) Find the low-frequency cutoff point for the output section.

THE CAPACITOR-COUPLED VACUUM-TUBE AMPLIFIER   203

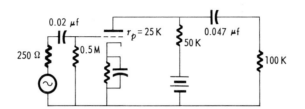

FIGURE 13-6 *Diagram for Probs. 13-4 to 13-6.*

13-5 What value of capacitance should take the place of the output coupling capacitor in Fig. 13-6 in order to provide a low-frequency cutoff point for the output section of 5 Hz?

13-6 The tube shown in Fig. 13-6 has an input capacitance of 6 pf and a plate-to-cathode capacitance of 2 pf. Assume a stray wiring capacitance of 0.8 pf hanging across the output.
 (*a*) Sketch the high-frequency equivalent circuit.
 (*b*) Calculate the high-frequency cutoff point of the input section of the amplifier shown as Fig. 13-6.
 (*c*) Calculate the high-frequency cutoff point of the output section of the amplifier shown as Fig. 13-6.

13-7 For the circuit shown in Fig. 13-7 find:
 (*a*) Equivalent circuit showing all capacitances
 (*b*) Mid-frequency gain
 (*c*) Low-frequency equivalent circuit
 (*d*) Low-frequency cutoff point for the input section of the circuit
 (*e*) Low-frequency cutoff point for the output section of the circuit
 (*f*) High-frequency equivalent circuit
 (*g*) High-frequency cutoff point for the input section
 (*h*) High-frequency cutoff point for the output section
 (*i*) Response curve of the amplifier

13-8 A two-stage triode amplifier is described as follows:

Stage I	Stage II
$R_G = 0.1$ megohm	$R_G = 0.05$ megohm
$R_P = 50$ kilohms	$R_P = 50$ kilohms
$C_{in} = 6$ pf	$C_{in} = 5$ pf
$C_{PK} = 0.31$ pf	$C_{PK} = 1.3$ pf
$\mu = 20$	$\mu = 18$
$r_p = 6000$ ohms	$r_p = 7000$ ohms

A coupling capacitor of 0.1 μf is used between stages and a 0.01-μf coupling capacitor is used to couple a 100-kilohm external load to the amplifier. Neglect the stray wiring capacitance and the output impedance of the signal source. A coupling capacitor of 0.05 μf is being used at the input of stage 1 to block any dc level that may be accompanying the input signal.
 (*a*) Draw a schematic diagram of the circuit.
 (*b*) Draw a mid-frequency equivalent for this circuit.
 (*c*) Calculate the mid-frequency gain for each stage.

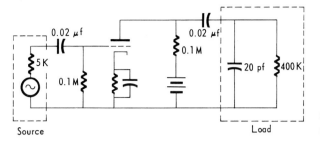

FIGURE 13-7   *Diagram for Prob. 13-7.*

Source   Load

(d)   What is the overall mid-frequency gain of the amplifier?

(e)   Draw an equivalent circuit to be used in the determination of the low-frequency cutoff point of the input section of the first stage.

(f)   Determine the low-frequency cutoff point for the input section of the first stage.

(g)   Draw an equivalent circuit to be used in the determination of the low-frequency cutoff point of the interstage section of the amplifier.

(h)   Calculate the low-frequency cutoff point for the interstage section of the amplifier.

(i)   Draw an equivalent circuit for determining the low-frequency cutoff point of the output section of stage two.   What is the value of this low-frequency cutoff point?

(j)   Repeat (e) to (i) for the high-frequency cutoff points.

(k)   Estimate the upper and lower cutoff frequencies of the entire amplifier.

14 THE CAPACITOR-COUPLED TRANSISTOR AMPLIFIER

Just as it was necessary to consider the coupling capacitors when determining the low-frequency cutoff point for vacuum-tube amplifiers, it is necessary to do the same for transistor amplifiers.

LOW-FREQUENCY RESPONSE

The internal capacitances within the transistor do not have to be taken into account for the low-frequency analysis because we will see that they appear in parallel with the input and output terminals of the transistor and at low frequencies they appear as an open circuit.

Figure 14-1a is a circuit diagram of a complete transistor amplifier. Figure 14-1b depicts the equivalent circuit of the amplifier. R_E and C_E have been omitted because including them makes the problem too complex at this stage. Though R_E and C_E will have an effect on the low-frequency cutoff point, it will be assumed that their values are such that their effect is negligible.

Recall from previous chapters that because of laboratory experiences we expect an amplifier to have a constant gain over a band of frequencies which we call the mid-frequency band. As the frequency of the signal is raised or lowered so that we leave this mid-frequency region, we find that the voltage and current gains decrease. The frequencies at which the gain is down to 0.707 of what it was in the mid-frequency region are called *cutoff frequencies*.

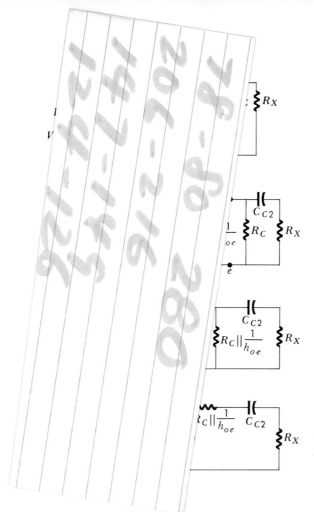

FIGURE 14-1 (a) Complete transistor amplifier; (b) equivalent circuit of transistor amplifier; (c) equivalent circuit after combining parallel resistors; (d) equivalent circuit after Norton-Thévenin transformation of the output section.

By combining many circuit components in Fig. 14-1*b* and *c* the familiar circuit shown as Fig. 14-1*d* is developed. This of course is one of the circuits studied in Chap. 12.

The following low-frequency cutoff-point formulas can now be written (*Note:* Remember the cutoff-frequency equations in Chap. 12):

$$f_{lco,\text{in}} = \frac{1}{2\pi R C_{c1}} \qquad \text{where } R = R_S + (R_1 \| R_2 \| h_{ie})$$

$$f_{lco,\text{out}} = \frac{1}{2\pi R_{\text{eq}} C_{c2}} \qquad \text{where } R_{\text{eq}} = R_X + \left(R_C \,\Big\|\, \frac{1}{h_{oe}} \right)$$

THE CAPACITOR-COUPLED TRANSISTOR AMPLIFIER   207

Illustrative Problem 14-1

The amplifier shown in Fig. Prob. 14-1 is to be used as an audio amplifier in an inexpensive transistor radio. The hybrid parameters for the transistor used are

$$h_{ie} = 900 \text{ ohms} \qquad h_{fe} = 80 \qquad \frac{1}{h_{oe}} = 75 \text{ kilohms}$$

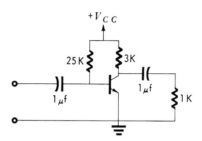

Calculate the low-frequency cutoff point for the input section of the circuit and then repeat the calculation for the output section. The output impedance of the previous stage feeding the amplifier is 1000 ohms.

SOLUTION

Given: Circuit shown in Fig. Prob. 14-1; $h_{ie} = 900$ ohms; $h_{fe} = 80$; $1/h_{oe} = 75$ kilohms; $R_S = 1000$ ohms

Find:

(a) $f_{lco,\text{in}}$
(b) $f_{lco,\text{out}}$

(a) $f_{lco,\text{in}} = \dfrac{1}{2\pi R C_{c1}}$

$$R = R_S + (R_B \| h_{ie})$$
$$= 1000 + (25 \text{ kilohms} \| 900)$$

$$25 \text{ kilohms} \| 900 = \frac{25{,}000 \times 900}{25{,}000 + 900} = 870 \text{ ohms}$$

$$R = 1000 + 870 = 1870 \text{ ohms}$$

$$f_{lco,\text{in}} = \frac{1}{2\pi(1870)(1 \times 10^{-6})}$$

$$\boxed{f_{lco,\text{in}} = 85 \text{ Hz}}$$

(b) $\quad f_{lco,\text{out}} = \dfrac{1}{2\pi R_{eq} C_{c2}}$

$\qquad R_{eq} = R_X + \left(R_C \,\middle\|\, \dfrac{1}{h_{oe}} \right)$

$\qquad 3 \text{ kilohms} \| 75 \text{ kilohms} = \dfrac{3 \times 75}{3 + 75} \text{ kilohms} = 2890 \text{ ohms}$

$\qquad R_{eq} = 3890 \text{ ohms}$

$\qquad f_{lco,\text{out}} = \dfrac{1}{2\pi(3890)(1 \times 10^{-6})}$

$\qquad \boxed{f_{lco,\text{out}} = 41 \text{ Hz}}$

HIGH-FREQUENCY RESPONSE

In studying the high-frequency response of the transistor amplifier we must take the internal capacitances of the transistor into ac-

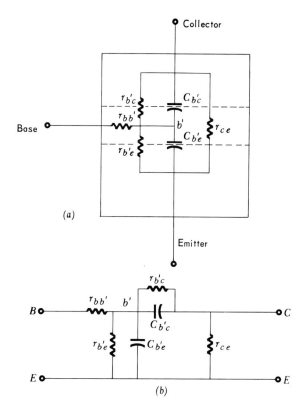

FIGURE 14-2 (a) Descriptive diagram showing the location of internal capacitances and resistances of a transistor; (b) equivalent circuit of internal capacitances and resistances of the transistor.

THE CAPACITOR-COUPLED TRANSISTOR AMPLIFIER   209

count. The first step in such an analysis is a study of a physical diagram of the transistor with all its capacitances shown. Let us begin this study by referring to Fig. 14-2a, which obviously must be redrawn before it can work for us.

In the common-emitter amplifier the input to the transistor is applied between the base and emitter terminals. Looking into the transistor between the base and emitter terminals, we immediately see $r_{bb'}$ in series with the parallel combinations of $r_{b'e}$ and $c_{b'e}$. Adding $r_{b'c}$, $c_{b'c}$, and r_{ce} to the picture provides us with the equivalent circuit shown as Fig. 14-2b. This equivalent circuit, however, does not have any provision for indicating the amplifying properties of the device. We must therefore add an internal signal source across the collector-to-emitter terminals.

This source should be directly proportional to that portion of the input signal which can get to the base-emitter junction. Transistor manufacturers publish a parameter g_m, transconductance, for use in high-frequency analysis of transistor circuits. It is this parameter g_m multiplied by $V_{b'e}$, the input signal voltage across the base-emitter junction, that is used to indicate the magnitude of the necessary output signal source.

The equivalent circuit shown in Fig. 14-3 is called the *hybrid-π equivalent*.

Using the hybrid-π equivalent directly in high-frequency analysis of amplifiers would result in rather unwieldy equations because the input and output sections of the amplifier have not been separated. When they are separated, the equivalent circuit of Fig. 14-4 results.

In developing Fig. 14-4, $r_{b'c}$ was considered as an open circuit because in most cases $r_{b'c}$ is of the order of tens of megohms. Note

FIGURE 14-3 *Hybrid-π equivalent circuit of a transistor.*

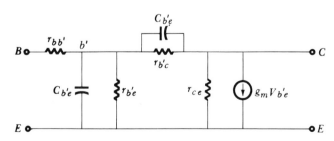

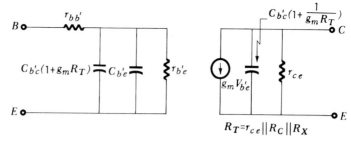

FIGURE 14-4 Hybrid-π equivalent circuit with input and output sections separated.

in Fig. 14-4 that input and output capacitance is dependent on R_T, the total resistance across the output terminals both internal and external

$$R_T = r_{ce}\|R_C\|R_X$$

When we complete the amplifier by adding the required additional components and capacitances normally associated with an amplifier, the result is Fig. 14-5b, which is the equivalent circuit for the schematic shown as Fig. 14-5a. Figure 14-5b can immediately be simplified to the circuits shown in Fig. 14-5c and d. Figure 14-6 is a familiar circuit, studied in Chap. 12. Referring back to Chap. 12, we can write the formulas for the determination of the high-frequency cutoff points.

Again note that each portion of the circuit should be taken into account only once. If a component in the input section of the second stage of a two-stage amplifier is considered when studying the output section of the first stage, it should not be reconsidered when studying the input section of the second stage

$$f_{hco,\text{in}} = \frac{1}{2\pi R_{\text{in}}C_{\text{in}}}$$

$$f_{hco,\text{out}} = \frac{1}{2\pi R_T C_{\text{eq}}}$$

where

$$R_{\text{in}} = (R_{SB} + r_{bb'})\|r_{b'e} \qquad R_T = r_{ce}\|R_C\|R_X$$
$$R_{SB} = R_S\|R_B \qquad R_B = R_1\|R_2$$
$$C_{\text{in}} = C_{b'e} + C_{b'c}(1 + g_m R_T)$$
$$C_{\text{eq}} = C_X + C_S + C_{b'c}\left(1 + \frac{1}{g_m R_T}\right)$$

THE CAPACITOR-COUPLED TRANSISTOR AMPLIFIER 211

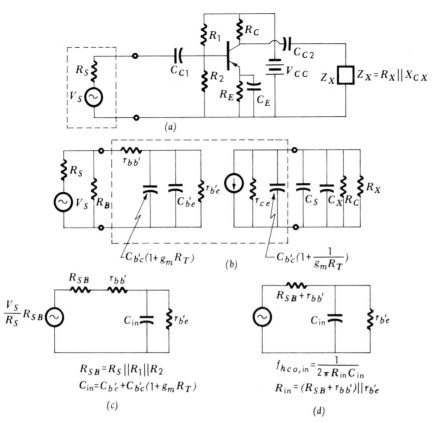

FIGURE 14-5 Development of a simplified hybrid-π equivalent circuit for the circuit shown schematically in (a).

FIGURE 14-6 Simplified hybrid-π equivalent of the schematic in Fig. 14-5a (a) Norton equivalent and (b) Thévenin equivalent.

$$Z_X = R_X \| X_{CX}$$

$$R_{SB} = R_S \| R_1 \| R_2$$
$$C_{in} = C_{b'e} + C_{b'c}(1 + g_m R_T)$$

(c)

$$f_{hco,in} = \frac{1}{2\pi R_{in} C_{in}}$$
$$R_{in} = (R_{SB} + r_{bb'}) \| r_{b'e}$$

(d)

$$R_T = r_{ce} \| R_C \| R_X$$

$$C_{eq} = C_X + C_S + C_{b'c}\left(1 + \frac{1}{g_m R_T}\right)$$

$$f_{hco,\,out} = \frac{1}{2\pi R_T C_{eq}}$$

Illustrative Problem 14-2

Determine the high-frequency cutoff point of the input portion of the amplifier shown in Fig. Prob. 14-2 and then determine the high-frequency cutoff point of the output section of the same amplifier. Assume a stray capacitance in this problem of 10 pf across the collector to emitter.　Properties of the transistor are

$$r_{bb'} = 15 \text{ ohms} \qquad g_m = 25 \text{ mmhos}$$
$$r_{b'c} = 20 \text{ megohms} \qquad C_{b'e} = 90 \text{ pf}$$
$$r_{b'e} = 200 \text{ ohms} \qquad r_{ce} = 40 \text{ kilohms}$$
$$C_{b'c} = 2 \text{ pf}$$

SOLUTION

Given: Circuit shown in Fig. Prob. 14-2; transistor properties given above

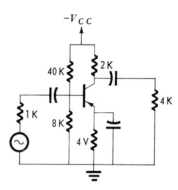

FIGURE PROB. 14-2

Find:

(a) $f_{hco,\text{in}}$

(b) $f_{hco,\text{out}}$

(a) $f_{hco,\text{in}} = \dfrac{1}{2\pi R_{\text{in}} C_{\text{in}}}$

$R_{\text{in}} = (R_{SB} + r_{bb'}) \| r_{b'e}$

$R_{SB} = R_S \| R_B$

$= 1 \text{ kilohm} \| 8 \text{ kilohms} \| 40 \text{ kilohms}$

$= \dfrac{1 \times 8}{9} \text{ kilohm} \| 40 \text{ kilohms}$

$= 890 \| 40 \text{ kilohms} = \dfrac{890 \times 40 \text{ kilohms}}{40.89 \text{ kilohms}}$

$= 873 \text{ ohms}$

$R_{\text{in}} = (873 + 15) \| 200 = 888 \| 200$

$= \dfrac{888 \times 200}{888 + 200} = \dfrac{888 \times 200}{1088} = 162$

$= 162 \text{ ohms}$

$R_T = r_{ce} \| R_C \| R_X$

$= 40 \text{ kilohms} \| 2 \text{ kilohms} \| 4 \text{ kilohms}$

$$= 40 \text{ kilohms} \left\| \frac{4 \times 2}{4 + 2} \text{ kilohms} = \frac{40 \times 1.33}{41.33} \text{ kilohms} \right.$$

$$= 1290 \text{ ohms}$$

$$
\begin{aligned}
C_{in} &= C_{b'e} + C_{b'c}(1 + g_m R_T) \\
&= 90 \text{ pf} + 2 \text{ pf} \left[1 + (25 \times 10^{-3} \times 1.29 \times 10^{3}) \right] \\
&= 90 \text{ pf} + 2 \text{ pf} \times 33.3 \\
&= 156.6 \text{ pf}
\end{aligned}
$$

$$
\begin{aligned}
f_{hco,in} &= \frac{1}{2\pi R_{in} C_{in}} \\
&= \frac{1}{2\pi (1290)(156.6 \times 10^{-12})}
\end{aligned}
$$

$$\boxed{f_{hco,in} = 795 \text{ kHz}}$$

(b)

$$
\begin{aligned}
C_{eq} &= C_X + C_S + C_{b'c}\left(1 + \frac{1}{g_m R_T}\right) \\
&= 10 \text{ pf} + 2 \text{ pf}\left(1 + \frac{1}{25 \times 10^{-3} \times 1290}\right) \\
&= 10 \text{ pf} + 2 \text{ pf}\,(1 + 0.0309) \\
&= 12 \text{ pf}
\end{aligned}
$$

$$
\begin{aligned}
f_{hco,out} &= \frac{1}{2\pi R_T C_{eq}} \\
&= \frac{1}{2\pi (1290)(12 \times 10^{-12})}
\end{aligned}
$$

$$\boxed{f_{hco,out} = 10.3 \text{ MHz}}$$

THE SIGNIFICANCE OF THE FREQUENCY RESPONSE

Of course the first thoughts about frequency response relate to the fact that an amplifier will not produce the expected gain if the given data are taken for mid-frequency range and the amplifier is then used beyond one of the cutoff points.

With a more sophisticated outlook we realize that an amplifier whose mid-frequency region is not wide enough will produce distortion (changed waveshape) when used with nonsinusoidal waveforms. To understand why we must have a basic understanding of the Fourier theorem, which states that any repetitive wave, no matter how complex, can be made up by the addition of sine waves. Thus any complex wave can be considered as being composed of a number of sine waves.

If a complex waveshape is presented to an amplifier which has a rather limited mid-frequency range, those sine-wave components whose frequency falls outside the mid-frequency range will be amplified less than those which fall within the mid-frequency range. The output waveshape will then have a different proportional composition of sine waves and thereby a different waveshape than the input. The fidelity of the signal the amplifier was presented with will not be maintained. This presents a serious problem in the reproduction of music. Consider the complex signal generated by an orchestra. If the amplifier does not have an adequate mid-frequency bandwidth, the music coming from the loudspeakers of a phonograph will not be the same music the orchestra produced. In designing high-fidelity equipment an attempt is made to maintain the mid-frequency band broad enough to cover the 20-Hz to 20-kHz range, the human hearing range.

TESTING AMPLIFIERS FOR FREQUENCY RESPONSE

The most obvious way to test an amplifier for frequency response is to use a signal generator to feed the amplifier with a signal of constant amplitude and varied frequency. The output signal of the amplifier is then measured. A plot of the response of this test will be the frequency-response curve of the amplifier (V_{out}/V_{in} vs. frequency). The main problem with this method is that it is very time-consuming and can be allowed only for the most expensive equipment. A much easier and less time-consuming method makes use of the Fourier theorem and requires that only one constant signal be impressed on the amplifier. The signal richest in sine-wave makeup turns out to be the square wave. If a signal which is a square wave having almost perfectly vertical sides and almost perfectly horizontal top and bottom is impressed on the input of the amplifier, the amount of slope of the originally vertical sides and the originally horizontal top of the square wave contain information about the frequency response of the amplifier under test. Because this test is so rapid and simple, it can be used in the mass-production testing of commercially produced amplifiers.

Since we have used both the h-parameter equivalent circuit and the hybrid-π equivalent circuit to represent the transistor, there must be some relationship between the parameters used in each. Figure 14-7 shows both the h-parameter equivalent circuit and the equivalent circuit we developed by simplifying the hybrid-π equivalent.

If we now consider both equivalent circuits at frequencies low enough for the input and output capacitances to be negligible,

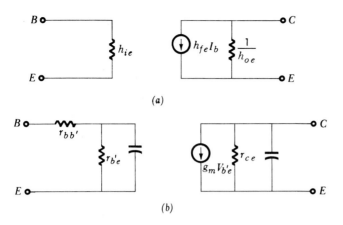

FIGURE 14-7 (a) h-parameter equivalent circuit and (b) simplified hybrid-π equivalent circuit of a transistor.

the following relationships become quite obvious:

$$h_{ie} \approx r_{bb'} + r_{b'e}$$

$$\frac{1}{h_{oe}} \approx r_{ce}$$

$$g_m \approx \frac{h_{fe}}{r_{b'e}}$$

You may wonder why these relationships are not written as an equality rather than an approximation. Recall that in the h-parameter equivalent the h_{re} parameter has been considered negligible and in the case of the simplified hybrid π, $r_{b'c}$ has been considered as open circuit.

Another question is whether the h-parameter equivalent circuit can be used in the determination of the high-frequency cutoff points. The answer is that it can be, providing that the input and output capacitances are known. Though the h-parameter equivalent circuit adapted for high-frequency analysis provides a more rapid solution and is therefore more desirable, at times the hybrid-π equivalent provides a more accurate solution, the reason being that the h parameters are frequency-dependent. Figure 14-8 depicts the h-parameter equivalent circuit for high-frequency calculations.

Illustrative Problem 14-3

Determine the high-frequency cutoff point for the input and output sections of the circuit shown in Fig. Prob. 14-3a. Assume that the

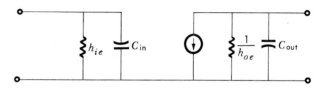

FIGURE 14-8 *h-parameter equivalent circuit at high frequencies.*

following parameters describe the transistor:

$$h_{ie} = 1000 \text{ ohms} \qquad \frac{1}{h_{oe}} = 100 \text{ kilohms}$$

$$C_{in} = 300 \text{ pf} \qquad C_{out} = 20 \text{ pf}$$

Neglect stray wiring capacitance. The collector resistor is 5 kilohms, and the external load is a 10-kilohm resistance. The output impedance of the signal source is 500 ohms.

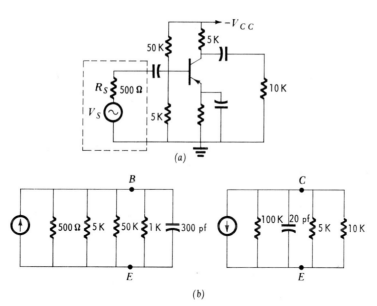

(a)

(b)

FIGURE PROB. 14-3

SOLUTION
Given: $h_{ie} = 1000$ ohms; $1/h_{oe} = 100$ kilohms; $C_{in} = 300$ pf; $C_{out} = 20$ pf
Find:
(a) $f_{hco,in}$
(b) $f_{hco,out}$

See Fig. Prob. 14-3*b*.

THE CAPACITOR-COUPLED TRANSISTOR AMPLIFIER 217

(a) $\quad f_{hco,\mathrm{in}} = \dfrac{1}{2\pi R_{\mathrm{in}} C_{\mathrm{in}}}$

$\quad\quad R_{\mathrm{in}} = 500\|5\ \mathrm{kilohms}\|50\ \mathrm{kilohms}\|1\ \mathrm{kilohm}$

$\quad\quad\quad = 280\ \mathrm{ohms}$

$\quad\quad f_{hco,\mathrm{in}} = \dfrac{1}{2\pi (280)(300 \times 10^{-12})}$

$\quad\quad\quad\quad = \dfrac{10^{12}}{5.25 \times 10^{5}}$

$$\boxed{f_{hco,\mathrm{in}} = 1.9 \times 10^{6}\ \mathrm{Hz}}$$

(b) $\quad f_{hco,\mathrm{out}} = \dfrac{1}{2\pi R_T C_{\mathrm{out}}}$

$\quad\quad R_T = 100\ \mathrm{kilohms}\|5\ \mathrm{kilohms}\|10\ \mathrm{kilohms}$

$\quad\quad\quad = 3.3\ \mathrm{kilohms}$

$\quad\quad f_{hco,\mathrm{out}} = \dfrac{1}{2\pi R_T C_{\mathrm{out}}}$

$\quad\quad\quad\quad = \dfrac{1}{2\pi (3.3 \times 10^{3})(20 \times 10^{-12})}$

$\quad\quad\quad\quad = \dfrac{10^{12}}{412 \times 10^{3}}$

$\quad\quad\quad\quad = 2.43 \times 10^{6}\ \mathrm{Hz}$

$$\boxed{f_{hco,\mathrm{out}} = 2.43\ \mathrm{MHz}}$$

PROBLEMS

14-1 What is meant by the term "cutoff frequencies"?

14-2 Why must coupling capacitors be taken into account during the low-frequency analysis?

14-3 An *NPN* transistor is being used as the active device in a common-emitter fixed-bias amplifier. The following components are peripheral to the transistor:

$R_B = 25\ \mathrm{kilohms} \quad\quad C_{c1} = 20\ \mu\mathrm{f}$

$R_C = 4.5\ \mathrm{kilohms} \quad\quad C_{c2} = 10\ \mu\mathrm{f}$

$R_X = 3\ \mathrm{kilohms} \quad\quad$ Signal source resistance $= 50\ \mathrm{ohms}$

The transistor parameters are

$h_{ie} = 1200\ \mathrm{ohms} \quad\quad h_{fe} = 90 \quad\quad \dfrac{1}{h_{oe}} = 90\ \mathrm{kilohms}$

(a) Sketch a schematic diagram of this circuit.

(b) Draw an equivalent circuit of this amplifier appropriate for low-frequency analysis.

(c) Determine the low-frequency cutoff point for the input portion of the amplifier.

(d) Find the low-frequency cutoff point of the output section of the amplifier.

(e) Calculate mid-frequency voltage gain of this amplifier.

14-4 Determine the low-frequency cutoff point for the input circuit and the output circuit of the amplifier shown in Fig. 14-9 if $h_{ie} = 800$ ohms and $1/h_{oe} = 50$ kilohms.

14-5 What will the new low-frequency cutoff points be if both coupling capacitors of Fig. 14-9 are replaced by 1-μf capacitors? When $h_{ie} = 800$ ohms and $1/h_{oe} = 50$ kilohms?

14-6 A transistor amplifier consists of two identical common-emitter stages. Each stage is biased by a voltage divider made up of a 5- and a 50-kilohm resistor. Coupling between stages is through a 5-μf capacitor. The input resistance of each transistor h_{ie} is 1 kilohm, and the output resistance $1/h_{oe}$ is large enough to be neglected. The collector load resistor R_{c1} of stage 1 is 4 kilohms; h_{fe} is 100.

(a) Draw a schematic diagram of the amplifier.

(b) Sketch an equivalent circuit including the output section of stage 1 and the input section of stage 2 which will be useful for determining the low-frequency cutoff point for this interstage section of the amplifier.

(c) Calculate the low-frequency cutoff point of the interstage section of the amplifier.

(d) Find the mid-frequency voltage gain of the first stage.

(e) What is the voltage gain of the first stage at the low-frequency cutoff point?

14-7 Sketch the high-frequency equivalent circuit of a transistor.

14-8 A fixed-bias common-emitter transistor amplifier has a base bias resistor of 100 kilohms, a collector resistor of 4 kilohms, and a capacitor coupled external load of 6 kilohms. The amplifier is being fed from a signal source whose output resistance is 300 ohms. The parameters for the transistor used are

$r_{bb'} = 80$ ohms	$C_{b'c} = 8$ pf
$r_{b'c} = 10$ megohms	$C_{b'e} = 300$ pf
$r_{b'e} = 1800$ ohms	$g_m = 200$ mmhos
$r_{ce} = 500$ kilohms	

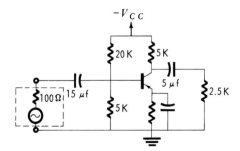

FIGURE 14-9 *Diagram for Probs. 14-4, 14-5, and 14-9.*

THE CAPACITOR-COUPLED TRANSISTOR AMPLIFIER   219

The stray capacitance for the circuit can be taken into account by considering a 200-pf capacitance hanging across the output.

(a) Draw a schematic diagram of the amplifier.

(b) Sketch an equivalent circuit of this amplifier for use in a high-frequency analysis.

(c) Determine the high-frequency cutoff point for the output section of the amplifier.

(d) Calculate the high-frequency cutoff point for the input section of the amplifier.

14-9 Assume that the transistor used in the circuit of Fig. 14-9 has the following parameter values:

$$r_{bb'} = 120 \text{ ohms} \qquad C_{b'c} = 4 \text{ pf}$$
$$r_{b'c} = 15 \text{ megohms} \qquad C_{b'e} = 175 \text{ pf}$$
$$r_{b'e} = 1500 \text{ ohms} \qquad g_m = 150 \text{ mmhos}$$
$$r_{ce} = 800 \text{ kilohms}$$

The stray wiring capacitance is 100 pf.

(a) Sketch an equivalent circuit which can be used to represent the amplifier during high-frequency analysis.

(b) Determine the high-frequency cutoff point for the input section of the amplifier.

(c) Calculate the high-frequency cutoff point for the output section of the amplifier.

14-10 A fixed-bias common-emitter amplifier uses a 2.5-kilohm collector resistor. The basis bias resistor is 150 kilohms, and the input and output coupling capacitors are 20-μf electrolytic capacitors. The external load has a resistance of 10 kilohms and negligible capacitance. The transistor itself has an input capacitance of 400 pf and an output capacitance of 10 pf. The h parameters of the transistor are

$$h_{ie} = 600 \text{ ohms} \qquad h_{fe} = 110 \qquad \frac{1}{h_{oe}} = 50 \text{ kilohms}$$

Neglect stray wiring capacitance and the output impedance of the signal source.

(a) Draw a schematic diagram of the amplifier.

(b) Calculate the mid-frequency gain of the amplifier.

(c) Determine the low-frequency cutoff point of the input section.

(d) Determine the low-frequency cutoff point of the output section.

(e) Determine the high-frequency cutoff point of the input section.

(f) Calculate the high-frequency cutoff point of the output section.

(g) Draw a frequency-response curve for the amplifier.

15 TRANSFORMER COUPLING

Let us recall how we differentiate between an amplifier and all other devices. We defined an amplifier as a unit which provides power gain, then we classified amplifiers into two categories, voltage amplifiers and power amplifiers. We found that although both provide power gain, the designer may place greater emphasis on obtaining a large voltage gain or a large power gain.

In general, the first stages of a multistage amplifier are voltage amplifiers. The function of these voltage amplifiers is to increase the signal voltage to a level large enough for it to drive the final stage, which is a power amplifier. The function of the power amplifier is to deliver signal power to an external load.

The aim of this chapter is to develop a means of delivering *maximum* power to a load.

HOW TO PROVIDE MAXIMUM POWER TO A LOAD

In order to keep the analysis as simple as possible, let us represent the output section of our power amplifier by a current source I in parallel with an output resistance R_O as in Fig. 15-1.

Let us now determine the relationship between R_O and R_X that must exist for maximum power to be delivered to R_X. If R_X is made very large, the current that flows through it becomes small and the power taken by it also becomes small. If R_X is made very small, the voltage dropped across it becomes small and the power taken by it again becomes small.

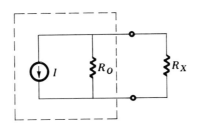

FIGURE 15-1 *Current source representation of the output section of a power amplifier.*

In attempting to bring the search for maximum power transfer to a satisfactory conclusion, let us give values to R_0 and I. We can make a table of the power P_X taken by R_X as R_X varies and then plot a graph of R_X vs. P_X.

If we allow I to be 1 amp and R_0 to be 10 kilohms, we can develop Table 15-1. Using the data from Table 15-1, we can then plot the curve of R_X vs. P_X shown in Fig. 15-2. Note that the maximum power is delivered to R_X when it is equal to 10 kilohms. It is *not* a coincidence that the maximum power is delivered to R_X when R_X *is equal to* R_0, the output impedance of the amplifier. A more rigorous approach to determining the relationship that exists between R_0 and R_X for maximum power transfer is to write a general equation for P_X. A graph of P_X vs. R_X/R_0 is then plotted. When this is done, the curve shown in Fig. 15-3 results. From Table 15-1 and Figs. 15-2 and 15-3 we see that for maximum power to be transferred to the load, the external load resistance R_X must equal the output impedance of the amplifier R_0. This appears to

FIGURE 15-2 *Power to the load vs. load resistance for the circuit of Fig. 15-1.*

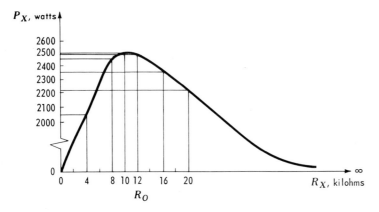

TABLE 15-1

$R_0 = 10$ kilohms	$I = 1$ amp
R_X, kilohms	**P_X, watts**
0	0
4	2040
8	2460
10	2500
12	2490
16	2360
20	2220
∞	0

create a problem because the final external load which an amplifier is expected to feed into is usually predetermined, and the output impedance of the amplifier, r_p, r_d, or $1/h_{oe}$, may be of a different order of magnitude. For example, consider the need to feed a 4-ohm loudspeaker from the final stage of an amplifier. The output impedance of a vacuum tube, a MOSFET, or a transistor is usually at least a few thousand ohms.

Before giving up in despair and relegating the result so far obtained to the scrap heap, let us consider the effect of looking at a load resistance through a transformer. Since current and voltage

FIGURE 15-3 *Power to the load vs. R_x/R_0 for the circuit of Fig. 15-1.*

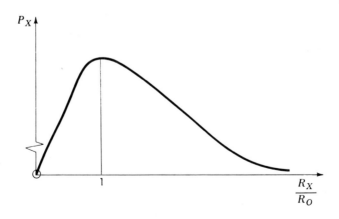

are changed when an electric signal is passed through a transformer, we suspect that the resistance of a transformer and resistor combination might prove interesting.

A TRANSFORMER AND RESISTOR COMBINATION

Let us investigate what the combined impedance is of the resistor R_2 and the transformer, as drawn in Fig. 15-4. In essence, we are interested in determining V_1/I_1, the resistance of the transformer and resistor combination.

To begin,

$$\frac{V_2}{V_1} = \frac{N_2}{N_1} \quad \text{and} \quad \frac{I_1}{I_2} = \frac{N_2}{N_1}$$

Therefore,

$$\frac{V_2}{V_1}\frac{I_1}{I_2} = \frac{N_2}{N_1}\frac{N_2}{N_1}$$

$$\frac{V_2/I_2}{V_1/I_1} = \left(\frac{N_2}{N_1}\right)^2$$

$$\frac{R_2}{R_1} = \left(\frac{N_2}{N_1}\right)^2$$

$$\boxed{R_1 = R_2 \left(\frac{N_1}{N_2}\right)^2}$$

where R_1 is the resistance represented by the combination of the transformer and R_2.

This is a significant conclusion. Through proper choice of a transformer turns ratio, a fixed value of resistance R_2 can be made to appear as any desired value when seen through a transformer. So we see that it is possible to provide an external load to an amplifier which is *impedance-matched* to the amplifier. By proper choice of transformer, any load can appear to have a resistance equal to the output resistance of the power amplifier. When an external load

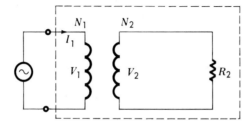

FIGURE 15-4 *Transformer-resistor combination.*

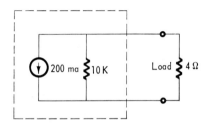

FIGURE 15-5 *Equivalent circuit of the output section of a transistor and its load.*

is equal to the output impedance of an amplifier, an *impedance match* is said to exist.

An Example Consider a situation in which a transistor amplifier is feeding a loudspeaker.   If the output resistance $1/h_{oe}$ of the transistor is 10 kilohms and the speaker impedance is 4 ohms, it is a very bad mismatch.   Figure 15-5 shows the equivalent circuit for the output section of the amplifier.

As an illustration, let us make $h_{fe}I_B$ equal to 200 ma rms.   Using the formula

$$P_X = \frac{R_O^2(R_X)}{(R_O + R_X)^2} I^2$$

we can determine how much power is delivered to the speaker

$$P_X = \frac{10,000^2 \times 4}{(10,000 + 4)^2} 0.2^2$$

$$\boxed{P_X = 0.16 \text{ watts}}$$

Having just developed the fact that the best case for power transfer is that in which $R_X = R_O$, let us determine how much power would have been delivered to the load had an impedance match been arranged by using a properly chosen transformer.   In this case, the speaker and transformer combination would appear as 10 kilohms, and the situation depicted in Fig. 15-6 would result.

The power to the speaker and transformer combination can

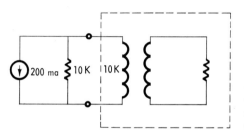

FIGURE 15-6 *Equivalent circuit of the output section of a transistor feeding a transformer and resistor combination.*

be determined from

$$P_X = \frac{R_O^2 R_X}{(R_O + R_X)^2} I^2$$

$$= \frac{10{,}000^2 \times 10{,}000}{(10{,}000 + 10{,}000)^2} \times 0.2^2$$

$$\boxed{P_X = 100 \text{ watts}}$$

Since the transformer absorbs a negligible amount of power, a huge increase in power to the speaker results.

Now that we have developed a need for transformer-coupling a load to an amplifier, let us attempt to analyze amplifiers which make use of this technique.

Figure 15-7 depicts a transistor amplifier, a vacuum-tube am-

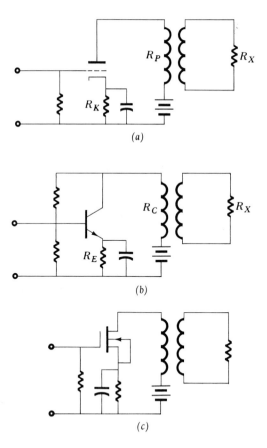

(a)

(b)

(c)

FIGURE 15-7 Amplifiers with transformer-coupled loads. (a) Vacuum-tube triode; (b) transistor; and (c) MOSFET.

plifier, and a MOSFET amplifier, each with transformer-coupled loads. Note that coupling capacitors are not needed because the transformer will pass only the ac portion of any signal that appears on its input.

Our next major concern is the construction of the four-quadrant graph that will represent the operation of the transformer-coupled amplifier.

LOAD LINES FOR TRANSFORMER-COUPLED AMPLIFIERS

The situation is similar to that encountered with capacitance coupling. Two load lines are required because the only resistance that appears for the dc currents and voltages is the small dc resistance of the transformer-primary winding. For ac currents and voltages, the impedance due to the combination is the impedance seen at the transformer terminals, $(N_1/N_2)^2 R_X$, the external load times the turns ratio squared (see Fig. 15-7).

The static load line (dc load line) is practically vertical, since its slope, due to the small resistance of the transformer primary plus R_K, R_E, or R_S, is almost infinity (slope $= -1/R$). R_K, R_E, or R_S is now important in the determination of the static load line because its value is significant compared to the dc resistance of the transformer primary. For most cases, the static load line is assumed to be vertical.

After the operating point is determined by the intersection of the static load line and the grid bias line of the plate characteristic, the dynamic load line (ac load line) can be drawn through the Q point at a slope equal to the impedance of the load as seen through the transformer, $(N_1/N_2)^2 R_X$, using the point-slope method of load-line construction (see Fig. 15-8).

Illustrative Problem 15-1

A 40358 power transistor is to be used as the final stage of an amplifier whose function is to drive a loudspeaker. The speaker impedance is 8 ohms and is to be transformer-coupled to the amplifier. It is desired that the speaker-transformer combination appear as a

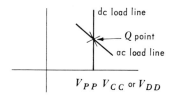

FIGURE 15-8 *Dc and ac load lines for a transformer-coupled amplifier.*

50-ohm load. A collector supply of 3 volts is available, and 3 ma quiescent base current should be used.

(a) What transformer turns ratio is required?
(b) Determine the quiescent operating point.
(c) Draw the ac load line.
(d) Find the output voltage for a base current signal of 2 ma peak-to-peak.

SOLUTION
Given: 40348 transistor; $R_X = 8$ ohms; $R_C = 50$ ohms; $V_{CC} = 3$ volts; $I_{BQ} = 3$ ma
Find:
(a) N_1/N_2
(b) Q point
(c) The ac load line
(d) V_{out} for 2 ma peak-to-peak I_B

(a) $\left(\dfrac{N_1}{N_2}\right)^2 = \dfrac{50}{8}$

$\qquad \dfrac{N_1}{N_2} = \sqrt{\dfrac{50}{8}} = 2.5:1$

$$\boxed{N_1:N_2 = 2.5:1}$$

(b) See Fig. Prob. 15-1b.

(c) $\dfrac{\Delta v_{ce}}{\Delta i_c} = 50$

Let $\Delta v_{ce} = 2$ volts

$\qquad \dfrac{2}{\Delta i_c} = 50$

$\qquad \Delta i_c = {}^2/_{50} = 40$ ma

$$\boxed{\Delta i_c = 40 \text{ ma}}$$

(d) From the graph (Fig. Prob. 15-1b)

$\qquad \Delta v_{ce} = 5.2 - 1.0 = 4.2$ volts peak-to-peak

$\qquad V_{out} = V_{ce} \dfrac{N_2}{N_1}$

$\qquad\qquad = 4.2 \dfrac{1}{2.5} = 1.68$ volts peak-to-peak

$$\boxed{V_{out} = 1.68 \text{ volts peak-to-peak}}$$

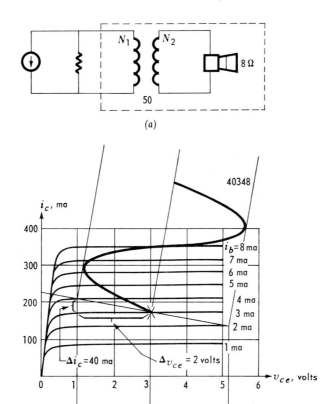

(a)

(b)

FIGURE PROB. 15-1

Illustrative Problem 15-2

A 6J5 triode amplifier is to be used to drive a 4-ohm speaker voice coil. The grid bias is −6 volts, and the B+ supply is 200 volts. The dc resistance of the transformer primary is 200 ohms.

For maximum power transfer to the speaker:

(a) What is the required value of R_K?   For this part of the problem approximate the static load line by a vertical line.
(b) Determine the Q point.
(c) Draw the dynamic load line.
(d) Determine the required transformer ratio.

SOLUTION

Given: 6J5; $R_X = 4$ ohms; $V_{GG} = -6$ volts; $V_{PP} = 200$ volts; $R_{TP} = 200$ ohms

Find:

(a) R_K

(b) Q point

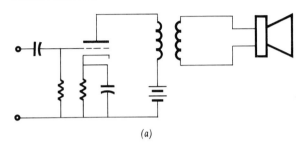

(a)

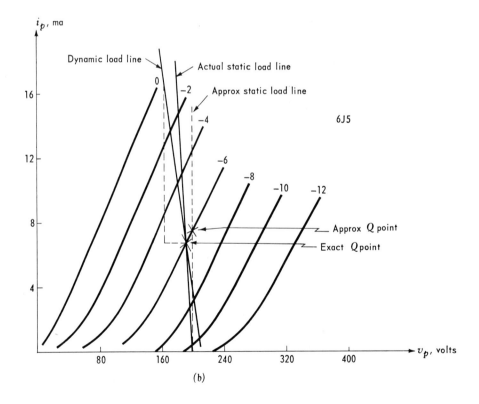

(b)

(c) Dynamic load line
(d) Transformer ratio

(a) From the approximate static load line, $I_{PQ} = 7.5$ ma.

$$7.5 \times 10^{-3} R_K = 6$$

$$\boxed{R_K = 800 \text{ ohms}}$$

(b) Two points are needed for the determination of the static load line. One is the v_p intercept at 200 volts. The i_p intercept cannot be used because it is way off scale. By point-slope technique

$$R = R_K + R_{TP}$$
$$= 800 + 200$$
$$= 1000$$

$$\frac{\Delta v_p}{\Delta i_p} = 1000$$

Let $\Delta i_p = 16$ ma

$$\frac{\Delta v_p}{16 \times 10^{-3}} = 1000$$

$$\Delta v_p = 16 \text{ volts}$$

Coordinates of second point

$$200 - 16 = 184 \text{ volts}$$

$$\boxed{184 \text{ volts, 16 ma}}$$

Note that the actual load line varies only slightly from the approximated one.

(c) For maximum power transfer

$$R_P = r_p$$

From the tube manual, $r_p = 2800$ ohms; therefore R_P should be made 2800 ohms

$$\frac{\Delta v_p}{\Delta i_p} = 2800 \text{ ohms}$$

Let $\Delta i_p = 10$ ma

$$\frac{\Delta v_p}{10 \times 10^{-3}} = 2800 \text{ ohms}$$

$$\Delta v_p = 28 \text{ volts}$$

(d) $$\frac{R_p}{R_X} = \left(\frac{N_{\text{prim}}}{N_{\text{sec}}}\right)^2$$

$$R_p = 2800 \text{ ohms}$$
$$R_X = 4 \text{ ohms}$$
$$\frac{2800}{4} = \left(\frac{N_{\text{prim}}}{N_{\text{sec}}}\right)^2$$

$$\boxed{\left(\frac{N_{\text{prim}}}{N_{\text{sec}}}\right) = 26.4}$$

PROBLEMS

15-1 In what portion of a multistage amplifier would you find a voltage-amplifier stage? A power-amplifier stage? Why?

15-2 To obtain maximum power transfer from a power source to a load, what must be the relationship between the output resistance of the source and the load resistance?

15-3 Refer to Fig. 15-1. Calculate the power absorbed by R_X for a current of 1 amp rms when:
(a) $R_O = 100$ ohms, $R_X = 100$ ohms
(b) $R_O = 100$ ohms, $R_X = 200$ ohms
(c) $R_O = 100$ ohms, $R_X = 50$ ohms

15-4 What is the resistance seen when looking into the primary side of a step-up transformer that has a 50-ohm load resistor across its secondary? The turns ratio of the transformer is $1:25$.

15-5 Determine the necessary transformer turns ratio for transferring maximum power to a 500-ohm load from a source that has an output impedance of 50,000 ohms. What is the voltage across the external load if the terminal voltage of the source is 10 volts rms?

15-6 A fixed-bias common-emitter amplifier uses a transistor having the following h parameters: $h_{ie} = 700$ ohms, $h_{fe} = 100$, $1/h_{oe} = 15$ kilohms. A 50-ohm load is transformer-coupled to the amplifier. A signal source with a terminal voltage of 350 mv peak-to-peak is applied to the input of the amplifier.
(a) Draw a schematic diagram of the amplifier.
(b) Sketch an h parameter equivalent of the circuit.
(c) Determine the transformer turns ratio necessary for maximum transfer of power to the load.
(d) Calculate the base signal current.
(e) How much signal current flows in the primary of the transformer?
(f) How much signal current flows in the secondary of the transformer?
(g) Find the amount of signal power being taken by the external load.

15-7 A common-emitter transformer-coupled transistor amplifier is to have a dynamic load line and a quiescent operating point as shown in Fig. 15-9. The final load R_X is 50 ohms.

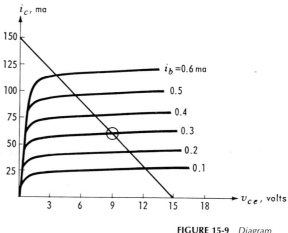

FIGURE 15-9 *Diagram for Prob. 15-7.*

(*a*) Draw a schematic diagram of the circuit.
(*b*) What is the necessary voltage value of the collector supply?
(*c*) Determine the impedance presented by the combination of the transformer and the final load.
(*d*) Calculate the necessary transformer turns ratio.
(*e*) Determine the peak-to-peak voltage across the external load for a base current of 400 μa peak-to-peak.

15-8 The base bias current in the circuit shown in Fig. 15-10 is 2 ma.
(*a*) Locate the static load line.
(*b*) Indicate the quiescent operating point.
(*c*) Construct the dynamic load line.
(*d*) Complete the four-quadrant graph for a base signal of 3 ma peak-to-peak.
(*e*) Making use of the input characteristics of the transistor, determine the voltage necessary to obtain the base signal current of 3 ma peak-to-peak with a case temperature of 25°C.

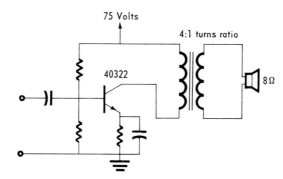

FIGURE 15-10 *Diagram for Prob. 15-8.*

TRANSFORMER COUPLING 233

15-9 A 6AV6 triode is used to drive five 8-ohm speakers (8 ohms $\equiv$ ac resistance) in parallel. The plate supply voltage is 150 volts, and the grid bias is -1 volt. The dynamic plate resistance of a 6AV6 is 80,000 ohms. It is desired that maximum power transfer occur between the amplifier and the speaker arrangement. Disregard the deviation of the static load line from the vertical.

(a) Find the Q point.

(b) Determine the required value of R_K.

(c) What is the required transformer turns ratio?

(d) Draw the dynamic load line.

(e) Plot the four-quadrant graph for an input signal that is 2 volts peak-to-peak.

(f) Determine the voltage across each speaker. (Remember the transformer!)

16 OUTPUT CIRCUIT POWER AND EFFICIENCY

In the early chapters of this unit, we defined an amplifier as any circuit that provided a power gain. Then we discussed the abilities of an amplifier to provide voltage gain. It was soon discovered that certain amplifiers did a better job of providing voltage gain while others did a better job of providing power gain. Consider the formula for the voltage gain of a common-emitter transistor amplifier

$$A_V = \frac{-h_{fe}R_C}{h_{ie}}$$

If we were interested in providing a maximum voltage gain we would make R_C extremely large, but if we were interested in providing maximum power gain, an impedance match would be necessary, requiring that R_C be the same as the output resistance of the transistor.

So we see that the criterion for obtaining maximum power gain is not the same as that for obtaining maximum voltage gain.

POWER GAIN

We can classify amplifiers according to which of the above results is desired when we design the amplifier. If obtaining power gain is most important to us during the design, we classify the amplifier as a *power amplifier*. If voltage gain is most important, we classify the amplifier as a *voltage amplifier*.

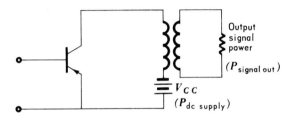

FIGURE 16-1 *Transistor amplifier, showing the origin of the output circuit power and the location of the output signal power.*

However, remember that *all* amplifiers provide power gain since this is inherent in our definition of an amplifier.

What do we mean when we say that an amplifier provides power gain? We mean that the output signal power is greater than the input signal power. Where does this increased power come from? All the output power comes from the output circuit dc supply, V_{PP}, V_{CC}, or V_{DD}. Thus, an amplifier provides the means for a small signal to shape large amounts of power, obtained from the output supply, to its own shape, differing only, we hope, in amplitude and power content (see Fig. 16-1).

EFFICIENCY

Since the major reason for the existence of a power amplifier is for conversion of power from the dc supply to signal power, the efficiency with which this is done is of great importance.

Let us now define a new term—*output circuit efficiency:*

$$\text{Output circuit efficiency} = \eta_{\text{out ckt}} = \frac{P_{\text{signal out}}}{P_{\text{dc supply}}} \times 100$$

Is the output circuit efficiency an important figure of merit for an amplifier? Yes, very definitely, because power which is taken from the supply and which does not become output signal power is not only wasted but is detrimental to the operation of the circuit, since it generates heat which must be dissipated by the active device. This heat is a major problem, especially when dealing with transistor amplifiers, since excessive heat can destroy the transistors.

ACTIVE-DEVICE POWER DISSIPATION

It is important whenever designing an amplifier that the designer calculate the amount of power the active device must dissipate itself.   Reference is then made to the manufacturer's published ratings to determine whether the active device can safely dissipate the required amount of power.   If the chosen device cannot dissipate the required amount of power safely, the amplifier must be redesigned.

Another important consideration refers to amplifiers designed for portable use.   Dissipated power represents a useless loss requiring that larger power packs be carried.   Consider the problems of equipment to be carried in a space capsule.   If all the electronic gear were dissipating excessive power, not only would a heat problem arise but also a weight problem due to the larger power supplies required.

POWER INTO THE OUTPUT CIRCUIT

Refer to Fig. 16-2.   The power that the power supply is providing is the product of the average current flowing through it and the dc voltage across it

$$P_{\text{dc supply}} = V_{\text{dc supply}} I_{\text{supply av}}$$

For a transistor amplifier

$$P_{\text{dc supply}} = V_{CC} I_{C,\text{av}}$$

For a tube amplifier

$$P_{\text{dc supply}} = V_{PP} I_{P,\text{av}}$$

For a MOSFET amplifier

$$P_{\text{dc supply}} = V_{DD} I_{D,\text{av}}$$

OUTPUT SIGNAL POWER

Now that we have established the dc power being delivered to the output section of the amplifier, let us determine the amount of signal power the amplifier delivers to the load.

Assuming that the output signal is an undistorted sine wave,

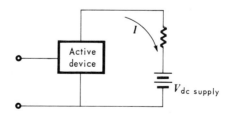

FIGURE 16-2

$$P_{\text{dc supply}} = V_{\text{dc supply}} I_{\text{supply av}}.$$

OUTPUT CIRCUIT POWER AND EFFICIENCY   237

the output signal power is calculated from

$$P_{out} = V_{rms\ out}I_{rms\ out}$$

Various forms of this equation can be written. A few of these forms are developed and shown below.

$$P_{out} = \frac{V_{peak\ out}}{\sqrt{2}}\frac{I_{peak\ out}}{\sqrt{2}}$$

$$= \frac{V_{p\text{-}p}}{2\sqrt{2}}\frac{I_{p\text{-}p}}{2\sqrt{2}}$$

$$= \frac{V_{p\text{-}p\ out}I_{p\text{-}p\ out}}{8}$$

$$\boxed{P_{out} = \frac{(V_{max\ out} - V_{min\ out})(I_{max\ out} - I_{min\ out})}{8}}$$

Referring to Fig. 16-3, we note that the average values of both the dc plus ac and the dc alone are the same. The power taken from the dc supply is $V_{CC}I_{C.av}$. Therefore, the dc power is independent of output signal variations. Power taken from the dc supply that does not become output signal power must be dissipated as heat in the active device. In a transformer-coupled situation, the worst case to consider is when there is no ac signal passing through the amplifier. In this case all the power delivered by the dc source must be dissipated by the active device. Thus, if

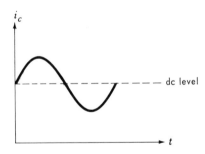

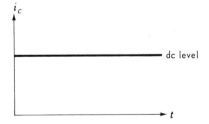

FIGURE 16-3 *Comparison of average value of a sine wave riding on a dc level with the dc level alone.*

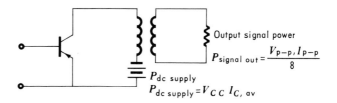

Output signal power

$$P_{\text{signal out}} = \frac{V_{\text{p-p}}, I_{\text{p-p}}}{8}$$

$P_{\text{dc supply}}$

$$P_{\text{dc supply}} = V_{CC} I_{C, \text{av}}$$

FIGURE 16-4 *Summary of power relationships.*

the power-dissipation rating of an active device is larger than $P_{\text{dc supply}}$, it will be well within safe limits during active conditions.

Figure 16-4 gives a summary of the relationships developed in this chapter.

Illustrative Problem 16-1

For the four-quadrant graph shown in Fig. Prob. 16-1 depicting the operation of the given circuit of a power amplifier, determine:

(a) Power output from the dc supply
(b) Output power delivered to the load
(c) Output circuit efficiency
(d) Required power dissipation rating of the transistor

Solution

Given: Four-quadrant graph
Find:

(a) $P_{\text{dc supply}}$
(b) $P_{\text{signal out}}$
(c) η_{out}
(d) $P_{\text{diss rating}}$

(a) $\begin{aligned} P_{\text{dc supply}} &= V_{CC}I_{C,\text{av}} \\ &= 9 \times 50 \times 10^{-3} \end{aligned}$

$$\boxed{P_{\text{dc supply}} = 450 \text{ mw}}$$

(b) $\begin{aligned} P_{\text{signal out}} &= \frac{(V_{CE,\text{max}} - V_{CE,\text{min}})(I_{C,\text{max}} - I_{C,\text{min}})}{8} \\ &= \frac{(12-6)(75 \times 10^{-3} - 25 \times 10^{-3})}{8} \\ &= \frac{6(50 \times 10^{-3})}{8} \end{aligned}$

$$\boxed{P_{\text{signal out}} = 37.5 \text{ mw}}$$

OUTPUT CIRCUIT POWER AND EFFICIENCY   239

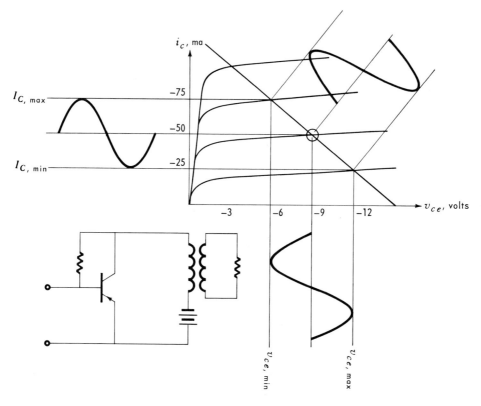

FIGURE PROB. 16-1

(c) $\quad \eta_{\text{out}} = \dfrac{P_{\text{signal out}}}{P_{\text{dc supply}}}$

$\qquad\qquad = \dfrac{37.5 \times 10^{-3}}{450 \times 10^{-3}}$

$\boxed{\eta_{\text{out}} = 8.35\%}$

(d) $\quad P_{\text{diss rating}} = P_{\text{dc supply}}$

$\boxed{P_{\text{diss rating}} = 450 \text{ mw}}$

PROBLEMS

16-1 What is the output circuit efficiency of an amplifier whose trans-former-coupled load receives 2 watts when the collector supply battery is delivering 10 watts? What happens to the remaining 8 watts of power?

16-2 Figure 16-5 shows the static and dynamic load lines that describe an amplifier.

(a) What type of coupling is used?

(b) What is the voltage of the dc supply?

(c) Determine the average current drawn from the dc supply.

(d) How much power is being supplied by the dc supply?

(e) Calculate the resistance of the load as seen by the output terminals of the active device.

16-3 An amplifier is delivering 10 watts of signal power to a loudspeaker. The amplifier is a common-emitter transformer-coupled unit with a collector supply battery providing 75 watts.

(a) Draw a schematic diagram of the amplifier showing a fixed-bias arrangement.

(b) Calculate the output circuit efficiency of the amplifier.

(c) How much power must the transistor dissipate?

(d) How much power would the transistor have to dissipate if the input signal voltage were reduced to zero?

(e) Can a transistor having a power rating of 50 watts be used in this circuit?

16-4 A vacuum-tube amplifier is transformer-coupled to its load. The plate supply voltage is 125 volts, and the quiescent plate current is 225 ma. The output signal is an undistorted sine wave. The instantaneous plate voltage swing is from 50 to 200 volts, while the plate current swings from 350 to 100 ma.

(a) Determine the rms value of the plate current swing.

(b) Calculate the rms value of the plate voltage swing.

(c) How much signal power is being delivered to the load?

(d) Find the amount of power being delivered to the circuit by the plate supply.

(e) Calculate the plate circuit efficiency of the amplifier.

16-5 A 2N2147 *PNP* transistor is to be used to drive a pair of 8-ohm speakers connected in parallel. The speaker combination is to be transformer-coupled to the amplifier. A 10-volt supply is available for use with the amplifier. A quiescent base current of 10 ma is chosen because a maximum input signal swing of 20 ma peak-to-peak is anticipated. A vertical-axis (collector-current) intercept

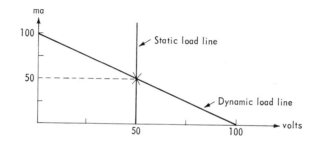

FIGURE 16-5 *Diagram for Prob. 16-2.*

OUTPUT CIRCUIT POWER AND EFFICIENCY   241

point of 5 amps is chosen so the dynamic load line will avoid the knee of the −20-ma base current curve.

(a) Construct a dc load line and locate the quiescent operating point.

(b) Construct the dynamic load line.

(c) Determine the resistance which the transformer and speaker combination must present to the amplifier so that the dynamic load line will be at the desired slope.

(d) Determine the required transformer turns ratio.

(e) Complete the four-quadrant graph for a 20-ma peak-to-peak input.

(f) How much power is being delivered to the circuit by the collector supply battery?

(g) Determine the signal power delivered to the load.

(h) What is the collector circuit efficiency for the operation described by the four-quadrant graph?

(i) Refer to the input characteristics of the transistor and determine the necessary base-to-emitter signal voltage needed for the 20-ma peak-to-peak base current.

(j) Calculate the voltage, current, and power gain of the amplifier.

17

CLASSES OF OPERATION

In examining the answers to the problems in Chap. 16 we note that the efficiencies of the amplifiers appear to be rather low compared to the efficiencies of other electric devices. This is of great concern because the major objective in a power amplifier is to provide power to an external load. Before attempting to find means of improving the efficiency let us determine whether or not there is a maximum attainable efficiency for the circuits with which we have been dealing.

MAXIMUM EFFICIENCY FOR A TRANSFORMER-COUPLED AMPLIFIER WITHOUT EXCESSIVE DISTORTION

The circuits we have been dealing with have been transformer-coupled ones. For simplicity, we will assume pure sine-wave input and set up for the maximum output circuit efficiency in Fig. 17-1. Maximum efficiency requires that the largest amount of output power be obtained for a given output circuit supply.

For a given load line and a given set of characteristics let us determine the maximum possible efficiency. In order to obtain the maximum undistorted output swing the quiescent point must be centrally located, as indicated on the load line in Fig. 17-1. We are interested in the maximum output swing because this corresponds to the maximum output power and therefore the largest output circuit efficiency. Let us examine the diagram in Fig. 17-1 in more detail.

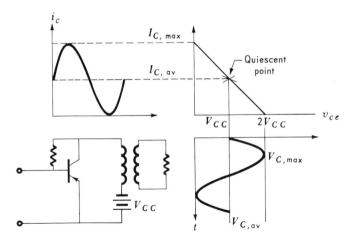

FIGURE 17-1 *Four-quadrant graph showing maximum output power without distortion for a transformer-coupled amplifier.*

Because a transformer-coupled situation is being studied, and because the static load line in such a case passes through the quiescent point, intercepting the horizontal axis at a voltage corresponding to the output circuit supply voltage, the horizontal axis of the characteristic curves of Fig. 17-1 can be marked off as indicated.

In order to eliminate the complications of notation, this analysis is being done with transistor notation, but it should be understood that the result holds for vacuum tubes and MOSFETs as well.

From Fig. 17-1 we note that the maximum undistorted swing of the output voltage is $2V_{CC}$ and that the maximum undistorted swing of output current is $I_{C,\max} = 2I_{C,\mathrm{av}}$.

With these facts in mind, these calculations follow directly from Fig. 17-1:

$$V_{C,\max} = 2V_{CC}$$

$$I_{C,\mathrm{av}} = \frac{I_{C,\max}}{2}$$

$$P_{\mathrm{dc\ supply}} = V_{CC}I_{C,\mathrm{av}}$$

$$= V_{CC}\frac{I_{C,\max}}{2}$$

$$P_{\mathrm{signal\ out}} = \frac{(V_{C,\max} - V_{C,\min})(I_{C,\max} - I_{C,\min})}{8}$$

$$V_{\min} = I_{\min} = 0$$

$$P_{\mathrm{signal\ out}} = \frac{2V_{CC}I_{C,\max}}{8} = \frac{V_{CC}I_{C,\max}}{4}$$

$$\eta_{\text{out ckt}} = \frac{P_{\text{signal out}}}{P_{\text{dc supply}}} \times 100 = \frac{V_{CC}I_{C,\text{max}}/4}{V_{CC}I_{C,\text{max}}/2} \times 100$$

$$\boxed{\eta_{\text{out ckt}} = 50\%}$$

This is a very interesting result. It says simply that the *maximum* output circuit efficiency for a transformer-coupled amplifier producing no distortion is 50 percent.

MAXIMUM EFFICIENCY WITHOUT A TRANSFORMER AND WITHOUT EXCESSIVE DISTORTION

Let us see what happens to the efficiency when we remove the transformer and couple directly to the load.

In Fig. 17-2 the four-quadrant graph construction for an amplifier in which the final load R_X is intimately a part of the amplifier is shown. In this case the quiescent operating point is again centrally located so that the maximum signal swing, and thereby maximum output signal power without distortion, is obtained. The maximum output efficiency for this situation, of the final load an intimate part of the amplifier (no transformer) and no major distortion allowed, can now be determined as follows:

$$I_{\text{av}} = \frac{I_{C,\text{max}}}{2}$$
$$V_{CC} = V_{C,\text{max}}$$

FIGURE 17-2 *Four-quadrant graph for an amplifier without a transformer and with the load an intimate part of the amplifier.*

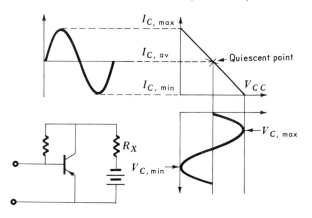

$$P_{\text{dc supply}} = V_{CC}I_{\text{av}}$$

$$P_{\text{dc supply}} = V_{C,\text{max}} \frac{I_{C,\text{max}}}{2}$$

$$P_{\text{out}} = \frac{(V_{C,\text{max}} - V_{C,\text{min}})(I_{C,\text{max}} - I_{C,\text{min}})}{8}$$

$$V_{C,\text{min}} = I_{C,\text{min}} = 0$$

$$P_{\text{out}} = \frac{V_{C,\text{max}}I_{C,\text{max}}}{8}$$

$$\eta_{\text{out ckt}} = \frac{P_{\text{out}}}{P_{\text{dc supply}}} \times 100$$

$$= \frac{V_{C,\text{max}}I_{C,\text{max}}/8}{V_{C,\text{max}}I_{C,\text{max}}/2}$$

$$= \frac{1/8}{1/2} = \frac{2}{8} = \frac{1}{4}$$

$$\boxed{\eta_{\text{out ckt}} = 25\%}$$

Eliminating the transformer has not improved the maximum attainable efficiency. In fact, the maximum attainable efficiency has actually been reduced to 25 percent.

INCREASING OUTPUT CIRCUIT EFFICIENCY

This problem of obtaining improved maximum efficiency can be approached in a more logical manner. How can the efficiency be increased? One way is to keep the output swing as great as before but reduce the input power by reducing V_{CC}. Such a move, however, will introduce drastic distortion.

If the quiescent operating point is moved lower down on the load line from Q_1 to Q_2, as shown in Fig. 17-3, the average current will be reduced and hence the dc power delivered to the amplifier will also be reduced. Let us investigate the case in which the Q point has been lowered all the way to the point at which it lies at the intersection of the load line and the horizontal axis, as shown in Fig. 17-4.

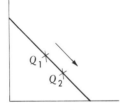

FIGURE 17-3 *Moving the quiescent point lower down on the load line to improve efficiency.*

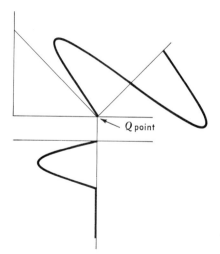

FIGURE 17-4 *Class B operation.*

This is called class B operation. More will be said about classes of operation shortly.

A huge amount of distortion is introduced in this type of operation because the collector current is equal to zero for half of the cycle (see Fig. 17-4).

Of what use is such an arrangement, if so much distortion is introduced that the original waveshape is drastically changed? A circuit arrangement which will be discussed in the next chapter uses two active devices in the same circuit, each one making up for the part of the wave the other leaves out. This eliminates the distortion introduced by this type of operation. Since each would be operating at the higher efficiency, the overall efficiency would also be immensely improved.

MAXIMUM EFFICIENCY OF CLASS B AMPLIFIER

Now to determine the efficiency of a circuit which is operating as shown in Fig. 17-4 (class B operation).

$$P_{\text{out}} = \tfrac{1}{2}V_{\text{rms}}I_{\text{rms}}$$
$$= \frac{\tfrac{1}{2}V_{\text{max}}}{\sqrt{2}}\frac{I_{\text{max}}}{\sqrt{2}} = \frac{V_{\text{max}}I_{\text{max}}}{4}$$
$$P_{\text{dc supply}} = V_{CC}I_{C,av}$$
$$\frac{I_{C,\text{max}}}{\pi} = I_{C,av}$$
$$\eta_{\text{out ckt}} = \frac{P_{\text{out}}}{P_{\text{dc supply}}} \times 100$$

$$= \frac{(V_{max}I_{max}/4)\ (100)}{V_{max}I_{max}/\pi} = \frac{\pi}{4} \times 100$$

$\eta_{\text{out ckt}} = 78.5\%$
Class B transformer-coupled

By allowing a major amount of distortion to be introduced the output circuit efficiency of the amplifier has been increased immensely. Obviously this presents another problem, that of an intolerable amount of distortion. We will discuss this further in the next chapter, when it will be found that by using two active devices in a particular configuration called *push-pull* we can eliminate most of the distortion.

FIGURE 17-5   *(a) Class A operation; (b) class B operation; and (c) class AB operation.*

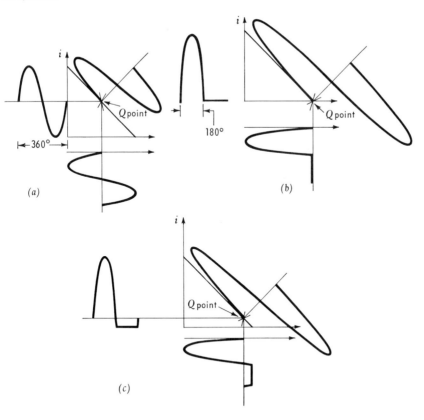

(a)

(b)

(c)

CLASSES OF OPERATION

When discussing power amplifiers, we differentiate between amplifiers in which the output circuit current flows for the entire period of the input wave and those for which current flows for a lesser time by the following classifications:

Class A   Bias and signal are such that plate, collector, or drain current (output circuit current) flows for 360° of the cycle.

Class AB   Bias and signal are such that output circuit current flows for *more than* 180° *but less than* 360°.

Class B   Input is biased to cutoff.   Output circuit current flows for *exactly* 180°.

Figure 17-5 depicts these three classes of operation.

There is one more class of operation, called *class C operation*, in which output circuit current flows for *less than* 180°.   This class of operation is usually reserved for use at radio frequencies.   Because of this and because the four-quadrant graph is not self-explanatory, it has not been shown in Fig. 17-5.

PROBLEMS

17-1   What is the effect on output circuit efficiency of moving the Q point lower down on the load line?

17-2   How can the amount of distortion introduced by class B operation be eliminated?

17-3   What is the difference between a class A, a class AB, and a class B operation?

17-4   What class of amplifier operation would result if no provisions were made for biasing an active device (zero bias)?

17-5   A 2N2147 transistor is to be used in an amplifier with a quiescent base current of 0 ma.   A collector supply of 15 volts is to supply the dc power.   An input signal of 20 ma peak-to-peak base current is driving the amplifier.   The load is a 5-ohm resistance.

  (a)   Sketch a four-quadrant graph of this operation.

  (b)   What class of operation is this?

  (c)   If the input signal were removed, how much power would the transistor draw from the collector supply?

CHAPTER

18

PUSH-PULL OPERATION

In previous chapters we found that a great improvement in output circuit efficiency was realized by operating power amplifiers in class B. The most obvious and overwhelming disadvantage of such operation is that only one-half the signal is being amplified, the output circuit current being cut off during the other half of the cycle, as shown in Fig. 18-1.

A rather obvious and simple proposal for correcting this disadvantage is to provide a second amplifier, also operating class B, which would amplify the other half of the signal.

TWO INPUTS WITH A PHASE DIFFERENCE OF 180°

Won't this second class B amplifier also amplify the same portion of the wave? Not necessarily; we can outwit this second class B amplifier by introducing a 180° phase shift immediately prior to its input, thereby making the negative-going portion of the wave the positive-going portion as far as the second amplifier is concerned.

Such a situation is shown in Fig. 18-2, where two active devices are being fed from opposite legs of a center-tapped transformer. Figure 18-3 presents the four-quadrant graph for the two active devices.

Now that both the positive-going and negative-going portions of the wave have been amplified, we are left with a signal that resembles a full-wave-rectified wave, both halves of the signal being

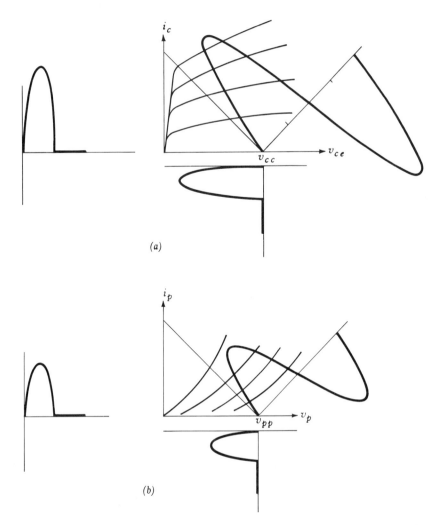

(a)

(b)

FIGURE 18-1 *Four-quadrant graph of class B operation. Note that the output current is cut off for 180°.*

on the same side of the horizontal axis. It is necessary that some provision be made to invert half the signal.

OUTPUT TRANSFORMER

What if we were to provide a center-tapped output transformer as shown in Fig. 18-4? Current would enter the transformer from

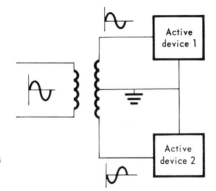

FIGURE 18-2 *Center-tapped transformer being used to provide two signals with a phase difference of 180°.*

FIGURE 18-3 *Two sets of four-quadrant graphs. One set showing the operation of active device 1 of Fig. 18-2 and the other set showing the operation of active device 2.*

Active device 1　　　　Active device 2

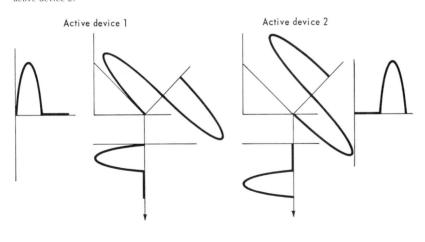

FIGURE 18-4 *How the output voltage is developed by passing the currents from each half of the push-pull amplifier through opposite ends of a center-tapped transformer.*

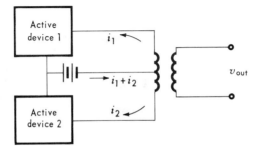

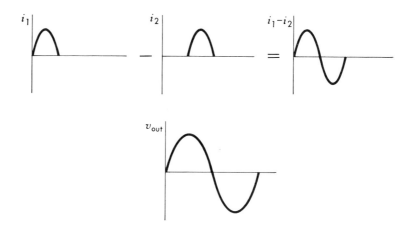

opposite ends of the primary, setting up opposing magnetic fields.

The magnetic field generated by the sum total of the two currents would be proportional to $i_1 - i_2$. It is this magnetic field that would provide the secondary coil with its voltage. Thus, the output voltage would be due to the *difference* between the two currents. Figure 18-5 gives a graphical description of these waveshapes.

THE SCHEMATIC DIAGRAM

In Fig. 18-6, the two sections of the amplifier that were just developed are joined together. This system is referred to as a *push-pull amplifier*.

Our task has been successfully completed. We have developed a circuit that permits the use of class B amplification with its inherent large output circuit efficiency without having to accept the huge distortion that accompanies it.

Now a schematic diagram for such an amplifier must be developed. Figure 18-7 shows schematic diagrams for both a transistor and a vacuum-tube push-pull amplifier.

Note the lack of provision for a bias current in the input portion of the transistor circuit of Fig. 18-7, though a bias has been provided in the vacuum-tube circuit. This can be understood by making reference to Fig. 18-8, which depicts the collector charac-

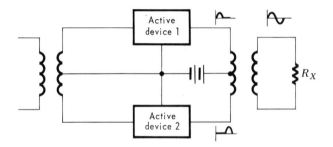

FIGURE 18-6 *A complete block diagram of a push-pull amplifier.*

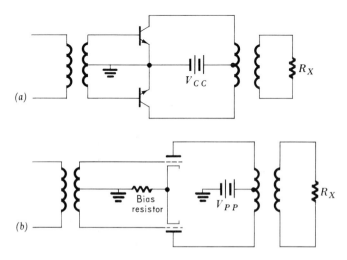

FIGURE 18-7 *Push-pull amplifiers using (a) transistors and (b) vacuum tubes.*

teristics and the plate characteristics. We note that the operating point required for class B operation of a transistor amplifier (as shown on the curve) requires a base current of 0 ma, while the grid voltage bias for class B operation requires the most negative voltage that the load line intercepts.

MATCHED PAIRS
Let us look into a few practical aspects of the push-pull circuit as far as design and analysis are concerned.

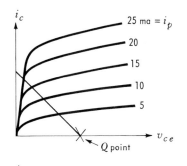

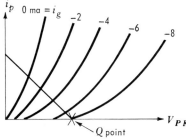

FIGURE 18-8 *Characteristic curves of a transistor and a vacuum tube with load line and Q point indicated.*

First, since we now have two active devices performing the function ordinarily performed by just one, it is necessary to ensure that the two devices are as close to being identical as is possible. In an attempt to do just that, manufacturers market *matched pairs* of active devices. Matched pairs are active devices the manufacturer has examined and feels come as close to being identical as is possible, given the limitations of the state of the art.

It will be necessary somewhere in the design of the circuit to relate the load line plotted on the characteristics to the external load and transformer combination. Because the transistors used in the push-pull circuit form, in most cases, a matched pair, an analysis of only one of the pair is necessary since the other one is identical in operation.

THE DYNAMIC LOAD LINE

In order to draw the dynamic load line for the circuit operation, it is necessary to determine the load on *each* transistor. We recall that to determine the dynamic load due to the external load R_X in combination with the transformer we multiply the impedance of the external load by the square of the transformer ratio. However, observe from Fig. 18-9 that *each* transistor is involved with only *half* of the primary turns, so that the dynamic load as seen by each

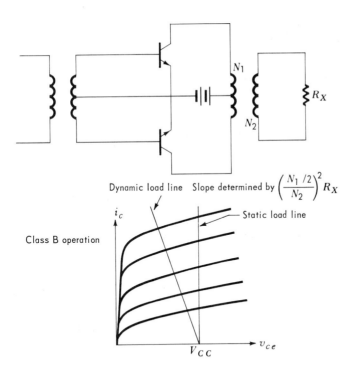

FIGURE 18-9 *A transistor push-pull amplifier and its load lines.*

transistor is only

$$R_C = \left(\frac{\frac{1}{2}N_1}{N_2}\right)^2 R_X$$

where N_1 is the *total* number of turns on the primary of the transformer and N_2 is the total number of turns on the secondary of the transformer.

Thus, the dynamic load line is drawn at a slope determined by $(\frac{1}{2}N_1/N_2)^2 R_X$.

Illustrative Problem 18-1

A push-pull amplifier shown in the Fig. Prob. 18-1a is using transistors whose collector characteristics are shown. An input current of 6 ma peak-to-peak is flowing in the primary of the input transformer:

(*a*) Draw the static load line.
(*b*) Draw the dynamic load line.

(c) Complete the four-quadrant graph.
(d) Find $P_{\text{dc supply}}$ for the complete push-pull circuit.
(e) Find P_{out} for the complete push-pull circuit.
(f) Determine the collector current efficiency for the amplifier.

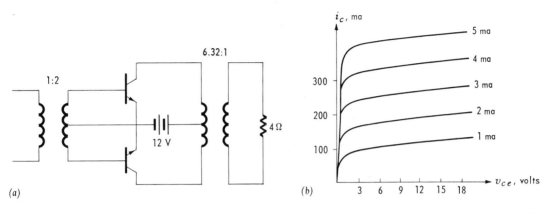

FIGURE PROB. 18-1a and b

SOLUTION
Given: $I_{\text{in}} = 6$ ma peak-to-peak
Find:
(a) Static load line
(b) Dynamic load line
(c) Four-quadrant graph
(d) $P_{\text{dc supply}}$
(e) P_{out}
(f) $\eta_{\text{coll ckt}}$

(a) See the four-quadrant graph (Fig. Prob. 18-1c).

(b) $\quad R_C = \left(\dfrac{\frac{1}{2}N_1}{N_2}\right)^2 R_X$

$\qquad = \left(\dfrac{\frac{1}{2} \times 6.32}{1}\right)^2 \times 4$

$\boxed{R_C = 40 \text{ ohms}}$

$\boxed{\dfrac{V_{CC}}{R_C} = \dfrac{12}{40} = 300 \text{ ma}}$

See Fig. Prob. 18-1c.

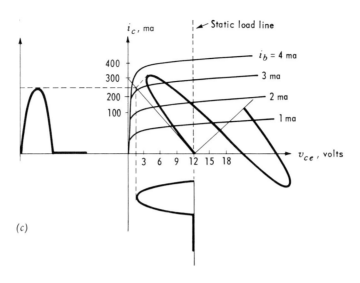

(c)

FIGURE PROB. 18-1c

(c) See Fig. Prob. 18-1c.

(d) $P_{\text{dc supply}} = V_{CC}I_{C,\text{av}}$

$$I_{\text{av}} = \frac{I_{\text{peak}}}{\pi} \qquad \text{from half-wave rectifier theory}$$

From graph:

$$I_{C,\text{peak}} = 250 \text{ ma}$$

$$I_{C,\text{av per transistor}} = \frac{250 \times 10^{-3}}{\pi}$$

$$= 79.6 \text{ ma}$$

$$P_{\text{dc supply per transistor}} = 12 \times 79.6 \times 10^{-3}$$
$$= 0.955 \text{ watts}$$

$$P_{\text{dc supply total}} = 2P_{\text{dc supply per transistor}}$$
$$P_{\text{dc supply total}} = 2 \times 0.955$$

$$\boxed{P_{\text{dc supply total}} = 1.91 \text{ watts}}$$

(e) $P_{\text{out}} = \dfrac{V_{\text{p-p out}}I_{\text{p-p out}}}{8}$

$$V_{\text{p-p}} = 2V_{\text{peak}}$$

From graph:

$$V_{\text{peak}} = 12 - 2.5 = 9.5 \text{ volts}$$
$$V_{\text{p-p}} = 2 \times 9.5 = 19 \text{ volts}$$
$$I_{\text{p-p out}} = 2I_{\text{peak}}$$
$$I_{\text{peak}} = 250 \text{ ma} \qquad \text{from four-quadrant graph}$$
$$I_{\text{p-p out}} = 2 \times 250 \times 10^{-3} = 0.5 \text{ amp}$$

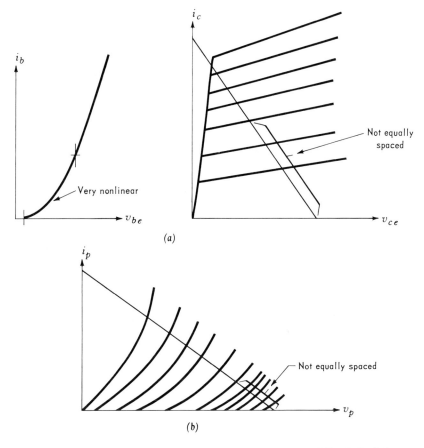

(a)

(b)

FIGURE 18-10 *Active-device characteristic curves. Note nonlinearity for low output currents.*

$$P_{\text{out total}} = \frac{19 \times 0.5}{8}$$

$$\boxed{P_{\text{out total}} = 1.19 \text{ watts}}$$

(f) $\quad \eta_{\text{coll ckt}} = \frac{P_{\text{out}}}{P_{\text{dc}}} \times 100 = \frac{1.19}{1.91} \times 100$

$$\boxed{\eta_{\text{coll ckt}} = 62.4\%}$$

CLASS AB OPERATION

As long as we are dealing with practical problems, we might as well discuss another important problem that arises when operating push-pull in class B. If we inspect the very bottom area of the collector characteristics of a transistor, we find that the curves for equal increments of constant base current are not equally spaced as we approach the horizontal axis (see Fig. 18-10).

A similar situation exists with triode vacuum tubes. As the horizontal axis of the plate characteristics are approached, the constant-grid-voltage curves take on a definite curvature and also become unequally spaced (see Fig. 18-10).

In addition, and most important for transistors, the input curve of a transistor, i_b vs. v_{be}, becomes very nonlinear for small values of i_b (see Fig. 18-10). In the case of vacuum tubes, since no input curves are involved, the main problem is the unequal spacing of the constant-grid-voltage curves as we approach the horizontal axis. Because of these nonlinearities and unequal spacings of curves, a particular type of distortion arises, known as *crossover distortion*, shown in Fig. 18-11. When such distortion cannot be tolerated, the best way to eliminate it is to operate the push-pull amplifier in class AB. Recall that class AB operation requires that the operating point be such as to allow collector current to flow for more than 180° but less than 360°. Figure 18-12 shows the load lines associated with operating a transistor amplifier in class AB.

To operate with an optimum quiescent point, each case must be analyzed individually to choose a quiescent point that is as close as possible to class B operation. Thus, we can reap the bene-

FIGURE 18-11 *Crossover distortion due to the nonlinearity indicated in Fig. 18-10.*

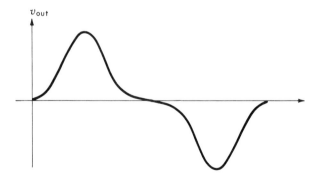

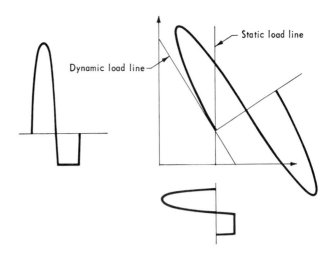

FIGURE 18-12 *Four-quadrant graph for class AB operation (such as Fig. 18-13).*

fits in increased efficiency yet be far enough into the class AB region to eliminate crossover distortion.

By referring to the input characteristics of the transistor, we can see the point at which the curve approaches its linear region and choose that point as the quiescent operating point. This is usually in the region of a v_{be} of 0.2 volt for germanium transistors and 0.6 or 0.7 volt for silicon transistors.

To find a proper bias point for the vacuum-tube triode, we study the characteristic curve with the dynamic load line superimposed on it and choose a point on the dynamic load line at which the constant grid lines become equally spaced (see Fig. 18-10).

BIASING THE CLASS AB PUSH-PULL AMPLIFIER

Now that we see a need for a class AB push-pull amplifier and have an idea of how to locate the quiescent operating point, how are we to provide the necessary bias? Figure 18-13 shows a schematic diagram for a complete push-pull class AB transistor amplifier with voltage-divider bias and emitter swamping. Other bias schemes can also be used, such as fixed or self-bias. However, as was discussed in an earlier chapter, voltage-divider bias with emitter swamping is preferred because of its effect on the stability of the amplifier.

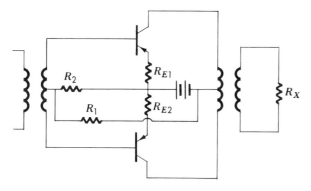

FIGURE 18-13 *Class AB transistor push-pull amplifier.*

COMPLEMENTARY SYMMETRY

Our last remaining problem with push-pull circuits is the expense, weight, and poor frequency response of the required transformers. Is it possible to eliminate these transformers? Yes, providing we have available in the same push-pull circuit two active devices that are the opposite of each other in their electric characteristics. *Given the identical input signal,* one should be delivering current to the load while the other is cut off, and the second should be delivering current to the load while the first is cut off. Do two such devices exist? Very definitely: the *PNP* and the *NPN* transistor.

This eliminates the need for the input transformer, but what of the output transformer? A study of Figs. 18-14 and 18-15 will show that the output transformer can also be eliminated because the currents due to each of the two transistors are flowing in opposite directions through the load, providing a signal to the load of $i_1 - i_2$ directly, without having to pass through opposite legs of a center-tapped transformer. Figure 18-16 shows a construction of the output signal.

Circuits of this type are said to make use of the *complementary symmetry* of the *NPN* and the *PNP* transistors.

In the case of both the *NPN* and the *PNP* transistors of Fig. 18-14 note that the input signal first goes positive and then 180° later goes negative. Why, then, do the incoming signals on the four-quadrant graphs of the two transistors appear to be out of phase? Closer examination reveals that they are *not* out of phase. In both the *NPN* and the *PNP* cases the incoming signal first goes positive and then negative. The appearance of the 180° phase

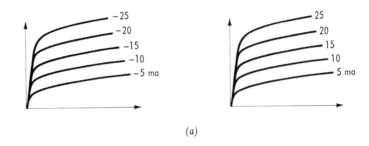

(a)

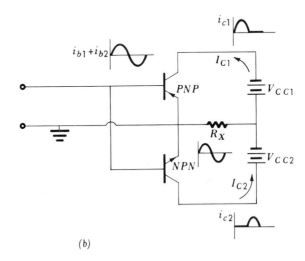

(b)

FIGURE 18-14 (a) Characteristic curves of complementary transistors. (b) A push-pull amplifier using complementary transistors and no transformer.

difference is due only to the fact that in the case of the *PNP* the constant base current lines become more *positive* as we go up the load line, and in the case of the *NPN* they become more *negative* as we go up the load line. Therefore, a positive-going input signal appears to be above the axis for the *NPN* transistor and below the axis for the *PNP*.

Note in Fig. 18-14 that this circuit requires two separate power supplies or one that is center-tapped.

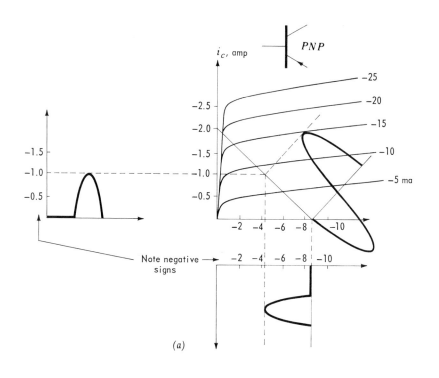

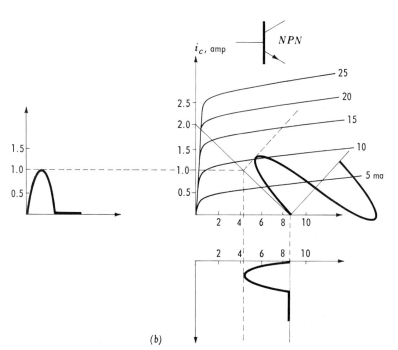

FIGURE 18-15 *Four-quadrant graph for the (a) PNP transistor and (b) the NPN transistor of Fig. 18-14.*

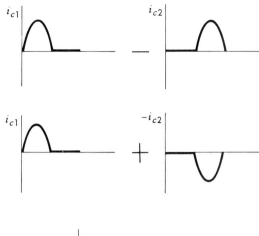

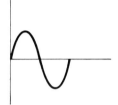

FIGURE 18-16 *Development of the output signal for the complementary transistor push-pull amplifier of Fig. 18-14.*

PUSH-PULL IN CLASS A

There are times when a push-pull amplifier is designed for class A operation. You may ask: Why bother with a push-pull arrangement for class A operation? First of all, since the two dc levels cancel out in the output section, a smaller transformer can be used than with single-ended operation (single-ended means standard operation with one active device). Second, there are times when the designer wants to take advantage of the reduced distortion inherent in push-pull operation. Another very important advantage is that ac hum picked up from the power line or the power supply by the push-pull stage cancels out.

THE SPLIT-LOAD PHASE INVERTER

Complementary symmetry allows us to eliminate the input and output transformers in the push-pull transistor amplifier. However, complementary symmetry does not exist in the domain of vacuum tubes.

Though we must tolerate the output transformer when dealing

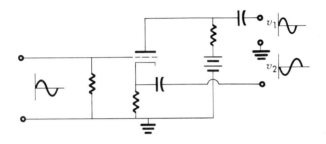

FIGURE 18-17 *The split-load phase inverter.*

with vacuum-tube push-pull amplifiers, it is possible to eliminate the input transformer. This can be done only if we are prepared to tolerate an additional stage of amplification preceding the push-pull circuit. The alternative to the input transformer, shown in Fig. 18-17, is called a *split-load phase inverter*.

The split-load phase inverter is a class A amplifier that provides two outputs each 180° out of phase with the other. This eliminates the need for an input transformer.

PROBLEMS

18-1 Why is it desirable to operate amplifiers in class B?

18-2 What is the chief advantage of operating a single-ended amplifier in class B?

18-3 Why don't we obtain identical outputs from both active devices of a push-pull amplifier?

18-4 A pair of *NPN* transistors is being operated push-pull class B. Each transistor is feeding the output transformer a 500-ma peak current signal and receives a 5-ma peak-to-peak base current sine-wave signal. Construct the following graphs:

(*a*) Input base current to each transistor

(*b*) Collector current from each transistor

(*c*) Final load output current assuming a 2:1 output transformer turns ratio

18-5 What is meant by the term "matched pair"?

18-6 The output transformer of a particular push-pull circuit is a 4:1 center-tapped unit. What resistive load does *each* of the two active devices see if the external load is 10 ohms?

18-7 A pair of 40318 *NPN* transistors is to be operated in class B push-pull. It is desired that each transistor see a dynamic load of 500 ohms. The final load is an 8-ohm speaker, and a power supply is available that supplies 100 volts dc. Each transistor is to be driven by a 2-ma peak-to-peak base current.

(*a*) Draw a schematic diagram of the circuit.

(*b*) Determine the necessary turns ratio of the output transformer.

(*c*) Construct a four-quadrant graph for the operation described above.

(*d*) Determine the total power delivered by the dc supply to the amplifier.

(*e*) Calculate the total signal power delivered to the speaker.

(*f*) What is the collector circuit efficiency of this amplifier?

18-8 A pair of 2N3055 *NPN* transistors operated in class B push-pull is being used to feed an external load whose resistance is 54 ohms. This external load is coupled to the amplifier by a transformer whose turns ratio is 2:3, the 2 side being center-tapped. The amplifier is to make use of a 30-volt dc supply. Each transistor is to be fed a signal of 100 ma peak base current.

(*a*) Draw a schematic diagram of the amplifier.

(*b*) Determine the dynamic load resistance seen by each transistor.

(*c*) Construct a four-quadrant graph that describes the operation of this amplifier.

(*d*) Construct a maximum-power-dissipation curve of 100 watts per transistor. Is this amplifier operating in a safe region? Why?

(*e*) Calculate the amount of power that the dc supply is being called upon to deliver.

(*f*) How much signal power is being delivered to the load?

(*g*) What is the collector circuit efficiency for this operation?

(*h*) From a study of the input curves of the transistor, determine the necessary voltage that must be supplied to each transistor in order to obtain the necessary base current.

18-9 What is crossover distortion? What causes it? How can it be prevented?

18-10 In designing a push-pull transistor amplifier, how can the input and the output transformers be eliminated?

18-11 The collector curves and load lines in Fig. 18-18 describe the operation of a push-pull amplifier.

(*a*) What class of operation is this?

(*b*) Draw a schematic diagram of the push-pull circuit this is describing.

(*c*) What is the maximum peak-to-peak undistorted collector current available from this amplifier?

(*d*) The external load being fed is a 100-ohm resistive device. Calculate the turns ratio of the output transformer.

(*e*) Determine the collector circuit efficiency of the amplifier.

18-12 The RCA transistor number 40396 is used to specify two different transistors. One is an *NPN*, and the other is a *PNP*, and they come packaged in separate cans. The reason they both have the same number is that they are designed to be used in complementary-symmetry push-pull amplifiers. A push-pull amplifier operating class B is to be designed using 40396 transistors and two dc supplies

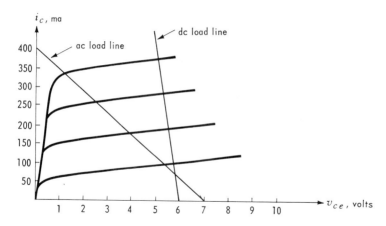

FIGURE 18-18 *Diagram
for Prob. 18-11.*

of 3 volts each.   The amplifier is to feed an 8-ohm speaker that is
directly coupled.

(*a*)   Draw a schematic diagram of the circuit described above.

(*b*)   Construct the load lines on both sets of characteristics, the
NPN and the PNP, and then complete both four-quadrant
graphs for the maximum undistorted output that can be obtained from this amplifier.

(*c*)   Using the waveshapes from part (*b*), construct the waveshape
of the current that is flowing in the 8-ohm load.

(*d*)   Calculate the collector circuit efficiency of the amplifier.

19

DISTORTION

Up to now we have been using the term distortion rather freely. This is not really proper since the term has a special technical meaning. Recall that we defined an amplifier as a device that provides power gain. In addition, we found that an amplifier will usually provide voltage and current gain simultaneously. We also tried to avoid operating an amplifier in a manner which would cause any waveshape difference between input and output other than amplitude.

DEFINITION

Distortion is defined as any difference in waveshape other than amplitude that exists between the input and output waveshapes. Every amplifier introduces some distortion. The better amplifiers introduce less than others.

THE FOUR-QUADRANT GRAPH

Let us begin our study of distortion by considering the four-quadrant graph of Fig. 19-1, which depicts the operation of an amplifier in a manner that causes drastic distortion to the waveshape. This provides us with distorted current and voltage waveforms.

In Fig. 19-2 we have set up a comparison between the waveshape we would have received from an amplifier had no distortion

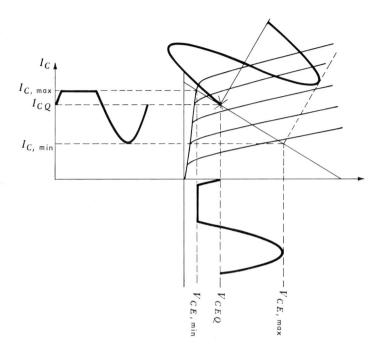

FIGURE 19-1 *Four-quadrant graph for an amplifier producing excessive distortion.*

FIGURE 19-2 *Comparison between (a) undistorted and (b) distorted waveshape.*

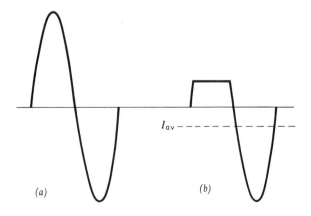

(a)

(b)

been introduced and the actual current waveshape that is being produced by the amplifier of Fig. 19-1.

FOURIER THEOREM

The first difference we observe between the two waveshapes of Fig. 19-2 is that the average value of the undistorted sine wave is the quiescent collector current I_{CQ} while the average collector current of the actual distorted waveshape is some other value. We can conclude that an additional dc level has been introduced.

Obviously, merely adding a dc level to the waveshape of Fig. 19-2a will not give us the waveshape shown as Fig. 19-2b. Some other differences also exist. At this point it will be wise to call on a theorem known as the Fourier theorem, which states:

Any repeating complex waveshape may be considered to be made up of a dc level and a sum of sine waves. The first of the sine waves has a frequency that is the same as the complex waveshape, and all others have a frequency some whole-number multiple of the frequency of the complex wave.

These sine waves, each of which has a frequency that is some whole-number multiple of the frequency of the complex wave, are known as *harmonics*. The sine wave whose frequency is equal to the frequency of the complex wave is called the *first harmonic* or *fundamental*, the one whose frequency is twice that of the complex wave is known as the *second harmonic*, and the one whose frequency is three times the frequency of the complex wave is called the *third harmonic*.

SYNTHESIS OF THE DISTORTED WAVESHAPE

Using the Fourier theorem, let us attempt to construct the waveshape of Fig. 19-2b by adding a dc level to the fundamental (first harmonic) and then adding a second harmonic to this composite. Should we expect an exact duplicate of the shape of Fig. 19-2b from this construction? No, of course not, because we are adding only the first two sine waves called for by the Fourier theorem. In actual practice, many harmonics must be taken together to come up with the total composite desired.

Figure 19-3 shows the waveshapes we are going to add to see if there is a *trend* toward producing the waveshape of Fig. 19-2b. In Fig. 19-4, the actual construction is shown.

As we anticipated, we have not really produced the waveshape

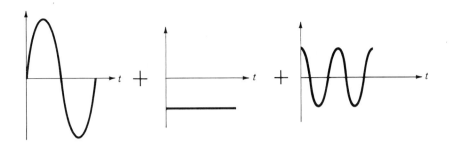

FIGURE 19-3 *Fourier waveshapes which go to make up the complex wave of Fig. 19-4.*

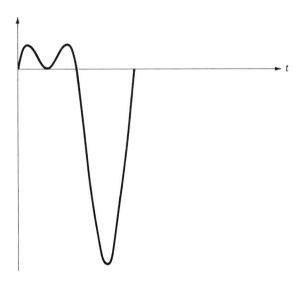

FIGURE 19-4 *Complex wave generated by the addition of a fundamental, a dc level, and a second harmonic such as those of Fig. 19-3.*

of Fig. 19-2*b*, but we can begin to see a trend. The top of the composite wave in Fig. 19-4 has begun to flatten, and the average value has been taken into account.

AMPLITUDE DISTORTION
One last word before turning to a quantitative study. There are other kinds of distortion that we will deal with later in this chapter.

For the present, we will limit our discussion to the kind of distortion referred to as *amplitude distortion*. Amplitude distortion is caused by driving an active device into its nonlinear region. This is the type of distortion that we have been discussing so far in this chapter.

We have seen that this type of operation produces sine waves having new frequencies. These new frequencies were given the name harmonics. Because of this, amplitude distortion is also called *harmonic distortion*.

QUANTITATIVE STUDIES

As in all our studies in this book, it is very important that we refer to actual values in our discussion. Let us now begin a quantitative analysis of distortion.

How can we describe different degrees of distortion to enable us to compare different amplifiers? One way is to start off with a pure sine-wave input to an amplifier and then compare the peak value of harmonics that are introduced. To do this, represent the peak value of the fundamental component of the output waveshape as A_1, the peak value of the second harmonic as A_2, etc. A_0 will represent the dc level that is introduced due to distortion.

If we are prepared to tackle the mathematics involved, it can be shown that

$$A_0 = A_2 \approx \frac{(I_{max} - I_{min}) - 2I_Q}{4}$$

$$A_0 = A_2 \approx \frac{(V_{max} - V_{min}) - 2V_Q}{4}$$

$$A_1 \approx \frac{1}{2}(I_{max} - I_{min})$$

$$A_1 \approx \frac{1}{2}(V_{max} - V_{min})$$

where I_{max} and V_{max} are the maximum values of the distorted waveshape and I_Q and V_Q are the quiescent values of current and voltage available from the amplifier when no signal is present (see Fig. 19-1).

Since, in many cases, the major contributor to distortion is the second harmonic, merely comparing the amount of second-harmonic distortion introduced by different amplifiers provides us with a fairly good idea of their quality as far as harmonic distortion is concerned.

Harmonic distortion is frequently represented as a percentage:

$$D_2 = \text{percent second-harmonic distortion} = \frac{A_2}{A_1} \times 100$$

If no distortion existed, A_2 would be zero and A_1 would be equal to the peak value of the waveshape in question. The percent second-harmonic distortion described by this equation would then be zero, as expected.

Illustrative Problem 19-1

For the waveshape shown in Fig. Prob. 19-1, determine:

(a) The peak value of the fundamental sine wave in its content
(b) The peak value of its second harmonic
(c) The dc level of its content
(d) The percent second-harmonic distortion, assuming that the waveshape was originally a sine wave

SOLUTION

Given: Waveshape shown in Fig. Prob. 19-1.

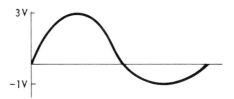

FIGURE PROB. 19-1

Find:

(a) A_1
(b) A_2
(c) A_0
(d) D_2

(a) $A_1 \approx \frac{1}{2}(V_{max} - V_{min})$
$\approx \frac{1}{2}[3 - (-1)]$

$$\boxed{A_1 \approx 2 \text{ volts}}$$

(b) $A_2 \approx \dfrac{(V_{max} - V_{min}) - 2V_Q}{4}$

$\approx \dfrac{[3 - (-1)] - 2(0)}{4} = \dfrac{4}{4}$

$$\boxed{A_2 \approx 1 \text{ volt}}$$

(c) $A_0 = A_2 \approx 1$ volt

(d) $D_2 = \dfrac{A_2}{A_1} \times 100$

$$\boxed{D_2 \approx 50\%}$$

ADDITIONAL HARMONICS

There are cases where the major contributor to distortion is not the second harmonic, one such case being where amplifiers are operated in push-pull. In push-pull amplifiers when the two active devices being used are identically matched, all *even-harmonic distortion* contributed by the two devices cancels out in the output section of the amplifier. Obviously, then, the contribution due to second-harmonic distortion will not provide us with a description of the amplifier's actual distortion. In such a case, we must go to higher harmonics, such as the third

$$A_3 \approx \frac{(I_{max} - I_{min}) - 2(I_1 - I_2)}{6}$$

or

$$A_3 \approx \frac{(V_{max} - V_{min}) - 2(V_1 - V_2)}{6}$$

I_1 and V_1 are the instantaneous values of the distorted wave at 45°, and I_2 and V_2 are the instantaneous values of the distorted wave at 135°.

We consider the third harmonic not only when dealing with push-pull circuits but also in cases in which the distortion introduced is quite large. When the contributions of the second- and third-harmonic distortion are of equal orders of magnitude, we must speak of the total distortion, and the following formulas are of significance:

$$A_T = \text{total harmonic distortion} = \sqrt{A_2{}^2 + A_3{}^2}$$
$$D_T = \text{percent total harmonic distortion} = \frac{A_T}{A_1} \times 100$$

Illustrative Problem 19-2

Determine the amplitude of the first, second, and third harmonics in the makeup of the waveshape shown in Fig. Prob. 19-2. Calculate the total harmonic distortion ànd the percent harmonic distortion due to the second and third harmonics.

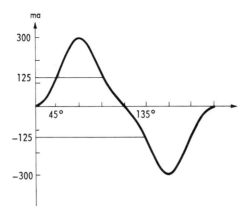

FIGURE PROB. 19-2

SOLUTION
Given: Waveshape as shown in Fig. Prob. 19-2.
Find:
(a) A_1
(b) A_2
(c) A_3
(d) A_T
(e) D_T

(a) $A_1 \approx \frac{1}{2}(I_{max} - I_{min})$
$\approx \frac{1}{2}[300 - (-300)]$

$$\boxed{A_1 \approx 300 \text{ ma}}$$

(b) $A_2 \approx \dfrac{(I_{max} - I_{min}) - 2I_Q}{4}$

$\approx \dfrac{[300 - (-300)] - 2(0)}{4} = \dfrac{600}{4}$

$$\boxed{A_2 \approx 150 \text{ ma}}$$

(c) $A_3 \approx \dfrac{(I_{max} - I_{min}) - 2(I_1 - I_2)}{6}$

$\approx \dfrac{[300 - (-300)] - 2[125 - (-125)]}{6}$

$\approx \dfrac{600 - 500}{6}$

$$\boxed{A_3 \approx 16.7 \text{ ma}}$$

(d) $A_T = \sqrt{A_2{}^2 + A_3{}^2}$
$$= \sqrt{150^2 + 16.7^2}$$
$$= \sqrt{22{,}500 + 279} = \sqrt{22{,}779}$$

$$\boxed{A_T = 151 \text{ ma}}$$

(e) $D_T = \dfrac{A_T}{A_1} \times 100 = \dfrac{151}{300} \times 100$

$$\boxed{D_T = 50.4\%}$$

OTHER TYPES OF DISTORTION

There are two other main types of distortion besides amplitude distortion, frequency distortion and phase-shift distortion.

Frequency distortion is the result of a complex wave changing shape as it passes through a circuit because the various harmonics that go to make it up are amplified by different amounts. Recall the frequency-response curves of earlier chapters of this unit.

The major difference between frequency distortion and amplitude distortion is that no new frequencies are introduced in the makeup of the wave when frequency distortion is encountered, while with amplitude distortion new frequencies *are* introduced. Frequency distortion becomes a consideration when dealing with a waveshape that is not a perfect sine wave before it enters the amplifier. If some harmonics in its makeup are outside the mid-frequency band, they will be amplified by different amounts. At the output the waveshape encountered will be composed of sinusoids whose proportional values are quite different from those which went to make up the original waveshape. Thus a different waveform is encountered at the output than that which we introduced at the input.

Phase-shift distortion results from the phase shifting of the sine waves of the Fourier series components by different amounts. This type of distortion is associated rather closely with frequency distortion and is caused by the same circuit components. Phase-shift distortion is also known as *delay distortion*. In general, phase-shift distortion does not create a problem when dealing with sound systems or AM radio work, but it creates a major problem with television and other systems requiring exact timing between various parts of the signal.

PROBLEMS

19-1 What is meant by the term "distortion"?

19-2 Referring to the Fourier theorem, describe the waveshapes that can be used as building blocks to compose a complex wave.

19-3 Why isn't an exact duplicate of the distorted wave obtained when all the waveshapes of Fig. 19-3 are added together?

19-4 What is the cause of amplitude distortion?

19-5 What is another name for amplitude distortion? Why is it used?

19-6 For each of the waveshapes shown in Fig. 19-5, determine:

(a) Its frequency

(b) The frequency of its first three harmonics

(c) The amplitude of the fundamental in its Fourier makeup

(d) The amplitude of the second harmonic in its Fourier makeup

(e) The dc level in its makeup

(f) Calculate the percent second-harmonic distortion introduced by a system that when fed a pure sine wave at its input produces this wave at its output

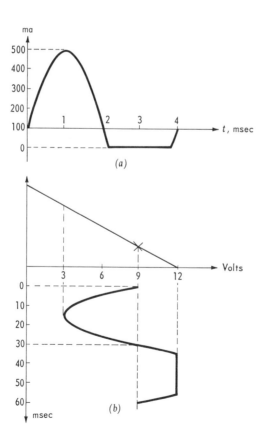

FIGURE 19-5 *Diagram for Prob. 19-6.*

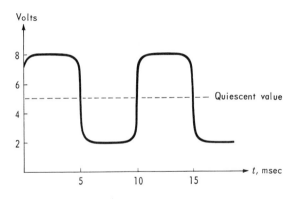

FIGURE 19-6 *Diagram for Prob. 19-8.*

19-7 Why isn't a comparison of second-harmonic distortion satisfactory when comparing push-pull amplifiers?

19-8 The waveshape shown in Fig. 19-6 resulted from overdriving an amplifier.

(a) What is the frequency of the waveshape?

(b) List the frequency of five sine waves that could be combined to approximate this wave.

(c) Calculate the amplitude of the fundamental component of the waveshape.

(d) Determine the amplitude of the second harmonic in the wave.

(e) Find the amplitude of the third-harmonic content of this wave.

(f) What is the total-harmonic-distortion content of this wave due to the second and third harmonics?

(g) Calculate the percent distortion due to the second and third harmonics.

19-9 Construct the waveshape that has the following harmonic components. Assume that all the different waveshapes start out in phase. $A_0 = A_2 = 4$ volts, $A_1 = 7$ volts, $A_3 = 1.5$ volts.

19-10 What is meant by the term "frequency distortion"? How can it be minimized?

20

THE EMITTER-FOLLOWER AND CATHODE-FOLLOWER CIRCUITS

THE POWER TRANSISTORS

Browsing through the literature that manufacturers publish to describe their transistors, we find that some transistors are classified as power transistors. Let us examine some of this literature and see some of the ways in which power transistors differ from those that are not classified as such.*

* An excellent reference is the "RCA Transistor Manual."

Consider the 40319 power transistor. The collector curves and the input curve for this transistor are shown in Fig. 20-1. The first very obvious and expected observation is that all currents—collector, base, and emitter—are an order of magnitude higher than for other transistors. This seems reasonable when we consider that the primary function of a power transistor is to deliver power to the final load.

Let us investigate the h_{ie} of the power transistor of Fig. 20-1, since this is the input resistance of the transistor when designed into a common-emitter transistor amplifier. Recalling the technique from previous chapters,

$$h_{ie} = \frac{\Delta v_{be}}{\Delta i_b}$$
$$= \frac{1.1 - 1.0}{(10 - 6) \times 10^{-3}}$$

$$\boxed{h_{ie} = 25 \text{ ohms}}$$

280

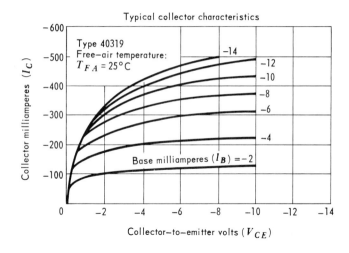

Typical collector characteristics

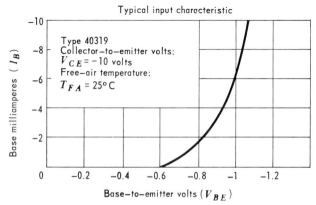

Typical input characteristic

FIGURE 20-1 *Collector and input characteristic curves of a typical power transistor.*

This is a very low value for h_{ie}. Yet, it is typical for power transistors. For other than power transistors, we expect h_{ie}'s on the order of 1000 ohms. The unusually low value of h_{ie} for power transistors raises havoc with the preceding amplifier stage that drives it. It presents to this previous stage a load resistance that looks almost like a short circuit compared to the relatively high output resistance of the previous stage, which is on the order of tens of kilohms. A power stage in the common-emitter configuration appears almost to be a short circuit on its previous stage. Recalling the voltage-gain formula, and realizing that the voltage gain of the previous stage is dependent upon the input resistance of its following stage, we see that this is a situation that cannot be tolerated, because the major function of this previous stage is to produce a voltage gain.

A NEW CIRCUIT CONFIGURATION

Next, we must seek an amplifier configuration with input resistance that is not limited to h_{ie}. Power transistors must be used in order to be able to pass the required collector current and develop the quantity of power necessary to drive loudspeakers and similar devices.

One way of providing a higher input resistance is to provide for the output circuit load to be a part of the input circuit as well. This can be done by putting the load in the emitter leg, as shown in Fig. 20-2a. This circuit is called an *emitter-follower* amplifier. It is also known as a *common-collector* amplifier.

INPUT RESISTANCE OF THE EMITTER FOLLOWER

Since this circuit was developed to provide a reasonably large input resistance, we will investigate its input resistance now.

Figure 20-2b is an equivalent circuit that can be used to determine the input resistance of the amplifier. Note that the internal resistance of the transistor from the base to the emitter is equal to approximately h_{ie}. However, h_{ie} is only part of the *entire* input resistance of the amplifier stage. Between the input terminals of

FIGURE 20-2 *The emitter-follower amplifier. (a) schematic; (b) equivalent circuit.*

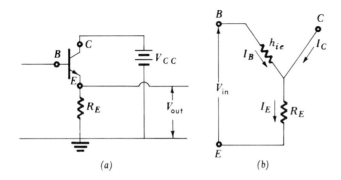

(a)   (b)

the amplifier, we also have the load resistance R_E. The input resistance cannot be determined simply by adding the two resistances h_{ie} and R_E because the two resistances have different currents flowing through them. The two resistances are *not* in series because they are not carrying identical currents. R_E has I_B and I_C flowing through it, while h_{ie} has only I_B flowing through it. The following is a rather simple mathematical exercise in which the input resistance of the emitter-follower amplifier is determined (see Fig. 20-2b).

$$V_{in} = h_{ie}I_B + R_E I_E$$

(The I's represent signal currents.)

$$I_E = I_C + I_B$$
$$V_{in} = h_{ie}I_B + R_E(I_C + I_B)$$
$$\frac{I_C}{I_B} = h_{fe}$$
$$I_C = h_{fe}I_B$$
$$V_{in} = h_{ie}I_B + R_E(h_{fe}I_B + I_B)$$
$$\phantom{V_{in}} = h_{ie}I_B + R_E(h_{fe} + 1)I_B$$
$$R_{in} = \frac{V_{in}}{I_B} = h_{ie} + R_E(h_{fe} + 1)$$

$$\boxed{R_{in} = h_{ie} + R_E(h_{fe} + 1)}$$

Note that in determining the input resistance, the resistance that appears in the emitter leg of the circuit is multiplied by $h_{fe} + 1$. In Fig. 20-2, it can be seen that this is because the current that flows through the emitter resistor I_E is $h_{fe} + 1$ times that which is flowing in the base leg of the transistor I_B.

We have attained an amplifier stage in which the input resistance of the transistor is not limited to h_{ie}. In this, the emitter-follower amplifier, the input resistance is h_{ie} plus $R_E(h_{fe} + 1)$. Since h_{fe} is of the order of 25 to 200 for a power transistor, a great increase in input resistance is obtained. This can solve our problem of finding a power stage that does not act almost as a short on the previous stage.

Illustrative Problem 20-1
Determine the input resistance of an emitter-follower amplifier whose load R_E is an 8-ohm resistance and whose transistor has an h_{ie} of 25 ohms and an h_{fe} of 100.

SOLUTION
Given: Emitter-follower circuit; $R_E = 8$ ohms; $h_{ie} = 25$ ohms; $h_{fe} = 100$

Find: R_{in}

$$R_{in} = h_{ie} + (h_{fe} + 1)R_E = 25 + 101 \times 8$$

$$\boxed{R_{in} = 833 \text{ ohms}}$$

GAIN

Now that a new amplifier configuration has been developed, let us determine equations for the various gains of the circuit. First, we shall develop the voltage-gain equation.

$$I_B = \frac{V_{in}}{R_{in}}$$
$$I_E = I_C + I_B$$
$$h_{fe}I_B = I_C$$
$$I_E = h_{fe}I_B + I_B = (h_{fe} + 1)I_B$$
$$V_{out} = I_E R_E = (h_{fe} + 1)I_B R_E$$
$$= (h_{fe} + 1)\frac{V_{in}}{R_{in}}R_E$$
$$\frac{V_{out}}{V_{in}} = (h_{fe} + 1)\frac{R_E}{R_{in}}$$
$$R_{in} = R_E(h_{fe} + 1) + h_{ie}$$

$$\boxed{A_v = \frac{V_{out}}{V_{in}} = \frac{(h_{fe} + 1)R_E}{(h_{fe} + 1)R_E + h_{ie}}}$$

When studying this formula for the voltage gain of the emitter-follower circuit, we find that the voltage gain it predicts is less than 1. This is certainly an interesting result. Why, if the voltage gain of the amplifier is to be less than 1, should the circuit be considered at all? The answer is obvious if we recall the original definition of an amplifier. An amplifier is a device that provides a *power gain*. As long as the circuit provides power gain, it will serve as an amplifier.

In investigating the current gain we find

$$I_E = I_C + I_B$$
$$h_{fe}I_B = I_C$$
$$I_E = h_{fe}I_B + I_B$$
$$= I_B(h_{fe} + 1)$$
$$A_i = \frac{I_E}{I_B}$$

$$\boxed{A_i = h_{fe} + 1}$$

The power gain of the amplifier, then, is

$$A_p = A_v A_i$$

$$A_p = \frac{(h_{fe} + 1)^2 R_E}{(h_{fe} + 1)R_E + h_{ie}}$$

The power gain will be a significantly large number when typical values are considered.

Let us assume that we are dealing with a power transistor that has the following parameters:

$$h_{fe} = 75 \qquad h_{ie} = 20 \text{ ohms}$$

Assume a load of 100 ohms resistance.

$$A_v = \frac{(h_{fe} + 1)R_E}{(h_{fe} + 1)R_E + h_{ie}}$$
$$= \frac{76 \times 100}{76 \times 100 + 20} = \frac{7600}{7620}$$
$$= 0.995$$
$$A_i = h_{fe} + 1 = 76$$
$$A_p = A_v A_i$$
$$= 0.995 \times 76 = 75.6$$

Since we are already considering some typical parameters, let us determine the input resistance for the circuit.

$$R_{in} = h_{ie} + (h_{fe} + 1)R_E$$
$$= 30 + 76 \times 100 = 7620 \text{ ohms}$$

The emitter-follower circuit provides for a significant current gain and a significant power gain while the voltage gain is less than 1. The input impedance of this circuit is much greater than that which would have been provided by the common-emitter circuit (7620 ohms vs. 20 ohms).

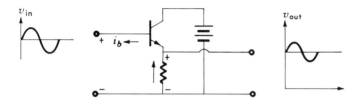

FIGURE 20-3 *The emitter-follower configuration.*

The second very interesting point to be observed is that the voltage-gain formula for the emitter-follower circuit does not predict a 180° phase shift (minus sign). Recall that the voltage-gain equation for the common-emitter amplifier did. Note in Fig. 20-3 that an instantaneous increase in the input voltage causes an increase in the instantaneous base current in the direction shown. This then causes an increase in the instantaneous emitter current in the direction shown, which creates an increase in the output voltage.

Figure 20-4 depicts the common-emitter circuit discussed in previous chapters. It is seen by way of comparison that the output signal voltage is 180° out of phase with the input signal. Let us examine why. An increase in the instantaneous value of the input voltage causes an instantaneous increase in the value of the base current, which in turn causes an instantaneous increase in the collector current. Observe, however, that the direction in which the collector current is flowing is such that an instantaneous increase in the collector current causes an instantaneous decrease in output voltage.

THE EFFECT OF BIAS RESISTORS ON THE OVERALL INPUT RESISTANCE OF AN AMPLIFIER

Bias resistors have been conspicuously missing from all amplifier diagrams in this chapter. This was done deliberately to simplify

FIGURE 20-4 *The common-emitter configuration.*

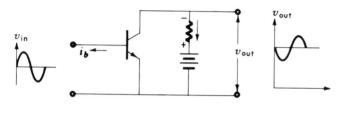

the situation. In practice, bias arrangements are provided for, as discussed in previous chapters. A very obvious question arises at this point: What effect do the bias resistors have on the total input resistance of the amplifier? The total input resistance, when taking bias resistors into account, is that of the bias resistors hanging on in parallel across the input resistance already calculated in this chapter.

In order to distinguish between the two, we shall refer to the input resistance of the transistor, which is $h_{ie} + R_E(h_{fe} + 1)$, and the total input resistance of the amplifier, which also takes into account the effect of the bias resistors.

THE EQUIVALENT CIRCUIT OF THE EMITTER-FOLLOWER AMPLIFIER CIRCUIT

According to Thévenin's theorem, any two-terminal network can be represented by a voltage source in series with an impedance. We have used this theorem before. Let us now attempt to develop a complete equivalent circuit for the emitter-follower circuit.

The following discussion refers to Fig. 20-5a to c. Two as-

FIGURE 20-5 *Development of the equivalent circuit of an emitter-follower amplifier.*

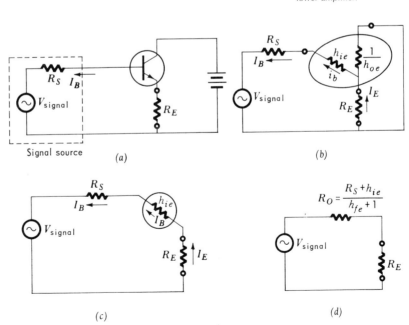

sumptions are made in this development. First, we will assume that any bias resistors used have a large enough resistance compared to the signal source resistance R_S to be ignored. Second, we shall assume that $1/h_{oe}$ of Fig. 20-5b is quite large compared to what R_S and h_{ie} appear to be as seen looking back through the transistor. With this in mind, proceeding from Fig. 20-5a to b to c should be self-explanatory.

It is very tempting in working with Fig. 20-5c just to add h_{ie} and R_S and put them in series with R_E. This cannot be done because different currents are flowing in R_E and in $h_{ie} + R_S$. Let us plod through a little algebra and see what develops.

$$I_E = I_C + I_B$$
$$h_{fe}I_B = I_C$$
$$I_E = h_{fe}I_B + I_B$$
$$\quad = (h_{fe} + 1)I_B$$
$$I_B = \frac{I_E}{h_{fe} + 1}$$

From Kirchhoff's voltage law

$$V_{sig} = I_E(R_S + h_{ie}) + I_E R_E$$
$$\quad = \frac{I_E}{h_{fe} + 1}(R_S + h_{ie}) + I_E R_E$$

$$\boxed{V_{sig} = I_E \left(\frac{R_S + h_{ie}}{h_{fe} + 1} + R_E \right)}$$

Using this equation, we can sketch Fig. 20-5d, which is the Thévenin equivalent circuit that can be used to represent the output section of the emitter-follower amplifier, since the Kirchhoff equation for this circuit is the same as that just developed above.

Note that the output resistance of the amplifier is dependent on h_{fe}, the signal source resistance R_S, and h_{ie}.

Further study of this equation will show that it predicts an output resistance that is considerably lower than $1/h_{oe}$, the output resistance of the common-emitter amplifier.

If, in a particular case, $1/h_{oe}$ is not large enough to be neglected, the output resistance becomes that which we just found, in parallel with $1/h_{oe}$

Illustrative Problem 20-2
Determine the input resistance, the output resistance, and the voltage gain of the circuit shown in Fig. Prob. 20-2. Consider that the bias resistor R_B is large enough to be neglected.

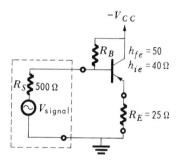

$-V_{CC}$

R_B $h_{fe} = 50$
  $h_{ie} = 40\,\Omega$

R_S $500\,\Omega$

V_{signal}

$R_E = 25\,\Omega$

FIGURE PROB. 20-2

SOLUTION

Given: $R_S = 500$ ohms; $R_E = 25$ ohms; $h_{fe} = 50$; $h_{ie} = 40$ ohms
Find: R_{in}; R_{out}; A_V

$$R_{in} = h_{ie} + R_E(h_{fe} + 1)$$
$$= 40 + 25(50 + 1)$$

$$\boxed{R_{in} = 1310 \text{ ohms}}$$

$$R_{out} = \frac{R_S + h_{ie}}{h_{fe} + 1} = \frac{500 + 40}{50 + 1}$$

$$\boxed{R_{out} = 10.6 \text{ ohms}}$$

$$A_V = \frac{(h_{fe} + 1)R_E}{(h_{fe} + 1)R_E + h_{ie}}$$
$$= \frac{51 \times 25}{51 \times 25 + 40} = \frac{1270}{1270 + 40}$$

$$\boxed{A_V = 0.97}$$

BIAS RESISTORS

Again, we have omitted bias resistors. What effect will bias resistors have on the output resistance of an amplifier?

Bias resistors can be taken into account by replacing R_S, the signal source resistance, with R_{SB}, the parallel combination of R_S and R_B, in the equation for output resistance of the emitter-follower amplifier.

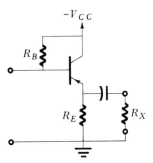

$-V_{CC}$

R_B

R_E

R_X

FIGURE 20-6 *The capacitor-coupled emitter-follower amplifier.*

TERMINOLOGY

It is appropriate at this point to consider the exact definitions of terms when dealing with the output resistance of an amplifier. It is possible for the term output resistance to take on more than one meaning. Consider Fig. 20-6, in which the external load R_X is not directly a part of the amplifier circuit but instead is capacitor-coupled to it. The term output resistance then refers to the resistance as seen by the final load R_X when looking back into the amplifier. In this case, the output resistance is the resistance that we previously called output resistance in parallel with R_E. In order to alleviate any difficulty that may arise due to this double meaning, we shall differentiate between the output resistance of the transistor in emitter-follower configuration and the output resistance of the complete amplifier.

$$R_{\text{out tran}} = \frac{R_S + h_{ie}}{h_{fe} + 1} \qquad R_{\text{out amp}} = R_{\text{out tran}} \| R_E$$

Illustrative Problem 20-3

The emitter-follower amplifier shown in Fig. Prob. 20-3 uses a transistor whose h_{fe} is 50 and whose h_{ie} is 20 ohms.

(a) Calculate the input resistance of the transistor.
(b) Determine the input resistance of the amplifier.
(c) What is the output resistance of the transistor?
(d) Calculate the output resistance of the amplifier.

SOLUTION
Given: $h_{fe} = 50$; $h_{ie} = 20$
Find:
(a) R_{in}
(b) $R_{\text{in total}}$
(c) $R_{\text{out tran}}$
(d) $R_{\text{out amp}}$

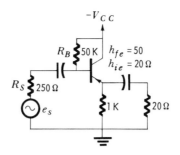

FIGURE PROB. 20-3

(a) $R_{in} = h_{ie} + R_L(h_{fe} + 1)$
   $R_L = R_E \| R_X$
      $= 1000 \| 20 = 19.6$
   $R_{in} = 20 + 19.6(50 + 1)$
      $= 20 + 1000$

   $$\boxed{R_{in} = 1020 \text{ ohms}}$$

(b) $R_{in\ total} = 50 \text{ kilohms} \| 1020 \text{ ohms}$

   $$\boxed{R_{in\ total} = 1000 \text{ ohms}}$$

(c) $R_{out} = \dfrac{h_{ie} + R_{SB}}{h_{fe} + 1}$
   $R_{SB} = R_S \| R_B$
      $= 250 \| 50 \text{ kilohms} \approx 250 \text{ ohms}$
   $R_{out\ tran} = \dfrac{20 + 250}{50 + 1}$

   $$\boxed{R_{out\ tran} = 5.4 \text{ ohms}}$$

(d) $R_{out\ amp} = 5.4 \| 1 \text{ kilohm} \approx 5.4 \text{ ohms}$

   $$\boxed{R_{out\ amp} \approx 5.4 \text{ ohms}}$$

THE VACUUM-TUBE CIRCUIT: THE CATHODE FOLLOWER

It might, at first thought, appear that a vacuum-tube counterpart of the emitter-follower circuit is not needed because the vacuum-tube common-cathode amplifier has a high enough input resistance and the emitter-follower circuit was developed, in this chapter, as a means of providing a high input resistance for transistor amplifiers. This is not quite the case. The vacuum-tube counterpart does

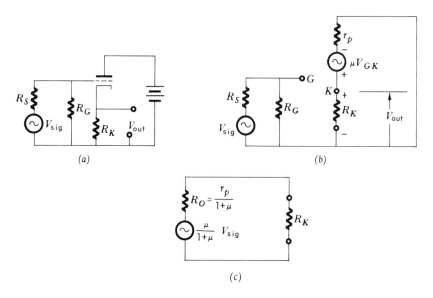

FIGURE 20-7 *The cathode-follower circuit. (a) Schematic diagram; (b) equivalent circuit; (c) simplified equivalent.*

exist and is in frequent use, but not because of the effect on the input resistance. Let us investigate the reasons for developing the cathode-follower circuit (see Fig. 20-7a).

Recall that it was necessary to introduce transformer coupling to attempt an impedance match so that a reasonably large amount of power could be transferred to the load. The transformer is required so that we can couple low resistances, like 4-ohm speakers, to the large output resistance of the vacuum tube. The r_p for most triodes runs about 10 kilohms. If the transformer was eliminated and no other provision made for an impedance match, such a small portion of the power developed would be transferred to the 4-ohm speaker that we could consider that none at all had been transferred.

Let us now recall one of the results of our study of the emitter-follower amplifier. It was found that the output resistance obtained with the emitter-follower was much lower than that which would have been obtained with the common-emitter circuit. Let us set up and analyze the vacuum-tube counterpart of this circuit, as in Fig. 20-7.

Our first approach to this circuit will be to write an equation describing the schematic of the cathode-follower circuit (see Fig. 20-7a). The next step is to replace the vacuum-tube schematic with its Thévenin equivalent (Fig. 20-7b). Next we write an equation, using Kirchhoff's voltage law to describe the circuit of Fig. 20-7b. The equation is then rearranged to describe the load resistance R_K, a single output resistance of the amplifier R_0, and a voltage source V_{thev}.

From Fig. 20-7b

$$\mu V_{GK} = r_p I_P + R_K I_P$$
$$V_{GK} = V_{\text{sig}} - V_{\text{out}}$$
$$\mu(V_{\text{sig}} - V_{\text{out}}) = r_p I_P + R_K I_P$$
$$V_{\text{out}} = R_K I_P$$
$$\mu V_{\text{sig}} = r_p I_P + R_K I_P + \mu R_K I_P$$
$$= r_p I_P + R_K(1 + \mu) I_P$$

$$\boxed{\frac{\mu}{1 + \mu} V_{\text{sig}} = R_K I_P + \frac{r_p}{1 + \mu} I_P}$$

This last equation describes a simple Thévenin equivalent circuit shown in Fig. 20-7c.

Figure 20-7c, then, is an equivalent circuit of the output section of the cathode-follower amplifier. From this, we see that the voltage gain of the circuit is less than 1, just like that for the emitter-follower. The output resistance of the cathode-follower amplifier is $r_p/(1 + \mu)$.

Let us look at our results. The output resistance has been re-

TABLE 20-1

Tube	Description	μ	r_p, ohms	R_{out}, ohms*
6J6A	Medium μ twin triode	38	7,100	181
6C4	Power triode	20	6,250	298
12AT7	High μ twin triode	60	15,000	246
6HG5	Beam power tube	210	52,000	246
6CK5	Power pentode	430	38,000	88.6
6AV6	Twin diode, high μ triode	100	62,500	625

*$R_{\text{out}} = r_p/(1 + \mu)$ in the cathode-follower configuration.

THE EMITTER-FOLLOWER AND CATHODE-FOLLOWER CIRCUITS   293

duced by a factor of $1 + \mu$. A typical value of μ is 50. Thus, by a proper choice of tube, we can have a combination of μ and r_p that will provide us with a wide range of resistance.

Let us look at some typical power tubes and see if possibly we can avoid using a transformer and still obtain a reasonable power match to a low-resistance load (see Table 20-1).

THE MOSFET SOURCE-FOLLOWER CIRCUIT

As you probably suspect, there exists a MOSFET circuit analogous to the emitter-follower circuit and the cathode-follower circuit. Such a circuit is called the *source follower*. The reason for the name is quite obvious, the source terminal of the MOSFET being the terminal which is the analog of the emitter and the cathode. Figure 20-8a is the schematic diagram of such a circuit. By analogy with the vacuum-tube case we can develop the Thévenin equivalents of Fig. 20-8b and c.

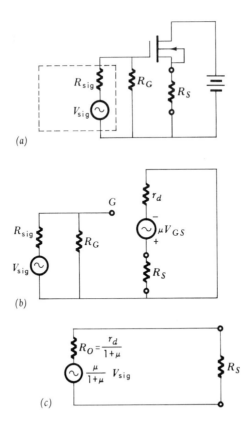

FIGURE 20-8 The source-follower circuit. (a) Schematic; (b) Thévenin equivalent; (c) simplified Thévenin equivalent.

PROBLEMS

20-1 How does the base-to-emitter resistance of a typical power transistor differ from other transistors?

20-2 Draw a schematic diagram of, and determine the input resistance of, an emitter-follower amplifier feeding an 80-ohm load and using a transistor having an h_{ie} of 50 ohms and an h_{fe} of 85. Repeat for the same amplifier in common-emitter configuration.

20-3 Calculate the current gain, voltage gain, and power gain of the two amplifiers described in Prob. 20-2.

20-4 Of what use is an amplifier that provides a voltage gain of less than 1?

20-5 An emitter-follower amplifier is feeding an 8-ohm load. It makes use of a 25-kilohm bias resistor, and the signal source has an output resistance R_S of 150 ohms. $h_{fe} = 50$ and $h_{ie} = 70$.

    (a) Draw a schematic diagram of the amplifier.
    (b) Determine the input resistance of the transistor.
    (c) Find the total input resistance of the amplifier.
    (d) Calculate the output resistance of the amplifier.
    (e) Determine the current gain, voltage gain, and power gain of the amplifier.

20-6 The amplifier shown in Fig. 20-9 makes use of a transistor having an h_{ie} of 40 ohms and an h_{fe} of 60.

    (a) Determine the combined resistance of R_E and R_X.
    (b) Calculate the input resistance of the transistor.
    (c) Find the total input resistance of the amplifier.
    (d) What is the combined parallel resistance of the bias resistors and the signal source resistance?
    (e) Determine the output resistance of the transistor in emitter-follower configuration.
    (f) Calculate the total output resistance of the amplifier.

20-7 What is the major advantage of a cathode-follower over a common-cathode circuit?

20-8 Draw a schematic diagram and determine the voltage gain and output resistance of a cathode-follower circuit that feeds a 50-ohm load and that uses a tube having a μ of 49 and an r_p of 5000 ohms. Repeat

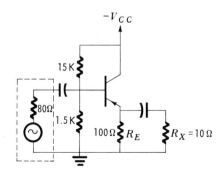

FIGURE 20-9 *Diagram for Prob. 20-6.*

THE EMITTER-FOLLOWER AND CATHODE-FOLLOWER CIRCUITS   **295**

the problem using the same components in common-cathode configuration.

20-9 A source-follower MOSFET amplifier is to feed a 20-ohm load and make use of a MOSFET having a dynamic drain resistance of 6 kilohms and a μ of 40. Draw a schematic diagram of the circuit. Determine the output resistance of the MOSFET as seen by the directly coupled load. If the input is a 4-volt peak-to-peak sine wave, determine the output voltage.

21 FEEDBACK

In Fig. 21-1 a pure sine wave is presented to the input of an amplifier. Passing through this amplifier, the signal becomes badly distorted, as shown. This presents the problem of whether or not we can reduce the amount of distortion the amplifier is introducing.

PREDISTORTING THE INPUT

One possible solution is to cause the input signal to be oppositely distorted before entering the amplifier. The distortion would then effectively be canceled out. Considering that the signal is inverted (undergoes a 180° phase shift) as it passes through a single stage, we can take a portion of the output and add it to the incoming signal, thereby effectively predistorting the incoming signal. This predistortion being opposite to that which will occur in the amplifier, we will effectively reduce the total distortion the signal undergoes.

In Fig. 21-2 a portion of the distorted output is added to the original input. A new input signal is thus obtained. By so doing, we initially distort the input signal opposite to the way in which it will be distorted as it passes through the amplifier. Figure 21-3 is a diagram of what the output signal will look like after passing the predistorted signal through the amplifier. Although it is not completely distortion-free, the percent distortion of the output has been appreciably reduced.

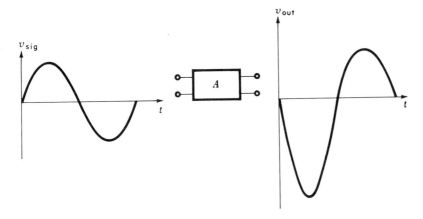

FIGURE 21-1 *Amplifier causing distortion.*

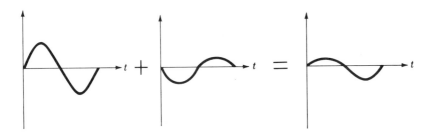

FIGURE 21-2 *Predistorting the input.*

FIGURE 21-3 *Output of the distortion-producing amplifier when the modified input signal of Fig. 21-2 is presented to it.*

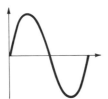

When a technique of returning a signal to an earlier section of the circuit is used, we say that we have introduced *feedback* into the circuit. Obviously we can return as much or as little of the output signal to the input of the amplifier as we wish.

FEEDBACK FRACTION

Can we develop a quantitative description of just how much feedback is being introduced? Yes, and to begin such a description, let us investigate the signal flow diagram of Fig. 21-4. A is the voltage gain of the amplifier *before* introducing feedback. B is called the *feedback fraction* and is the ratio of the signal being fed back and the output signal. By feeding back a portion of the output *in the manner that we have*, we have reduced the total signal being presented to the amplifier A (see Figs. 21-2 and 21-3). It would therefore be reasonable to define a new voltage gain of the overall system taking into account the feedback. We shall refer to this new voltage gain as A'. Referring to Fig. 21-4, $A' = V_{out}/V_{sig}$ and $A = V_{out}/(V_{sig} + BV_{out})$.

It would appear reasonable at this point to seek a relationship between A, B, and A'. Referring again to Fig. 21-4, we find

$$V_{total\ in} = V_{sig} + BV_{out}$$
$$\begin{aligned} V_{out} &= AV_{total\ in} \\ &= A(V_{sig} + BV_{out}) \\ &= AV_{sig} + ABV_{out} \end{aligned}$$
$$V_{out} - ABV_{out} = AV_{sig}$$
$$V_{out}\ (1-AB) = AV_{sig}$$
$$\frac{V_{out}}{V_{sig}} = \frac{A}{1-AB} = A'$$

$$\boxed{A' = \frac{A}{1-AB}}$$

NEGATIVE FEEDBACK

In addition, it can be shown that the percent distortion with feedback is related to the percent distortion without feedback by

$$D' = \frac{D}{1-AB}$$

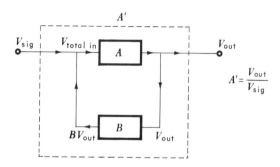

FIGURE 21-4 *Amplifier with feedback.*

$$A' = \frac{V_{out}}{V_{sig}}$$

where D' is the percent distortion with feedback and D is the percent distortion without feedback. Note that for feedback to reduce distortion, the denominator of the above equation must be greater than 1. This occurs only when the product AB is negative. Thus in order for the distortion to be reduced, A and B have to be of opposite sign. Refer back to the voltage-gain formula, $A' = A/(1 - AB)$, and note the effect this has on the overall gain of the system. With either A or B negative, we find that the overall voltage gain is reduced. For this reason, whenever the product of A and B is negative, we say that we have introduced *negative* or *degenerative feedback*.

The product AB is referred to as the *loop gain* or *feedback factor*. When the loop gain AB is negative, the portion of the output being fed back to the input is 180° out of phase with the input signal.

POSITIVE FEEDBACK

Note that the loop gain AB can also be positive. If this is the case, we say that we are dealing with *positive* or *regenerative* feedback. Then, the portion of the output returned to the input is in phase with the input signal.

In Fig. 21-5 are shown the four different possibilities for the signs of A and B. Note the phase relationships of the various waveforms.

Positive feedback creates a situation whereby a greater amount of distortion is encountered than without feedback since the denominator of the distortion equation, $D' = D/(1 - AB)$, becomes less than 1.

Since positive feedback causes an increase in distortion, you may be wondering why we even consider it. In the first place, positive feedback presents itself unintentionally in many cases and thereby forces the issue of whether we will or will not consider it, and second, a very interesting result appears when we examine the denominator of the gain equation, $A' = A/(1 - AB)$. Note what happens when $AB = 1$. The denominator goes to zero, thus predicting an infinite gain

$$A' = \frac{A}{1 - AB} = \frac{A}{0} = \infty$$

Is this ever encountered in practice, or is it a mathematical fiction? Recall the effect of placing the microphone of a public address system too close to the loudspeakers. A self-sustaining acoustical

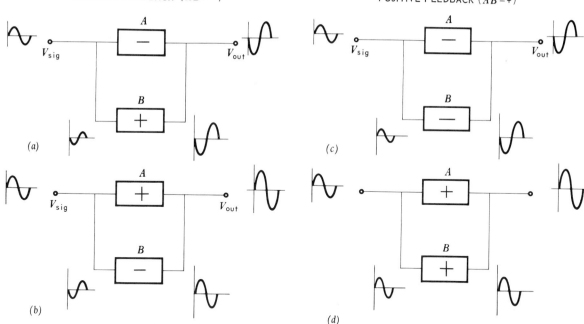

NEGATIVE FEEDBACK ($AB=-$)

POSITIVE FEEDBACK ($AB=+$)

FIGURE 21-5 *The four different possibilities for the signs of A and B.*

howl is generated. Thus the system itself can generate a signal with no apparent input. To start it off, all that is needed is a very minor electric or audible noise which is sent around the feedback loop appearing at the input again to feed into the amplifier even when the original disturbance has passed. This manner of providing a *primary* signal source is not unique to the audio system. It also happens in a completely electric system and is the basis for almost all the primary (original) signal sources, e.g., signal generators.

The requirement that the product AB be equal to 1 is called the *Barkhausen criterion*. In practice when designing oscillators (signal generators) the designer aims theoretically for AB to be greater than 1. With this the case, the signal goes around and around the loop getting bigger with each go-around until the amplifier is driven into its nonlinear region. This causes the voltage gain of the active device to be reduced until the condition of $AB = 1$ is realized. A great deal more will be said about oscillators in a separate chapter devoted to them.

Illustrative Problem 21-1

Before the switch was closed in Fig. Prob. 21-1, the voltage gain was -50 and the distortion was 12 percent. Calculate the loop gain that would result when the switch is closed. Determine the voltage gain and the percent distortion after the switch has been closed.

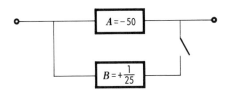

FIGURE PROB. 21-1

Solution
Given: $A = -50$; $D = 12\%$; $B = +1/25$
Find: AB; A'; D'

$$AB = -50 \left(+ \frac{1}{25} \right)$$

$$\boxed{AB = -2}$$

$$A' = \frac{A}{1 - AB} = \frac{-50}{1 - (-2)} = \frac{-50}{3}$$

$$\boxed{A' = -16.7}$$

$$D' = \frac{D}{1 - AB} = \frac{0.12}{1 - (-2)} = \frac{0.12}{3} = 0.04$$

$$\boxed{D' = 4\%}$$

VOLTAGE-CONTROLLED VS. CURRENT-CONTROLLED FEEDBACK

In the technical literature we find the two terms *voltage-controlled feedback* and *current-controlled feedback*. Examples of each are shown in Figs. 21-6 and 21-7.

In a voltage-controlled feedback situation, the signal being fed back is proportional to an output voltage, while in the current-controlled case, the signal being fed back is proportional to an output current. Note in Fig. 21-6a, the voltage-controlled case, that the feedback signal is dependent upon the load current and

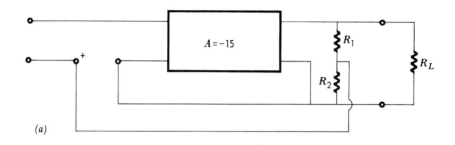

(a)

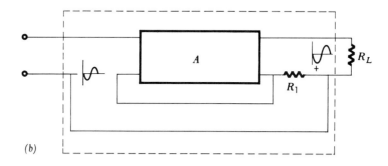

(b)

FIGURE 21-6 (a) Voltage-controlled feedback.

$$B = \frac{R_2}{R_1 + R_2}$$

(b) Current-controlled feedback.

$$B = \frac{R_1}{R_1 + R_L}$$

even if, somehow, a change in output current could be made to occur without an associated change in output voltage, the feedback signal would not change. In like manner, in the case of the current-controlled feedback (Fig. 21-6b) if a change in output voltage were to occur without an associated change in output current, the feedback signal would still remain constant. It should be clear at this point why the names voltage-controlled and current-controlled feedback are appropriate.

Figure 21-7 depicts actual circuits in which voltage-controlled feedback and current-controlled feedback are encountered.

In Fig. 21-7a, the voltage-controlled case, the output voltage V_{CE} is divided across the voltage divider consisting of R_1 and the input resistance of the transistor h_{ie}. Therefore B, the feedback

FEEDBACK 303

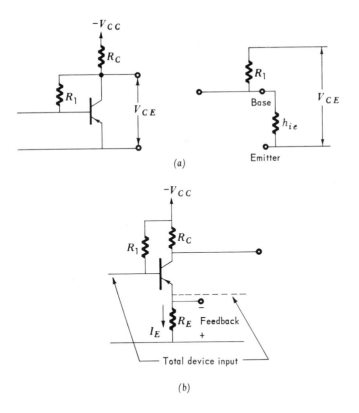

(a)

(b)

FIGURE 21-7 (a) Voltage-controlled feedback.

$$B \approx \frac{h_{ie}}{R_1 + h_{ie}}$$

(b) Current-controlled feedback.

$$B \approx \frac{R_E}{R_E + R_C}$$

fraction for this case, is equal to $h_{ie}/(R_1 + h_{ie})$.

In Fig. 21-7b the feedback voltage appears across R_E. Both R_C and R_E carry approximately the same current, so that the feedback fraction is approximately equal to $R_E/(R_E + R_C)$.

PROBLEMS

21-1 The waveshape shown in Fig. 21-8 is the output signal obtained from an amplifier that is being fed a pure sine wave. Draw the following:

(a) A wave similar to, but one-third the magnitude of, the output wave shown in the diagram.

(b) A pure sine wave with a peak voltage of 10 volts 180° out of phase with the waveshape of part (a).

(c) A point-by-point construction of the waveshape that is the sum of the waveshapes obtained in (a) and (b).

(d) An estimation of what the output from the amplifier would look like if the input to the amplifier looked like the waveshape constructed in (c).

21-2 A feedback loop is added to an amplifier that originally had a voltage gain of −35. What must be the value of the feedback fraction if the amplifier, after the feedback loop is completed, gives an output of 20 volts for an input of 1.5 volts? Draw a block diagram of the amplifier with the feedback loop.

21-3 An amplifier has a distortion of 15 percent and a voltage gain of −20 without feedback. What must the feedback factor be if a feedback loop is added to lower the distortion to 8 percent? Is this positive or negative feedback? Determine the gain of the amplifier after the feedback loop is added.

21-4 A three-stage common-emitter amplifier has a 5 percent negative feedback ($B = 0.05$). The gain of the amplifier with feedback is −10. Determine the gain of the amplifier if the feedback loop is removed.

21-5 A two-stage common-emitter amplifier without feedback has a voltage gain of +70 and a 20 percent distortion. It is desired that the distortion be reduced to 5 percent by the use of a feedback loop.
(a) Determine the required feedback factor.
(b) Calculate the required feedback fraction.
(c) Find the voltage gain that results when this feedback loop is added.

21-6 An amplifier with 1 percent feedback ($B = 0.01$) has a gain of −75. It introduces a total distortion of 6 percent. Determine the feedback factor required to reduce the distortion to 3 percent. What is the new value for the voltage gain when the required amount of feedback is introduced?

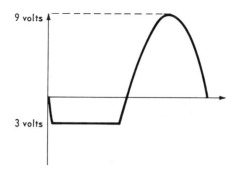

FIGURE 21-8 *Diagram for Prob. 21-1.*

21-7 An amplifier with feedback has a gain of +40 and 8 percent feedback ($B = 0.08$). Determine the gain that would result if the feedback loop were to open.

21-8 An amplifier has a gain with feedback of -30. The gain of the amplifier without feedback is -50. The distortion with feedback is 5%.
(*a*) Calculate the percent feedback.
(*b*) Determine the feedback factor.
(*c*) What would the percent distortion be if there were no feedback loop?

21-9 An amplifier has a gain of -20 without feedback. Determine the loop gain and the feedback fraction required to cause this amplifier to break into oscillation.

21-10 An amplifier has a gain of -80 without feedback. It is desired to convert this amplifier to an oscillator.
(*a*) What must the feedback factor be to perform this conversion?
(*b*) Determine the percent feedback and sign of this feedback in order to provide oscillation.

21-11 Refer to Fig. 21-7*a*, in which a self-biased circuit is depicted. $h_{fe} = 110$, $h_{ie} = 1200$ ohms, $R_1 = 10$ kilohms, and $R_C = 3$ kilohms. Determine the feedback fraction B. Is this positive or is it negative feedback? Why? What would the voltage gain of the amplifier be if no feedback had been introduced? What is the actual voltage gain of this amplifier taking feedback into account?

21-12 Consider the circuit shown in Fig. 21-7*b*. For an R_C of 2500 ohms, an R_E of 500 ohms, and an R_1 of 10 kilohms, determine the feedback fraction and the voltage gain of the amplifier. The transistor has the following values of h parameters: $h_{fe} = 150$, and $h_{ie} = 1$ kilohm.

22

PRIMARY SIGNAL SOURCES

So far we have assumed the availability of variable-magnitude and variable-frequency signal sources. Now we must attempt to provide for this availability. To begin, let us recall the gain formula for an amplifier which has had a feedback loop added to it

$$A' = \frac{A}{1 - AB}$$

BARKHAUSEN CRITERION

In the last chapter, mention was made of the Barkhausen criterion, which calls for $AB = +1$. When this condition prevails, the denominator of the A' formula goes to zero and A' goes to infinity, thus predicting an infinite gain. Infinite gain indicates that a signal is provided at the output terminals even though no external input signal is provided at the input terminals of the amplifier. The amplifier appears to be providing its own input signal. This is possible because a portion of the output is taken and fed back to the input, the amplifier thus providing its own input signal. The amplifier of Fig. 22-1 does not care where the input signal is coming from and takes and amplifies it in the same manner as though it were externally provided. $AB = +1$ merely requires that the fed-back portion of the signal which is appearing as an input to A does not decay with each pass around the feedback loop.

When an amplifier provides its own input and thus becomes a

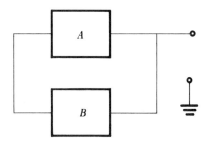

FIGURE 22-1 *Block diagram of an oscillator.*

primary signal source, we say that oscillation is taking place and refer to the system as an *oscillator*.

The Barkhausen criterion $(AB = +1)$ must be carefully considered when designing and constructing both amplifiers and oscillators. In the case of amplifiers, one must be wary lest the Barkhausen criterion be met and the amplifier break into unwanted oscillation. In the case of oscillators, care must be taken to ensure that the Barkhausen criterion is met in order that oscillation does occur.

To ensure oscillation, oscillators are generally designed so that AB is greater than $+1$. This seems to indicate that the voltage returned to the input is greater than the input voltage which initiated this feedback. If this were allowed to occur indefinitely, an infinite voltage would appear. This buildup of voltage reaches a limit, however. The active-device parameters are constant over a limited range of its characteristic curves. As the input voltage gets larger and larger, a limit is reached, since operation spills over into the cutoff and saturation region of the characteristic, thereby limiting the peak-to-peak magnitude of the output signal, as shown in Fig. 22-2. Since the input signal is a constant portion of the output signal BV_{out}, once the peak-to-peak magnitude reaches a limit due to saturation and cutoff, the input voltage also reaches a limit and also does not continue to increase. A stable situation then reigns. This stable situation occurs when $AB = +1$. Figure 22-2 indicates the input and output voltages as they appear on a four-quadrant graph of an active device, with AB limited to $+1$ because saturation and cutoff have taken place.

There is an advantage to designing for AB greater than $+1$ and then allowing saturation and cutoff to limit the value of AB to $+1$. If A, the gain of the amplifier without feedback, were to vary for some reason, the circuit would continue to function properly because A has been made somewhat independent of active-device parameters. A reason for the variation of A is active-device parameter variation due to age or replacement.

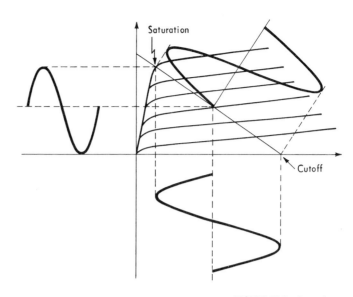

FIGURE 22-2 *Saturation and cutoff, limiting AB to a maximum value of +1.*

A BASIC OSCILLATOR

A circuit whose theory of operation is very easy to understand and which satisfies the Barkhausen criterion is shown in Fig. 22-3. Note that it is merely a two-stage capacitor-coupled amplifier with +100 percent feedback. Since this is a two-stage common-emitter amplifier, A is a positive quantity. Thus, oscillation will occur if A is large enough. This circuit will provide a primary signal, but it will not be a sine wave. Instead of providing a sine wave, this circuit provides the waveshape shown in the diagram. Note that the Barkhausen criterion did not predict the waveshape or frequency that would be produced by making $AB = +1$. In practice, then, if a sine wave is desired, something additional must be provided to ensure the generation of a sine wave at the desired frequency.

To begin, let us first look into the Fourier theorem. The Fourier theorem states that all repetitive complex waveshapes can be made up from, and broken down into, a set of sine waves. If we were then to pass the complex waveshape shown in Fig. 22-3 through some sort of filtering device, could we possibly extract one of these sine waves and eliminate all others? Filtering a particular sine wave from a complex waveshape and attempting to control the frequency at which oscillation occurs should point us in the direction of some combination of capacitor and inductor,

PRIMARY SIGNAL SOURCES   309

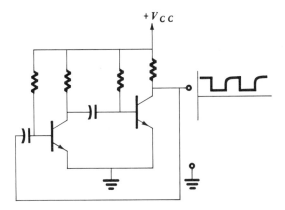

FIGURE 22-3 *The basic oscillator circuit.*

since the impedance of the capacitor and the inductor are frequency-sensitive.

$$Z_C = -X_C = \frac{-1}{2\pi fC}$$
$$Z_L = X_L = 2\pi fL$$

Series and parallel combinations of these components prove to be just what is needed to fulfill our requirements.

THE SERIES *LC* CIRCUIT

Figure 22-4 is a schematic representation of an ideal series *LC* circuit. It is interesting to study the condition which exists when $X_L = X_C$. In the series *LC* circuit (Fig. 22-4) the impedance of the total circuit is $X_L - X_C$. When $X_L = X_C$, the total impedance is zero. The frequency at which X_L is equal to X_C is known as the *resonant frequency* of the circuit.

If we were to add a series *LC* circuit as in the loop of Fig. 22-5, sine-wave currents having a frequency equal to the resonant frequency of the *LC* circuit would have a relatively low impedance path through the feedback loop. Thus, oscillator circuits could be designed which would provide $AB = 1$ at a particular frequency using a series *LC* circuit. An equation for finding the frequency

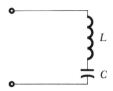

FIGURE 22-4 *Series LC circuit.*

310   **AMPLIFIERS**

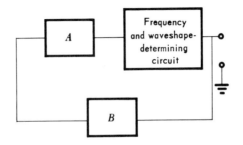

FIGURE 22-5 *Block diagram of an oscillator with a frequency- and waveshape-determining circuit.*

at which this resonance occurs can be derived as follows:

$$X_L = 2\pi f L$$
$$X_C = \frac{1}{2\pi f C}$$
$$X_L = X_C \quad \text{from the definition of resonance}$$
$$2\pi f L = \frac{1}{2\pi f C}$$
$$f^2 = \frac{1}{(2\pi)^2 LC}$$
$$\boxed{f_o = \frac{1}{2\pi \sqrt{LC}}}$$

Note that at the resonant frequency, the total impedance is equal to *zero*, since $Z_T = X_C - X_L$ and $X_C = X_L$ at resonance.

In practice, however, the ideal series resonant circuit is not encountered. The actual series resonant circuit is shown in Fig. 22-6. The resistor R is shown because inductors always have some internal resistance associated with them. In dealing with actual series RLC circuits, the total impedance at resonance is equal to R.

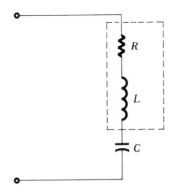

FIGURE 22-6 *A series combination of a real inductor and capacitor. The inductor has an associated resistance R due to the resistance of the many turns of wire.*

PRIMARY SIGNAL SOURCES   311

A figure of merit for both inductors and inductive circuits is defined as Q (the quality factor), $Q = X_L/R$.

Illustrative Problem 22-1
A 100-mh choke (inductor) is in a series resonant circuit with a capacitor so that the resonant frequency is 1000 Hz. The coil has a Q of 20. A 100-volt 1000-Hz signal is applied to the circuit.

(*a*)   What is the resistance of the choke?
(*b*)   Determine the value of the required capacitor.
(*c*)   How much current flows in the circuit?
(*d*)   Find the voltage across the capacitor.
(*e*)   How much voltage appears across the choke?

SOLUTION
Given: $L = 100$ mh; $Q = 20$; $f_o = 1000$ Hz; $V_{in} = 100$ volts at 1000 Hz
Find:
(*a*) R
(*b*) C
(*c*) I_0
(*d*) V_C
(*e*) V_{LR}

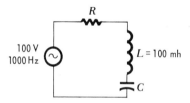

FIGURE PROB. 22-1

(*a*) $Q = \dfrac{X_L}{R}$

$R = \dfrac{X_L}{Q}$

$X_L = 2\pi f L = 2\pi (1000)(100 \times 10^{-3}) = 628$ ohms

$R = {}^{628}/_{20}$

$\boxed{R = 31.4 \text{ ohms}}$

(*b*) $f_o = \dfrac{1}{2\pi\sqrt{LC}}$

$f_o{}^2 = \dfrac{1}{4\pi^2 LC}$

$$C = \frac{1}{4\pi^2 L f_o^2}$$

$$= \frac{1}{4\pi^2 (100 \times 10^{-3})(10^6)}$$

$$\boxed{C = 0.253 \ \mu f}$$

(c) $\quad I_0 = \dfrac{V_{\text{in}}}{R} = \dfrac{100}{31.4}$

$$\boxed{I_0 = 3.19 \ \text{amp}}$$

(d) $\quad V_{CO} = X_C I_0 = 628 \times 3.19$

$$\boxed{V_{CO} = 1990 \ \text{volts}}$$

(e) $\quad V_{LR} = \sqrt{V_L^2 + V_R^2} = \sqrt{1990^2 + 100^2}$

$$\boxed{V_{LR} = 1990 \ \text{volts}}$$

THE PARALLEL LC CIRCUIT

Figure 22-7a depicts an ideal parallel LC circuit. For the ideal parallel resonant circuit, the total impedance is represented as

$$Z_T = \frac{-X_L X_C}{X_L - X_C}$$

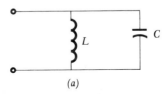

(a)

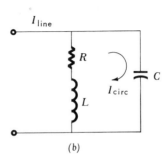

(b)

FIGURE 22-7 *Parallel LC circuit. (a) Ideal; (b) actual.*

Remembering that resonance occurs when $X_L = X_C$, it can be seen that at resonance the total impedance is infinite. However, since the ideal case is only occasionally of importance, the remainder of this discussion will deal with the actual parallel resonant circuit, shown in Fig. 22-7b.

It can be shown that for actual parallel circuits which have a Q greater than 10, the impedance at resonance can be found from

$$Z_{T_0} = QX_0$$

where X_0 is the inductive reactance at resonance.

It can be shown that at resonance a circulating current is present that circulates in the RLC loop. This current is equal to

$$I_{circ} = QI_{line}$$

Illustrative Problem 22-2

A 10-henry choke and a 0.1-μf capacitor are connected in parallel. A 100-volt signal is applied at the resonant frequency. The resistance of the coil is 400 ohms.

(a) What is the resonant frequency?
(b) Find the Q of the coil.
(c) Calculate the line current.
(d) What is the circulating current?

SOLUTION
Given: $L = 10$ henrys; $C = 0.1 \times 10^{-6}$ fd; $V_{in} = 100$ volts; $R = 400$ ohms
Find:
(a) f_o
(b) Q
(c) I_{line}
(d) I_{circ}

(a) $f_o = \dfrac{1}{2\pi\sqrt{LC}} = \dfrac{1}{2\pi\sqrt{10 \times 0.1 \times 10^{-6}}}$

$$\boxed{f_o = 158 \text{ Hz}}$$

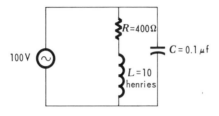

FIGURE PROB. 22-2

(b) $Q = \dfrac{X_L}{R} = \dfrac{2\pi fL}{R} = \dfrac{2\pi(158)(10)}{400}$

$$\boxed{Q = 24.9}$$

(c) $Z_{T0} = QX_0$
$\qquad = 24.9\ (2\pi)(158)(10)$
$\qquad = 247$ kilohms

$I_{\text{line}} = \dfrac{V_{\text{line}}}{Z_{T0}} = \dfrac{100}{247 \times 10^3} = 0.4 \times 10^{-3}$

$$\boxed{I_{\text{line}} = 400\ \mu\text{a}}$$

(d) $I_{\text{circ}} = QI_{\text{line}} = 24.9(400 \times 10^{-6})$

$$\boxed{I_{\text{circ}} = 9.96\ \text{ma}}$$

FREQUENTLY ENCOUNTERED CIRCUITS

In practice, merely adding a resonant circuit to the circuit configuration shown as Fig. 22-3 results in an unnecessarily costly circuit. We can allow block A of Fig. 22-1 to be a single stage, thus being negative if we provide for block B also to be negative. The following are a few circuits which have withstood the test of time and are frequently encountered. They are by no means the only possible configurations for oscillators.

THE TUNED-BASE OSCILLATOR

Figure 22-8a is a schematic representation of a tuned-base oscillator. It is one of the easier oscillator circuits to understand. The basic transistor amplifier, consisting of the transistor and its associated bias and stabilization circuit, is blocked off and labeled A, while the resonant circuit, consisting of the transformer secondary and the tuning capacitor C_1 remains. The transformer performs the function of the B in the block diagram of feedback theory shown as Fig. 22-8b. Note that the transformer is serving double duty in that not only is it coupling the output to the input circuits but the secondary of the transformer is part of the resonant circuit. The values of A and B are respectively the gain of the transistor amplifier without feedback and the transformer ratio.

As with all other transistor oscillators, the frequency of oscillation cannot be raised without limit merely by changing the res-

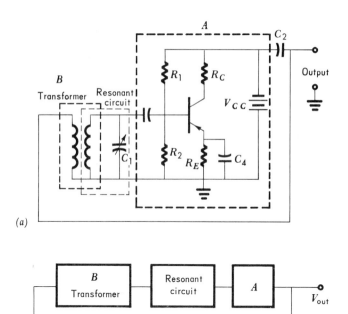

(a)

(b)

FIGURE 22-8 *The tuned-base oscillator. (a) Schematic; (b) block diagram.*

onant frequency of the resonant circuit. The upper value of frequency which can be obtained is limited by the frequency capability of the transistor.

THE TUNED-COLLECTOR OSCILLATOR

The tuned-collector oscillator shown in the schematic in Fig. 22-9 is very similar to the tuned-base oscillator previously discussed except that the tuned circuit is now placed in the collector circuit. The major differences are that the output is transformer-coupled to the load and the feedback is provided by a third coil on the transformer called a *tickler coil*.

THE COLPITTS OSCILLATOR AND THE HARTLEY OSCILLATOR

In Figs. 22-10 and 22-11 the Colpitts and Hartley oscillators are shown. Since the schematic diagrams appear a bit complicated and cluttered, they have been redrawn as Fig. 22-12*a* and *b*, with

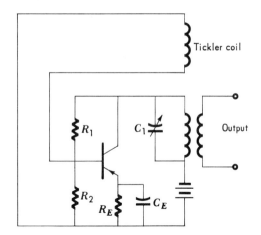

FIGURE 22-9 Tuned-collector oscillator.

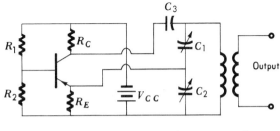

FIGURE 22-10 Colpitts oscillator.

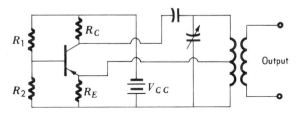

FIGURE 22-11 Hartley oscillator.

the biasing circuit removed to provide a less complicated diagram. Remember, however, that in order for the circuit to function properly, the bias circuit must be part of the operating circuit as shown in Figs. 22-10 and 22-11.

In studying Fig. 22-12, note that the feedback is provided in the Colpitts oscillator by C_1 and C_2 acting as a voltage divider, as well

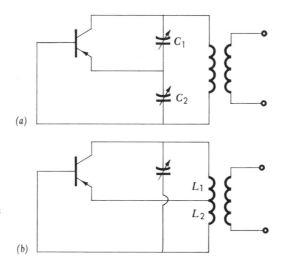

as being in the resonant circuit. In the Hartley oscillator, feedback is provided by the two portions of the transformer primary acting as a voltage divider in a similar manner. The B factor of the feedback loop is thereby determined by C_1 and C_2 in the Colpitts oscillator and by L_1 and L_2 in the Hartley oscillator.

CRYSTAL-CONTROLLED OSCILLATORS

The major disadvantage of the oscillators discussed thus far is their lack of frequency stability. This lack of stability can be overcome by replacing the LC circuit with a crystal. The replacement, however, introduces limitations on the circuit, since the frequency of oscillation is no longer continuously variable. The frequency can be changed only by the replacement of the crystal.

The use of a crystal as a frequency-determining device is based on the *piezoelectric effect*. When a voltage is applied to certain crystals (Rochelle salts, quartz, etc.), a mechanical stress is developed which causes the crystal to vibrate. The frequency of vibration is determined by the physical characteristics of the crystal.

The frequency stability of crystal-controlled oscillators is excellent as long as they are not subjected to large temperature variations.

It is sometimes desirable to replace the crystal with its equivalent circuit in order to facilitate the analysis of a crystal-controlled oscillator. Figure 22-13 shows the equivalent circuit of a crystal.

A crystal may be used as the frequency determinator in any of the oscillator circuits discussed. When using crystals for deter-

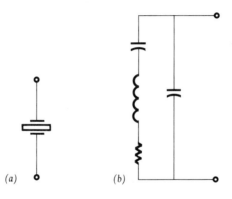

FIGURE 22-13 (a) *Crystal.* (b) *Equivalent circuit of a crystal.*

mining the frequency of oscillation in cases where accuracy to a high degree is essential, the crystal may be housed in a temperature-controlled oven to prevent variation of resonant frequency with temperature.

Although only transistor oscillators have been discussed, with only a few changes, all the circuits can be made to function with vacuum tubes.

AN ALTERNATE APPROACH TO OSCILLATOR THEORY

This section on oscillators has taken a strong feedback approach to oscillator theory, considering oscillation to be due primarily to the feeding back of part of the output power to the input. The tank circuit (*LC* circuit) was considered merely as a means of determining the waveshape and frequency of oscillation. An alternate approach to oscillator theory is to consider the oscillation as originating in the *LC* circuit or crystal, and the amplifier section of the circuit is considered to provide an electric kick during each cycle to prevent the damping out of the oscillation. This is referred to as the *flywheel approach.*

Reasons for preferring the feedback approach are:

1 Oscillation can occur without an *LC* circuit or crystal.
2 Oscillators designed for use in the generation of other than sine waves do not have tank circuits or crystals but can still be explained by the feedback approach.
3 The feedback approach builds directly from *LC* circuit and feedback theory, thereby eliminating the need for a brand new approach when attacking oscillator theory.
4 The feedback approach more readily explains multiple resonant frequencies when more than one possible frequency of oscillation is encountered in the same circuit. For example, $AB = 1$ may develop into a quadratic equation in L's and C's for a complicated *LC* arrangement.

PRIMARY SIGNAL SOURCES   319

PROBLEMS

22-1 A series circuit consisting of a 0.1-μf capacitor and a coil which has a dc resistance of 75 ohms is to be resonant at 1500 Hz. A 25-volt 1500-Hz source is applied to the circuit.
  (a) Determine the inductance of the choke.
  (b) Find the Q of the coil.
  (c) How can the resonant frequency be doubled?
  (d) What is the current that flows through the circuit?
  (e) What is the voltage across the capacitor?

22-2 A series circuit has a 10-pf capacitor and a 5-henry choke. The choke has a dc resistance of 500 ohms.
  (a) Find the resonant frequency of the circuit.
  (b) What is the Q of the coil?
  (c) Calculate the voltage across the capacitor if a 10-volt source is applied to the circuit whose frequency is the same as the resonant frequency of the circuit.

22-3 A series resonant circuit consists of a 0.002-μf capacitor and a 50-mh choke. The choke has a Q of 30.
  (a) Determine the resonant frequency of the circuit.
  (b) What is the resistance of the choke?
  (c) How much current flows if a 1.5-volt source is applied to the circuit and is tuned to the resonant frequency of the circuit?
  (d) Determine the voltage across the capacitor.

22-4 A series RLC circuit is to be resonant at 50 kHz. A coil with a Q of 25 at 50 kHz and an inductance of 30 mh is to be used.
  (a) Determine the required value of the capacitor.
  (b) Determine the resistance of the coil.

22-5 A parallel circuit is to be resonant at 200 Hz. The choke is 10 henrys and has a dc resistance of 100 ohms. A 50-volt 200-Hz source is applied to the circuit terminals.
  (a) Find the value of the necessary capacitor.
  (b) What is the Q of the coil?
  (c) Calculate the total impedance of the circuit.
  (d) What is the value of the line current?
  (e) Determine the value of the current which flows through the capacitor.

22-6 A parallel circuit consisting of a 15-henry choke with a Q of 25 and a 20-pf capacitance has a 50-volt source whose frequency is the resonant frequency of the circuit applied to its terminals.
  (a) Determine the resonant frequency of the circuit.
  (b) Find the dc resistance of the choke.
  (c) What is the impedance of the circuit at resonance?
  (d) Determine the line current.
  (e) What is the value of the circulating current?

22-7 A resonant circuit has a 0.02-μf capacitor in parallel with a coil of 5 mh and a Q of 15.
  (a) Determine the resonant frequency of the combination.

(b) Determine the resistance of the coil.

(c) Calculate the impedance of the circuit at resonance.

(d) How much current will be drawn from a 50-volt source which is tuned to the resonant frequency of the circuit?

(e) If an additional resistance of 150 ohms is added in series with the choke, what will be the new Q of the circuit?

22-8 A Hartley oscillator is to generate a 15-kHz signal. The inductor to be used has a total inductance of 10 mh. Find the value of the required capacitor.

22-9 It is desired to triple the frequency of the signal which is being produced by an oscillator. If the inductance is to remain the same, what change in value must the resonant circuit capacitance undergo?

22-10 A center-tapped 15-mh choke and two 1-μf capacitors are available.

(a) Using all three components, find the frequency of the output voltage of a Colpitts oscillator.

(b) Repeat (a) for a Hartley oscillator.

22-11 What is the major advantage of using a crystal-controlled oscillator?

22-12 (a) The tank circuit of a Hartley oscillator consists of a 250-mh choke and a capacitor which is variable from 100 to 300 pf. Determine the frequency range of the oscillator.

(b) A trimmer capacitor is in shunt with a 150-pf fixed capacitor in a Hartley oscillator tank circuit. The trimmer can be adjusted from 10 to 50 pf. If the inductance of the tank circuit is 0.1 henry, how much variation in frequency does this allow?

UNIT
THREE

PULSES AND THEIR APPLICATIONS

23

PULSES AND PULSE TRAINS

Many modern applications of electronics use signals other than the sine wave. The most frequently encountered waveshape in modern equipment other than the sine wave is the *pulse*.

In general the term pulse signifies any abrupt change in voltage or current. However, as we will use it pulse has a more limited meaning. It will refer only to waveshapes such as that shown in Fig. 23-1a and any other shapes which can be obtained by distorting this ideal pulse waveform. Radar, television, and computer systems make use of pulses.

PULSES AND RADAR

In a radar system, a high-frequency radio signal is fed to a highly directional antenna. The antenna rotates through an arc the size of which depends upon the area under surveillance. This arc can be as small as desired or may be as large as 360°. The radio signal is caused to be ON for short intervals and OFF for intervals long enough to allow an echo to return to the antenna if the radio beam strikes a reflecting object in its path. This series of ON and OFF intervals can be provided for by properly biasing the final stage of the transmitter. This final stage is designed to be off until an additional positive bias voltage is provided which will lift the stage out of this cutoff condition. This additional bias voltage is turned on and off at a given rate. Thus it can be described as a series of re-

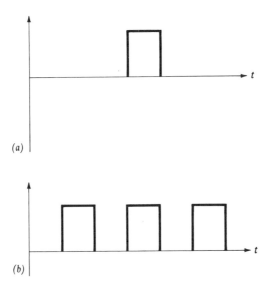

FIGURE 23-1 (a) The
ideal pulse. (b) A pulse
train.

curring pulses. A series of recurring pulses is called a *pulse train*
(see Fig. 23-1*b*).

PULSES AND COMPUTERS

In the solution of a problem by digital computer, only one step of
the problem is solved at a time; thus most of the computer sits idle.
A clock circuit within the computer provides a series of pulses that
keep the idle portion of the computer cut off. Also, most computers use a system of arithmetic called binary arithmetic. This
system depends on the presence or the absence of a fixed voltage
level. Again pulses are involved.

PULSES AND TELEVISION

When dealing with television, not only must picture and sound
information be transmitted, but information about synchronization
must also be provided. Synchronization information makes it
possible for all television receivers tuned to the same station to
have their electron beam pointing at the same spot on the screen at
the same time. While the transmitter is transmitting synchronization information, the picture on the receiver must be turned off
so the viewer will not be disturbed by this information appearing
on the screen. This calls for *blanking pulses* to be transmitted by
the television transmitter. These blanking pulses bias the picture
tube to cut off during the time that synchronization information is
transmitted.

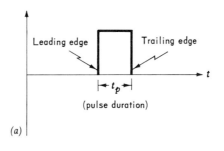

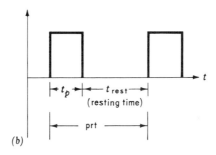

FIGURE 23-2 (a) A pulse.
(b) A pulse train.

THE PARTS OF A PULSE

In order to be able to discuss pulses and pulse trains intelligently we must provide names for their various parts. Figure 23-2a and b are descriptive diagrams. Note that the difference between the trailing edge and the leading edge is that the trailing edge occurs later in time than the leading edge.

Observe in Fig. 23-2b that the period of the pulse train is equal to the pulse duration plus the resting time. The period of the pulse train is also referred to as the pulse repetition time of the pulse train, abbreviated PRT. Just as with the sine wave, the inverse of the period of the signal is an important quantity. In the case of the pulse train, the inverse of the PRT is called the pulse repetition rate, abbreviated PRR. The analog of the PRR when dealing with sine waves was the frequency. The units of PRR are pulses per second (pps).

$$\text{PRT} = t_p + t_{\text{rest}}$$
$$\text{PRR} = \frac{1}{\text{PRT}}$$

Illustrative Problem 23-1

A radar installation located at a commercial airport is required to maintain surveillance over an area enclosed by a circle whose radius is 10 miles in all directions from the installation.

(a) How long would it take for a radio signal to travel to the outer perimeter of the area under surveillance? (The speed of electromagnetic waves is about 186,000 miles/sec.)

(b) How long would it take for an echo to return from the outer-most point?

(c) The final stage of the transmitter is cut off when the control pulse is not present. What is the required rest time of the pulse which is "keying" the transmitter?

(d) Make an annotated sketch of the required pulse train if the ON time of the transmitter is 12 μsec.

(e) Determine the PRT of this pulse train.

(f) Calculate the PRR of the pulse train.

SOLUTION

Given: Radius = 10 miles; rate = 186,000 miles/sec; ON time = 12 μsec

Find:

(a) t_{going} (b) $t_{\text{returning}}$
(c) OFF time (d) Sketch pulse train
(e) PRT (f) PRR

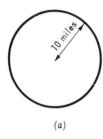

FIGURE PROB. 23-1   (a)   (b)

(a) Rate × time = distance
186,000 miles/sec × t = 10 miles

$$t = \frac{10}{186,000}$$

$$\boxed{t_{\text{going}} = 54 \ \mu\text{sec}}$$

(b) Same as (a)

$$\boxed{t_{\text{returning}} = 54 \ \mu\text{sec}}$$

(c)   OFF time $= t_{\text{going}} + t_{\text{returning}} + t_{\text{on}}$
$$= (54 + 54 + 12)\,\mu\text{sec} = 120\ \mu\text{sec}$$

$$\boxed{t_{\text{rest}} = 120\ \mu\text{sec}}$$

(d)   See Fig. Prob. 23-1b.
(e)   PRT $= 120 + 12$

$$\boxed{\text{PRT} = 132\ \mu\text{sec}}$$

(f)   PRR $= \dfrac{1}{\text{PRT}} = \dfrac{1}{132 \times 10^{-6}} = 7{,}600$ pps

$$\boxed{\text{PRR} = 7600\ \text{pps}}$$

THE IMPERFECT PULSE

Although a pulse train may start out consisting of perfectly shaped pulses, after passing through a number of stages of amplification, it will be found to have taken on the form shown in Fig. 23-3.

What can be causing this distortion of the pulse?   Recall that in dealing with amplifier distortion in previous chapters, the frequency response of the amplifier created problems which resulted in distortion of complex waveshapes.   Amplifiers were found to contain high-pass and low-pass filter sections.   Can these same high-pass and low-pass filters be the culprits in this case also?

Very slowly varying signals presented a problem when we were dealing with the response of an amplifier to sine waves.   The amplifier was said to have a low-frequency cutoff point.   Thus, it is not surprising to find that a pulse cannot maintain its constant level over the entire pulse duration but decays with time.

Low-pass filters found in capacitor-coupled amplifiers prevented instantaneous changes in voltage.   Note that for a perfect

FIGURE 23-3 *A distorted pulse.*

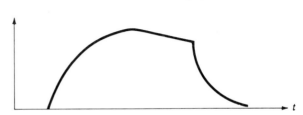

pulse to pass undistorted through an amplifier, instantaneous rises and falls in voltage are called for. Since the low-pass filter prevents these instantaneous changes from taking place, a distortion resulting in nonvertical leading and trailing edges of the pulse results.

It will simplify matters somewhat if we investigated the effect of the two types of filters, low-pass and high-pass, separately.

THE EFFECT OF A LOW-PASS FILTER ON A PULSE

Figure 23-4 depicts the situation we encounter when passing an ideal pulse through a low-pass filter. Note that since the voltage across the capacitor cannot change instantaneously, a finite time is required for the output pulse to initially come up to its full magnitude, because the output pulse is taken from across the capacitor. Likewise, at the end of the pulse, a finite amount of time is required for the capacitor to discharge and thereby end the pulse. To analyze the deterioration of the pulse, we must define some terms for a quantitative discussion.

The *rise time* of a pulse is defined as the amount of time it takes the pulse to rise from 10 to 90 percent of its largest value.

The *pulse duration* is taken as the time between the point at which the pulse has risen to 10 percent of its largest value and the point at which it has fallen to 90 percent of its largest value. The reason for defining the pulse duration in this manner is that this corresponds rather closely to the pulse duration of the undistorted (ideal) pulse.

The *decay time* of the pulse is taken as the amount of time required for the pulse to fall from 90 percent of its largest value to 10 percent of its largest value.

Figure 23-5 gives a pictorial description of the terms just defined.

FIGURE 23-4 *A low-pass filter causing the distortion of a pulse.*

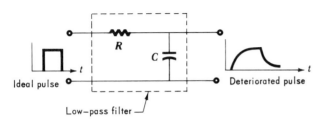

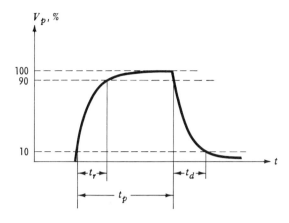

FIGURE 23-5 The distorted pulse; $t_r \equiv$ rise time; $t_p \equiv$ pulse duration; $t_d \equiv$ decay time.

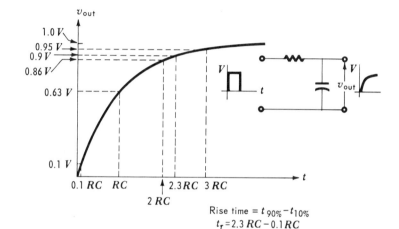

Rise time $= t_{90\%} - t_{10\%}$

$t_r = 2.3\,RC - 0.1\,RC$

$t_r = 2.2\,RC$

FIGURE 23-6 The distorted output from a low-pass filter.

Figure 23-6 is a plot of output voltage (voltage across C) vs. time (in RC time constants). A standard RC charge curve has been constructed and the points for 0.1 and 0.9 volt have been annotated. It is found from this sketch that the voltage rises to 10 percent of its largest value in $0.1RC$ and to 90 percent of its value in $2.3RC$. Therefore, the rise time of the distorted pulse is equal to $(2.3 - 0.1)\,RC$ or $2.2RC$.

$$\boxed{t_r = 2.2RC}$$

A similar construction can be done for the trailing edge of the pulse. This has been left as an exercise.

THE EFFECT OF A HIGH-PASS FILTER ON A PULSE

Like the low-pass filter, the high-pass filter causes a deterioration of the pulse shape. However, rather than rounding the sides of the pulse, as was the case with the low-pass filter, the high-pass filter creates a *tilt* in the upper and lower portions of the pulse which were previously flat (see Fig. 23-7).

Figure 23-8 depicts the waveshape after it has passed through the high-pass filter. The tilt is caused by the charging of the capacitor through the resistor R. Since the capacitor voltage cannot change instantaneously at the time of the initial instantaneous voltage change at the leading edge of the pulse, the entire input voltage appears across the resistor. As time passes, the capacitor charges, and the input voltage is shared by both the capacitor and

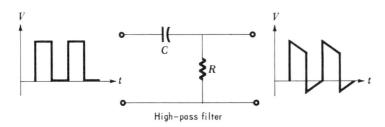

High–pass filter

FIGURE 23-7 *The effect of a high-pass filter on a pulse train.*

FIGURE 23-8 *A pulse train with tilt.*

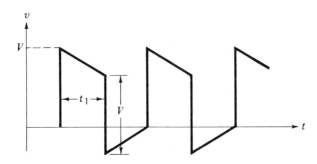

the resistor. (Remember Kirchhoff's voltage law!) Thus, the tilt is actually a portion of an RC discharge curve. Note that there is a tilt not only in the top of the wave but also at the bottom. At the trailing edge of the pulse, when the input voltage changes instantaneously by V, the voltage across the capacitor again cannot change instantaneously. The voltage across the resistor therefore undergoes an *instantaneous voltage change of V*.

Illustrative Problem 23-2
Determine the rise time of the output pulse which resulted from passing an ideal pulse through a low-pass filter composed of a 5-kilohm resistor and a 300-pf capacitor.

SOLUTION
Given: Ideal input pulse; $R = 5$ kilohms; $C = 300$ pf; low-pass filter
Find: t_r

$$t_r = 2.2RC = 2.2(5 \times 10^3)(300 \times 10^{-12})$$
$$= 3.3 \times 10^{-6}$$

$$t_r = 3.3 \ \mu\text{sec}$$

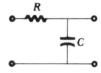

FIGURE PROB. 23-2

TELEVISION SYNCHRONIZATION PULSES
Figure 23-9 is a typical composite television signal. The important region for our purposes now is the blanking pedestal and synchronization pulse. For a portion of time the picture on a TV set is turned off while synchronization information is transmitted. During this time the electron beam is made to return to the starting side of the screen in order to be positioned for the beginning of a new sweep period. Note that the signal received at the viewer's end of transmission is very small in magnitude and in power content. It is necessary to pass the signal through several stages of amplification to restore adequate magnitude and power content to the signal. If the pulse is made to deteriorate excessively during amplification, the TV picture will tear and smear. It is therefore necessary that the high- and low-pass filters found in the amplifiers through which this signal passes have proper RC values to prevent excessive deterioration.

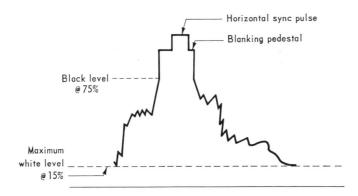

FIGURE 23-9 *A composite television signal.*

Horizontal sync pulse

Blanking pedestal

Black level @ 75%

Maximum white level @ 15%

RULES OF THUMB

As a reasonable rule of thumb, for the prevention of excessive pulse deterioration in most applications, high-pass filters should have a long time constant which is 10 or more times the pulse duration. Low-pass filters, on the other hand, should have a time constant of one-tenth or less of the pulse duration.

FIGURE 23-10 *Diagram for defining tilt.*

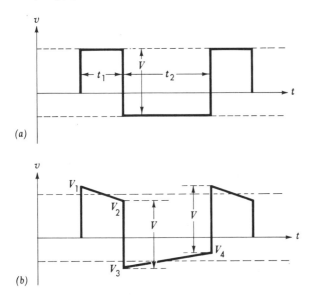

PERCENT TILT

At this point, a quantitative description of the tilt is required. *Percent tilt* is the term most frequently used for this purpose. To be most meaningful, the term will be defined with reference to Fig. 23-10.

$$\text{Percent tilt} \equiv \frac{V_1 - V_2}{V/2} \times 100$$

With the application of a little geometry, it can be shown that the percent tilt is equal to

$$\text{Percent tilt} = \frac{t_1 + t_2}{2RC} \times 100$$

Illustrative Problem 23-3

Calculate the percent tilt of the pulse train shown in Fig. Prob. 23-3.

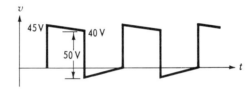

FIGURE PROB. 23-3

SOLUTION

Given: Waveshape as shown
Find: Percent tilt

$$\text{Percent tilt} = \frac{V_1 - V_2}{V/2} \times 100 = \frac{45 - 40}{50/2} \times 100 = {}^5\!/_{25} \times 100$$

$$\boxed{\text{Percent tilt} = 20\%}$$

THE CAPACITOR-COUPLED AMPLIFIER

Let us now apply what we have learned to a quantitative study of the capacitance-coupled amplifier.

Figure 23-11 shows the equivalent circuit of the interstage portion of a two-stage capacitor-coupled amplifier. We must determine which capacitors to take into account when calculating the rise time introduced by the interstage section of the amplifier and which to take into account when determining the tilt.

When doing *rise-time* calculations, we are dealing with a rapidly changing voltage, similar to that we encountered in *high-*

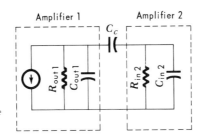

FIGURE 23-11 *An equivalent circuit of the interstage portion of a two-stage amplifier.*

frequency calculations. It would therefore seem reasonable to include in the rise-time calculations only those capacitances which we would include in high-frequency calculations. Recall that when determining the high-frequency performance of an amplifier, we neglected C_C because at high frequencies it has a low impedance. Because it is in series with both the output of one amplifier and the input of the other amplifier, a negligible voltage is dropped across it. The two shunt capacitors, C_{out1} and C_{in2}, on the other hand, being low impedances at high frequencies, provide paths for the signal current to bypass the input of the second stage. Thus for high-frequency considerations and, by analogy, rise-time calculations, the parallel combination of C_{out1} and C_{in2} is to be considered the capacitance in the time-constant calculations (see Fig. 23-12a).

In Fig. 23-12b, the capacitances and resistances which must be taken into account have been combined. In going from Fig. 23-12b to c, use has been made of the Norton-Thévenin equivalence, which was discussed in a previous chapter. The circuit

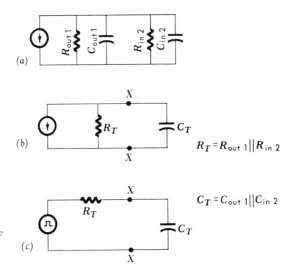

FIGURE 23-12 *An equivalent circuit of the interstage portion of a two-stage amplifier for rise-time considerations.*

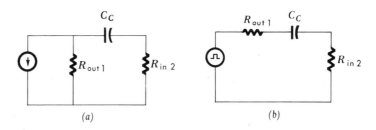

FIGURE 23-13 *An equivalent circuit of the interstage portion of a two-stage amplifier for tilt considerations.*

is broken at the points marked by X in Fig. 23-12b, the Norton-Thévenin equivalence performed, and then rejoined at the X's in Fig. 23-12c. In recalling the Norton-Thévenin equivalence, we note that though the source changes from a current source to a voltage source and the impedance changes from a shunt to a series position, the *value* of the impedance is identical in both the Thévenin and the Norton cases.

In Fig. 23-13 we have the situation which must be considered in tilt calculations. Tilt, being a relatively slow-occurring phenomenon, is analogous to the low-frequency studies of previous chapters. In the low-frequency case, the shunt capacitances of Fig. 23-11 present a relatively high impedance due to the low-frequency value of X_C. Since the shunt capacitances are relatively large in value, they provide a very limited shunt path and can be neglected. The coupling capacitor, however, now takes on an important role because its impedance becomes relatively large. Since it is a series component, it provides a place where signals can be dropped (recall Kirchhoff's voltage law). Figure 23-13a, then, represents the equivalent circuit of the interstage section of the two-stage amplifier. Performing a Norton-Thévenin equivalency, we obtain the circuit of Fig. 23-13b. It is obvious that the resistance and capacitance involved in tilt considerations are (R_{out_1} + R_{in_2}) and C_C.

Illustrative Problem 23-4

An 80,000-pps pulse train is passed through a two-stage vacuum-tube amplifier. The input impedance of the second stage consists of a capacitance of 150 pf in parallel with a resistance of 100 kilohms. The output impedance of stage 1 consists of a 5-kilohm resistance and a 4-pf capacitance. A 0.1-μf coupling capacitor is used between the two stages of amplification.

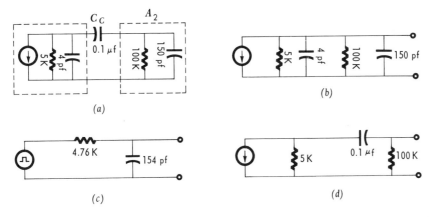

(a)   (b)

(c)   (d)

FIGURE PROB. 23-4

(a)   What will be the rise time?

(b)   What is the percent tilt?

SOLUTION

Given: 80,000 pps; two-stage amplifier; $Z_{in2} = 150$ pf$\|$100 kilohms; $Z_{out1} = 5$-kilohm resistance$\|$4 pf; $C_C = 0.1$ μf

Find:

(a) t_r

(b)   Percent tilt

(a)   Rise-time calculations are analogous to high-frequency calculations.   Therefore C_C is considered a short.   See Fig. Prob. 23-4b.

$$R_T = 5 \text{ kilohms}\|100 \text{ kilohms} = \frac{5 \times 100}{105} \text{ kilohms} = 4.76 \text{ kilohms}$$

$$C_T = 150 \text{ pf} + 4 \text{ pf}$$

Using the Norton-Thévenin equivalence (Fig. Prob. 23-4c),

$$\begin{aligned} t_r &= 2.2RC \\ &= 2.2(4.76 \times 10^3)(154 \times 10^{-12}) \\ &= 1.6 \times 10^{-9} \text{ sec} \end{aligned}$$

$$\boxed{t_r = 1.6 \text{ nsec}}$$

(b)   Tilt is analogous to low-frequency response, so that the only capacitance of significance is C_C (Fig. Prob. 23-4d).

$$\text{Percent tilt} = \frac{t_1 + t_2}{2RC} \times 100$$

$$\text{Period} = \frac{1}{\text{pps}} = \frac{1}{80,000} = 12.5 \times 10^{-6} \text{ sec}$$
$$R = R_{\text{out}_1} + R_{\text{in}_2}$$
$$R = (5 + 100) \times 10^3$$
$$\text{Percent tilt} = \frac{12.5 \times 10^{-6}}{2(105 \times 10^3) \times 0.1 \times 10^{-6}} \times 100$$

$$\boxed{\text{Percent tilt} = 0.0595\%}$$

PROBLEMS

23-1 Determine the following quantities for the pulse train in Fig. 23-14.
  (a) Pulse duration
  (b) Resting time
  (c) PRT
  (d) PRR
  (e) The time at which the leading edge of the third pulse occurs
  (f) The time at which the trailing edge of the third pulse occurs

23-2 A radar installation is to maintain surveillance over an area enclosed by a circle whose radius is 15 miles in all directions from the installation.
  (a) How long would it take for a radio signal to travel to the outer perimeter of the area under surveillance? (The speed of electromagnetic waves is about 186,000 miles/sec.)
  (b) How long would it take for an echo to return from the outermost point? The final stage of the transmitter is cut off when the positive portion of the control pulse is not present.
  (c) What is the minimum required rest time of the pulse which is keying the transmitter? The ON time of the transmitter is 12 μsec.
  (d) Make an annotated sketch of the required pulse train.
  (e) Determine the PRT of this pulse train.
  (f) Calculate the PRR of the pulse train.

23-3 What effect does a low-pass filter have on a pulse train passing through it? A high-pass filter?

23-4 Determine the rise time and pulse duration of the pulse shown in Fig. 23-15.

23-5 A pulse has a value of 10 volts when its trailing edge occurs. The pulse is being passed through a low-pass filter consisting of a

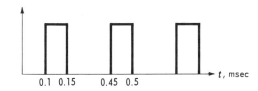

0.1 0.15   0.45 0.5 t, msec

FIGURE 23-14   *Diagram for Prob. 23-1.*

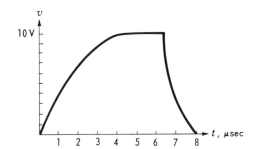

FIGURE 23-15 *Diagram for Prob. 23-4.*

3-kilohm resistor and a 100-pf capacitor. Sketch the resulting trailing edge to scale and determine the decay time for the pulse. How many time constants is this equal to?

23-6 Calculate the rise time and the decay time which results from passing an ideal pulse through a low-pass filter consisting of a 2-kilohm resistor and a 50-pf capacitor. Make an approximate annotated sketch of this pulse if its pulse duration is 2 μsec.

23-7 Determine the percent tilt that results from passing a pulse train having a pulse duration of 6 msec and a resting period of 10 msec through a high-pass filter having a time constant of 40 msec.

23-8 Determine the percent tilt of the waveshape shown in Fig. 23-16.

23-9 Using the rules of thumb mentioned in this chapter, determine the maximum permissible time constant of a low-pass filter and the minimum permissible time constant of a high-pass filter when dealing with a pulse train whose pulses have a pulse duration of 50 nsec.

23-10 A 10,000-pps pulse train is to be passed through a two-stage amplifier. Determine the rise time and the percent tilt for an amplifier with the following characteristics. The output impedance of stage 1 consists of a 5-kilohm resistance in parallel with a 10-pf capacitance. The input impedance of the second stage consists of a 1-kilohm resistance with a 200-pf capacitance in parallel. The coupling capacitor is 0.1 μf.

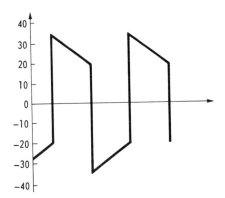

FIGURE 23-16 *Diagram for Prob. 23-8.*

24

WAVESHAPING
WITH *RC* CIRCUITS

In the previous chapter we attempted to avoid distorting our wave-shapes as they passed through high-pass and low-pass filters. Interesting results are obtained, however, if we deliberately allow the filter circuits to introduce large amounts of distortion. We expect new and different waveshapes to appear at the output of these circuits when the distortion is *maximized*.

THE INTEGRATOR

Consider the low-pass filter shown in Fig. 24-1. Recall that in the last chapter we decided that the *RC* time constant should be very small in order to keep distortion to a minimum. Now that we are interested in maximizing distortion, *RC* should be made very large.

Figure 24-2 depicts a case in which a pulse train is used as an input to the circuit of Fig. 24-1. The rise time of the circuit is very large, and the output waveshape does not reach its maximum value before the pulse begins its decay. Note that the output waveshape between the time intervals t_1 and t_2 is an *RC* charge curve. If the time constant of this charge curve is made very very large, only a very small portion of the charge curve is encountered, thereby providing what seems to be almost a straight line.

Now, as the trailing edge of the pulse appears, the capacitor starts to discharge through *R*. Again, an *RC* curve results. This time it is a discharge curve. It appears as a straight line for the

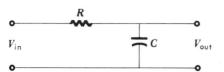

FIGURE 24-1 *Low-pass filter.*

same reason as the charge curve did, because only a small portion of the total curve is involved if the RC time constant is made very large. This discharge occurs during the time interval t_2 to t_3 of Fig. 24-2b.

A close study of the waveshapes in Fig. 24-2 shows that the output signal appears to keep track of the area enclosed by the input waveshape and the horizontal axis. Area above the horizontal axis is taken as positive, while area below the axis is considered negative. As each interval of time elapses, more or less area is added to the total area enclosed. The area enclosed by a single pulse increases linearly with time for a rectangular pulse.

In the study of the calculus a curve which keeps track of the area bounded by another curve is called the *integral* of the first curve. For this reason we can say that the incoming pulse of Fig. 24-2a undergoes an *integration* in passing through the circuit.

Further study would indicate that any waveshape undergoes integration as it passes through a low-pass filter with a large RC time constant. For most purposes of integration a large time constant is taken to mean that the RC time constant should be greater than or equal to 10 times the period of the waveshape being processed ($RC \geq 10T$).

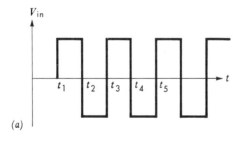

(a)

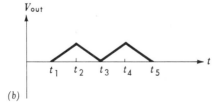

FIGURE 24-2 (a) *Pulse train applied to the input of the low-pass filter.* (b) *Output of the low-pass filter.*

(b)

Integrators are used extensively in analog computers to perform the mathematical operation of integration. Generally, an integration circuit used in an analog computer is included as part of an amplifier.

Integrators are also used frequently to produce new waveshapes.

THE DIFFERENTIATOR

It should also prove interesting to investigate the high-pass filter with a very short time constant. Such a situation is depicted as Fig. 24-3.

Again, let us study the effect of applying a pulse train to the circuit in question. Note that as the leading edge of the pulse of Fig. 24-3 is encountered at t_1, the voltage across the capacitor cannot change instantaneously. Therefore the voltage across R must rise immediately (remember Kirchhoff's voltage law). However, because of the small time constant the capacitor will charge rapidly, causing the output voltage to decay quickly, as shown. This decay of the output voltage is obviously an RC discharge curve.

As the trailing edge of the pulse is encountered at t_2, the output voltage must change by the same amount that the input changes because the voltage across the capacitor cannot change instantaneously. Again, because of the small RC time constant the voltage across the capacitor will take on the value of the input voltage quickly. Thus the output voltage returns to zero as a rapid RC discharge curve.

Because the effect on a waveshape as it passes through this circuit resembles the calculus operation of differentiation, it is frequently referred to as a *differentiator*.

FIGURE 24-3 *High-pass filter.*

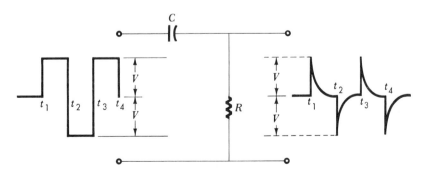

For the purpose of designing differentiator circuits a small time constant will be considered as one which is less than one-tenth the period of the waveshape being processed. Such a circuit is used in some analog computers to solve calculus problems, although this circuit is not used nearly as often as is the integrator circuit. The second and more extensive use which this circuit finds is that of converting pulse trains to marker pips for timing purposes.

The conversion of a pulse train to a series of timing pips is required in the synchronization circuit of television receivers. As will be shown in the next chapter, the synchronization pulses of an incoming television signal are removed from the total signal. These synchronized pulses must be converted to pips and are then used to *trigger* the horizontal oscillator circuit. More will be said about the horizontal oscillator of television receivers in later sections of this book.

Illustrative Problem 24-1

It is desired that the pulse train shown in Fig. Prob. 24-1a be converted to:

(a) A triangular waveshape
(b) A series of spikes

Determine the limitations on the circuit required for the triangular pulse and then for the series of spikes.

SOLUTION
Given: Waveshape shown in Fig. Prob. 24-1a
Find:
(a) The limitations on RC for the production of a triangular wave
(b) The limitations on RC for the production of spikes

FIGURE PROB. 24-1

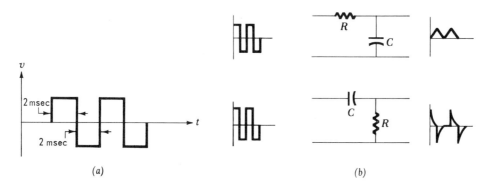

(a)   (b)

(a) See Fig. Prob. 24-1*b*.

$$RC > 10T$$
$$T = 4 \text{ msec}$$

$$\boxed{RC > 40 \text{ msec}}$$

(b) $RC < \dfrac{T}{10} = \dfrac{4 \text{ msec}}{1}$

$$\boxed{RC < 0.4 \text{ msec}}$$

PROBLEMS

24-1 A pulse train consisting of pulses whose two levels are 0 and 10 volts is to be passed through a low-pass filter with a time constant equal to one-half the pulse duration of the pulses in the pulse train. The pulse duration and the resting time are equal. Construct the input waveform and the waveform which appears at the output of the filter.

24-2 Repeat Prob. 24-1 for the case in which the *RC* time constant is equal to the pulse duration.

24-3 (*a*) What is the meaning of the term "integration" as used in the study of electronics?

(*b*) The waveshape shown in Fig. 24-4 is to be passed through an integrator. Sketch the output waveshape.

(*c*) Determine the limitation on the time constant of the integrator to be used in this problem in order for a reasonably good integration to take place.

(*d*) If a 500-kilohm resistor is used, what is the limitation on the value of the capacitor?

24-4 The pulse train described in Prob. 24-1 is fed into a high-pass filter whose *RC* time constant is one-third the pulse duration of the pulses in the pulse train. Construct the waveform appearing at the input to the filter and that appearing at the output. If the PRR of the pulse train is 15,000 pps, what is the limitation on the time

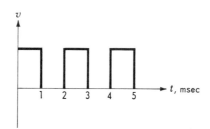

FIGURE 24-4 *Diagram for Prob. 24-3.*

WAVESHAPING WITH RC CIRCUITS **345**

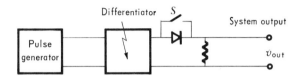

FIGURE 24-5 *Diagram for Prob. 24-5.*

constant of the RC combination in order for the output to be a reasonably good approximation to a differentiation of the input?

24-5 Consider the system represented in Fig. 24-5. The pulse generator is producing a series of 25-volt pulses at the rate of 30,000 pps. The resting time of the pulse train is equal to one-half the pulse duration.

(a) Sketch the pulse train that appears at the output of the pulse generator.

(b) Sketch the waveshape that appears at the output of the differentiator.

(c) Sketch the output of the system with switch S closed.

(d) Sketch the system output with switch S open.

(e) Sketch the system output with switch S open and the diode reversed.

25

CLIPPING, LIMITING, AND CLAMPING CIRCUITS

Consider the composite television signal of Fig. 25-1. Somewhere within a television receiver it is necessary to separate the horizontal synchronization pulses from the rest of the composite signal. The horizontal signal pulses and the remainder of the signal are then sent to different portions of the set.

CLIPPERS AND LIMITERS

The horizontal synchronization pulses are included in the composite television signal to ensure that the horizontal oscillator within the receiver begins its cycle simultaneously with the horizontal oscillator in the television camera. To perform the separation of the horizontal synchronization pulses from the rest of the signal we should expect a dc reference voltage to be required. The function of such a dc voltage is to determine the level at which the separation takes place. In addition we expect that a diode is needed. Recall the rectifier circuits studied previously in which diodes were used to separate sine waves into portions above the zero level and portions below the zero level.

Consider passing the composite television signal through a circuit consisting of a reference voltage and a diode as shown in Fig. 25-2. Note that the diode is not permitted to conduct until the input signal exceeds V, the battery voltage. Prior to this, no current flows, and the voltage across the output is the battery voltage V. No voltage drop appears across R since no current is flowing at

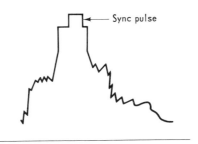

FIGURE 25-1 *Composite television signal.*

Sync pulse

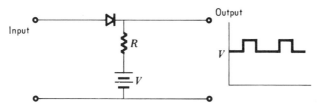

FIGURE 25-2 *Series synch separator.*

Input

Output

R

V

V

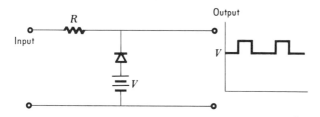

FIGURE 25-3 *Shunt synch separator.*

Input

R

Output

V

V

this time. Once the input signal voltage exceeds V, the diode conducts. It will be assumed that the diode involved is an ideal diode so that when it is conducting, it may be considered a short circuit. Thus, once the diode begins conducting, the input signal appears directly across the output terminals of the circuit.

Another circuit which can be used to separate the synchronization pulses from the rest of the television signal is shown in Fig. 25-3. In this circuit the diode conducts until the input voltage exceeds the reference voltage V. Before the input reaches this level, the dc supply V appears across the output. Once the input signal voltage exceeds V, the diode stops conducting and the input voltage appears across the output.

In both the circuits just discussed the diode serves as an automatic switch, alternately placing the input signal and the battery voltage across the output terminals.

DEFINITIONS

In general, the term *clipper* is used to represent any circuit which separates a waveshape into two component parts, as just described. Another term which we will use interchangeably with the term clipper is *limiter*. In some texts a distinction is made between the two terms, the term limiter being reserved for those circuits whose output is always below a certain value, while the term clipper is reserved for those circuits whose output is always above a certain value. We, however, will use the terms clipper and limiter interchangeably since in most cases a limiter can be used as a clipper, and vice versa, merely by changing the place from which the output is taken.

Figures 25-4 and 25-5 show additional circuits which might be used to implement the clipper-limiter function.

Note in Fig. 25-4 that the input signal is directly coupled to the output through the series resistor as long as the input signal remains below the value of V. Once the input signal exceeds V, the diode starts to conduct, thereby placing the battery V directly across the output terminals. The output voltage is thus forced to remain at the voltage V until the diode opens due to the input voltage having returned to a value less than V.

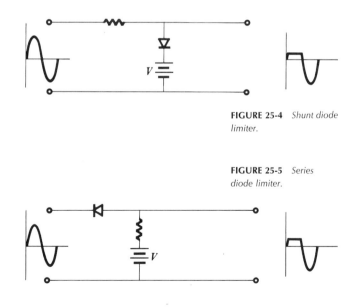

FIGURE 25-4 *Shunt diode limiter.*

FIGURE 25-5 *Series diode limiter.*

The circuit of Fig. 25-5 functions in a somewhat similar fashion except that the diode conducts until the input reaches V and then opens. The input signal is placed directly across the output until the input reaches V. Once V is reached, the diode no longer conducts. The battery voltage V then is coupled to the output through the series resistor.

Illustrative Problem 25-1

Develop a series diode clipper circuit which will separate a signal as shown in Fig. Prob. 25-1a.

SOLUTION
See Fig. Prob. 25-1b.

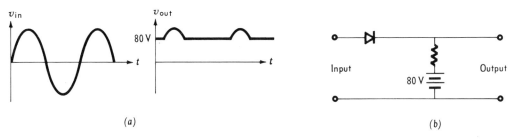

(a)   (b)

FIGURE PROB. 25-1

THE TWO-LEVEL SLICER

On occasion it proves helpful to be able to slice out a portion of a signal and dispose of the remainder, as is done by the black box in Fig. 25-6. A circuit which can perform such a function is shown in Fig. 25-7. In this circuit, diode D_1 conducts until the input voltage exceeds V_1. When V_1 is finally exceeded, both diodes become nonconducting and remain nonconducting until V_2 is exceeded.

When D_1 is conducting, voltage V_1 appears across the output. During the time when both D_1 and D_2 are not conducting the input voltage appears across the output. When V_2 is exceeded, D_2 begins to conduct. During that time interval when D_2 is conducting, V_2 appears across the output.

The circuit of Fig. 25-7 is therefore an implementation of the function described in Fig. 25-6. This circuit is known as a *two-level slicer* or a *double-ended clipper*.

Figure 25-8 is an interesting variation of the two-level slicer. The circuit shown as Fig. 25-8 clips the signal on both the upper and the lower half of the wave. Circuits of the type shown in

FIGURE 25-6 *Block diagram of a two-level slicer.*

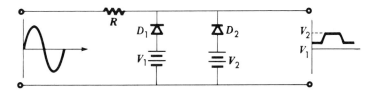

FIGURE 25-7 *Two-level slicer. Note that $V_2 > V_1$.*

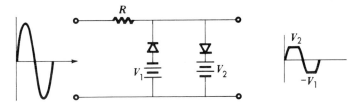

FIGURE 25-8 *A two-level slicer.*

Figs. 25-7 and 25-8 can be used to provide an approximation to square waves when a supply of sine waves is available. If the sine waves are of large enough amplitude for the portion being sliced out and passed on to the output to be only a relatively small portion of the total amplitude, then the edges of the waveshape approach being vertical.

Illustrative Problem 25-2

A circuit is desired that can produce a waveshape which resembles a pulse train when fed a sine wave. The upper level of the pulse train should be 10 volts, while the lower level should be 2 volts. A 120-volt-rms sine wave is available as a source of sine waves.

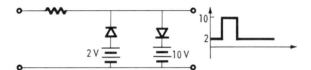

FIGURE PROB. 25-2

THE TRANSISTOR AMPLIFIER AS A CLIPPER CIRCUIT

Consider the effect of providing a transistor amplifier with an ex-cessively large input signal as is done in Fig. 25-9. Note that such a situation provides double-ended clipping.

As the input signal increases in value and the operating point travels up the load line, a point is reached at which the voltage between collector and emitter v_{ce} cannot decrease any further. The transistor is said to have reached *saturation*.

On the other extreme of operation, the operating point travels down the load line until practically no current is flowing in the collector circuit. At this point the transistor is said to be cut off. Note that attempting to drive the amplifier beyond the saturation point on one extreme and beyond the cutoff point on the other ex-

FIGURE 25-9 *Double-ended clipping provided by overdriving a transistor amplifier.*

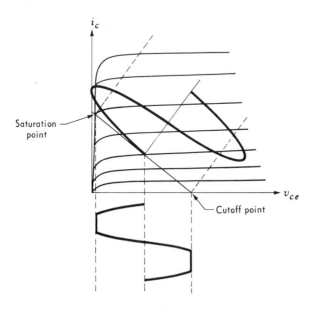

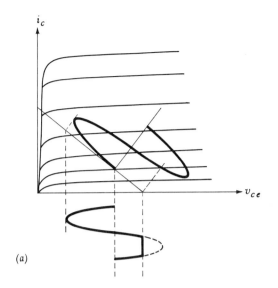

(a)

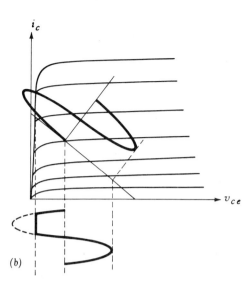

(b)

FIGURE 25-10 *Single-ended clipping due to properly placing the Q point and then overdriving the amplifier on only one end.*

treme results in clipping. The situation depicted in Fig. 25-9 provides double-ended clipping. Single-ended clipping can also be obtained by overdriving the amplifier. By an appropriate choice of operating point, clipping due to either cutoff (Fig. 25-10*a*) or saturation (Fig. 25-10*b*) can be obtained. Bear in mind that a major advantage of using transistor-amplifier clipping rather than diode clipping is that amplification is obtained at the same time.

Illustrative Problem 25-3

A transistor amplifier is to operate as a single-ended clipper (see Fig. Prob. 25-3*a*). The transistor is to use a fixed-bias common-emitter configuration (assume $V_{BEQ} = 0.2$ volt). Determine:

(*a*) Schematic
(*b*) V_{CC}
(*c*) R_C
(*d*) R_B

SOLUTION
Given: Fixed bias CE; $V_{BEQ} = 0.2$ volt; characteristics and input as shown

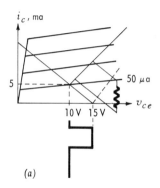

(a)

Find:

(a) Schematic
(b) V_{CC}
(c) R_C
(d) R_B

(a) See Fig. Prob. 25-3b.

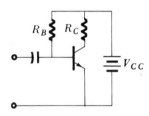

(b)

(b) $\boxed{V_{CC} = v_{ce,\text{intercept}} = 15 \text{ volts}}$

(c) $R_C = \dfrac{1}{\text{slope of load line}} = \dfrac{\Delta v_{ce}}{\Delta i_c}$

$$= \dfrac{15 - 10}{5 \times 10^{-3} - 0} = \dfrac{5}{5 \times 10^{-3}} = 1\text{K}$$

$\boxed{R_C = 1 \text{ kilohm}}$

(d) $|I_{BQ}R_B| + |V_{BEQ}| = V_{CC}$
$50 \times 10^{-6}R_B + 0.2 = 15$

$$R_B = \frac{14.8}{50 \times 10^{-6}} = 0.296 \times 10^6$$

$$\boxed{R_B = 296 \text{ kilohm}}$$

CLAMPING CIRCUITS: THE DC RESTORER

Figure 25-11 depicts the effect of passing a television signal through a circuit which has a series blocking capacitor. Note that the dc level which the signal originally contained has been removed. The second signal, though it resembles the first in most respects, is not acceptable since the dc level which represents the general brightness level of the picture has been removed. As a matter of fact, as shown in Fig. 25-11, only the raster will appear on the screen; the entire signal is whiter than white. This is because the entire signal is below the level of maximum brightness. Obviously some means must be provided for the restoration of the dc level in order to provide an acceptable picture.

Such a circuit for the restoration of the dc level of the television signal is called a *dc restorer*. It is one of a group of circuits called *clamping circuits*, so called because one end of the signal, either the extreme maximum excursion or the extreme negative excursion, is rigidly held at a reference voltage (clamped). Let us now investigate the type of circuit best suited to restoring the dc level of the television signal.

The uppermost level of the television signal is the horizontal synchronization pulse, whose level is known. A circuit which

FIGURE 25-11 *The loss of dc level due to passing a signal through a coupling capacitor.*

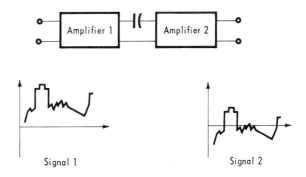

Signal 1   Signal 2

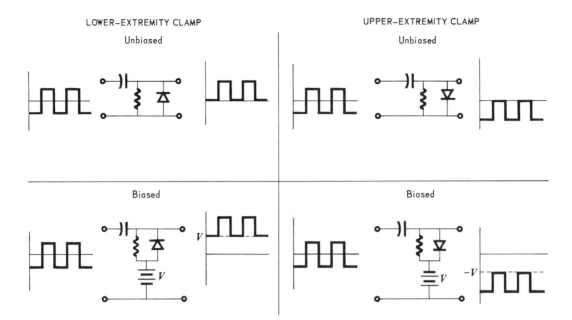

LOWER–EXTREMITY CLAMP

UPPER–EXTREMITY CLAMP

Unbiased

Unbiased

Biased

Biased

FIGURE 25-12 *Clamp circuits.*

could clamp the maximum excursion of the signal at this predetermined level would suit our needs quite satisfactorily.

Figure 25-12 is a series of schematics of clamping circuits which indicate the effect each circuit has on the signal which passes through it. Rather than going through an analysis of each of the circuits shown in Fig. 25-12, one circuit, typical of the set, will be analyzed. It is the one described as a *biased lower-extremity clamp*. For convenience it has been duplicated as Fig. 25-13.

THE BIASED LOWER-EXTREMITY CLAMP

During the few beginning cycles of operation the capacitor is being charged. This charging occurs through the diode and only during the time that the sum of the input voltage and the battery voltage V is a positive number (see Fig. 25-13). The capacitor charges to $V_2 + V$. This is the maximum voltage that the sum of the input and battery voltage combination attains in a direction which causes the diode to conduct. The diode acts as a one-way valve, allowing

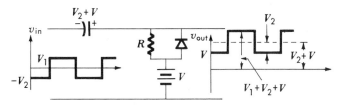

FIGURE 25-13 *Biased lower-extremity clamp.*

the capacitor to charge when the charging voltage ($V_2 + V$) is positive but not allowing the capacitor to discharge when the charging voltage is decreased.   Only a very negligible charging takes place through the resistor, which shunts the diode because it is chosen such that $R \times C$ is large, thereby creating a large time constant through the path of R and C.   The resistor was included in order to provide a path for the capacitor to discharge through, in the event that the level of the signal extremities should change.   This discharge, if it is required, will take a fairly long time because of the long time constant deliberately designed into the circuit.

After the capacitor has come up to $V_2 + V$ with the polarity shown in Fig. 25-13, the diode no longer conducts and will conduct only in order to make up for charge which may be lost because of current flowing from the capacitor to the final load or because of a change in the extremity levels of the input.   The voltage seen looking in through the output terminals is that represented by the input signal plus the voltage across the capacitor (Kirchhoff's voltage law).

Observe that the lower extremity of the output waveshapes of Fig. 25-13 appears to be clamped at the voltage V.   Thus the name of the circuit, the lower-extremity clamp.

CLAMPING VS. ADDING A DC LEVEL

The difference in the output signal between that obtained from a clamp circuit and that obtained by merely adding a dc level to a signal is the level that remains constant as the input varies in amplitude.   In the case of a clamp circuit, depending on whether we are dealing with an upper- or lower-extremity clamp, one of the extremities remains fixed at the clamp voltage regardless of how the input varies.

When we merely add a dc level, both the extremities of the output vary as the input signal is made to vary, the average value remaining fixed at V, the reference voltage.

PROBLEMS

25-1 Sketch the schematic diagram and indicate the reference-voltage value required of a circuit which will separate the synchronization pulses from the waveshape shown in Fig. 25-14.

25-2 Determine the battery voltage for the situation in Fig. 25-15.

25-3 It is desired that a pulse train be generated by passing a sine wave through a double-ended clipper. The pulse train is to have an upper level of 35 volts and a lower level of 20 volts. The PRT is to be 5 msec.

    (*a*) Draw a schematic diagram of the appropriate clipper circuit indicating the reference-voltage levels.

    (*b*) What should the frequency of the sine wave be?

    (*c*) Sketch the input and output waveshapes.

    (*d*) Indicate the periods of time when each of the diodes is conducting.

25-4 Sketch the waveshapes at points I to V of Fig. 25-16. Indicate all pertinent voltage levels and times.

25-5 (*a*) Sketch a set of transistor collector characteristics with a superimposed load line. Indicate the saturation point and the cutoff point.

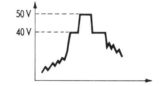

FIGURE 25-14 *Diagram for Prob. 25-1.*

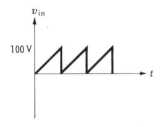

FIGURE 25-15 *Diagram for Prob. 25-2.*

FIGURE 25-16 *Diagram for Prob. 25-4.*

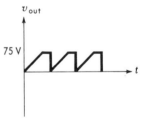

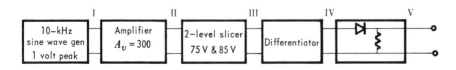

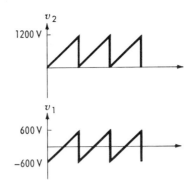

FIGURE 25-17 *Diagram for Prob. 25-7.*

(b) What is meant by the terms "saturation clipping" and "cut-off clipping"?

(c) What is the advantage of using transistor limiting rather than diode limiting?

25-6 A self-biased transistor amplifier is being used to reshape a pulse which has deteriorated because tilt and noise have affected its positive extremity. This deteriorated pulse has extreme values of 0 and +50 μa. A 2N2953 transistor is to be used in the amplifier. A new pulse is to be generated which has extremity values of −5 and −10 volts. The base is to be biased to −30 μa.

(a) Draw a schematic diagram of the circuit.

(b) Prepare a layout for a four-quadrant graph. Include the output voltage waveshape.

(c) Locate the quiescent operating point.

(d) Draw the load line.

(e) Draw the collector output waveshape.

(f) Determine V_{CC}, R_C, and R_B (assume $V_{BEQ} = 0.2$ volt).

25-7 (a) When would you consider using a clamping circuit?

(b) What is the advantage of using a clamping circuit over merely adding a dc level to a signal?

FIGURE 25-18 *Diagram for Prob. 25-8.*

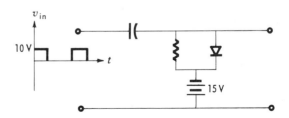

CLIPPING, LIMITING, AND CLAMPING CIRCUITS 359

(c) What is the difference between an upper-extremity clamp and a lower-extremity clamp?

(d) Draw a schematic diagram of a clamp circuit which can be used to convert the waveshape V_1 into the waveshape V_2 (Fig. 25-17).

25-8 Sketch the output waveshape for the situation depicted in Fig. 25-18. The peak-to-peak value of the input wave doubles. Sketch the new output waveshape.

26

COMPUTERS AND DIODE LOGIC CIRCUITS

As our civilization advanced and scientific knowledge and business relationships grew more sophisticated, it became necessary to perform many mathematical operations on data growing out of these endeavors. Often, the maximum size of business and government ventures was limited by the capacity of any one organization to handle and process large amounts of data repetitively. In the pursuit of scientific knowledge many problems remained unsolved. It was not possible to allocate the immense number of people to the tasks of accumulating and processing the huge amounts of data. Performing mathematical operations on data was not the only hindrance to efficiency. If was becoming impossible to conveniently retrieve information. An unreasonable amount of time and personnel had to be allocated to this function. It was necessary to develop an automated means of keeping track of, and operating on, accumulated data. Complex filing and retrieval systems were developed for this purpose. However, it was not until the middle of the twentieth century, with the advancement of electronic technology, that we were able to effectively cope with the ever increasing load of paper work (information handling). It was at this time that modern-day computers were born.

These machines cannot do anything that a human being cannot do. The rapidity with which these machines perform their tasks is what makes them so valuable.

Modern-day computers are classified into one of three categories: analog, digital, or hybrid computers. Hybrid computers are a combination of the other two.

THE ANALOG COMPUTER

Scientists, mathematicians, and engineers found in their studies of electric circuits that many of the equations they wrote were similar in form to equations describing other natural phenomena. They reasoned that it might be possible to design circuitry with properties similar to the properties of devices which were physically different but mathematically similar. For example, the mathematical description of a spring is quite similar to that of an inductor and capacitor combination; applied force to that of voltage; friction to that of resistance. A detailed study of electric circuitry indicated that almost any mathematical equation could be simulated by some combination of electric components. In making use of the analog computer a set of equations is first written describing the physical situation to be studied. The electric network is then arranged on the computer, simulating these equations. It is then possible, by studying the currents and voltage involved, to determine the behavior of the physical quantities of the original system under study. As an example of the strength of the analog computer consider its ability to eliminate the need of building, testing, and flying an aircraft in order to see if it is flightworthy. Consider also the effort and expense saved by not having to build a dam to determine whether it is capable of withstanding all the stresses to which it may be subjected. Actually, even if the analog computer was not available one would hardly run off and build aircraft or dams to determine whether they were worthwhile; analysis of the rather complex equations involved would be undertaken first. Such an analysis usually requires a great deal of time and effort by highly trained and skilled personnel. Use of the analog computer reduces the amount of time required to a very tiny fraction of what would have been required otherwise. As an example, consider the analysis of the equations describing a navigation system. This analysis would require a highly trained mathematician to work for approximately a full work week, while the analog computer can produce the same results in less than one minute, once the circuitry has been set up.

THE DIGITAL COMPUTER

The digital computer, at first glance, is not as "smart" a machine as the analog computer. It depends for its usefulness not upon its ability to solve sophisticated mathematical equations but upon its speed in performing ultrasimple arithmetic operations. All mathematical operations which a digital computer is called upon to do, no matter how complex, are broken down into either an addition or a subtraction process. Actually, the digital computer is even dumber than that. Modern digital machines do not even have the ability to do simple arithmetic in the decimal system. All work is done in the binary system. The binary system of numbers has only two digits, 0 and 1. Table 26-1 is a list of a few binary num-

TABLE 26-1

Binary number	Decimal equivalent
0	0
1	1
10	2
11	3
100	4
101	5
110	6
111	7
1000	8
1001	9
1010	10
1011	11

bers and their decimal equivalents. Such a dumb machine finds unlimited usefulness because while it can do only ridiculously simple operations, it can do them at fantastic speeds. At present, the time per operation is being measured in nanoseconds (10^{-9} sec) with the state of the art looking toward still greater speeds in the near future.

Thus, though it may take many simple operations to implement a single more complicated mathematical operation, the time needed to accomplish the simple operations is small.

DATA STORAGE

Because of the many simple operations a digital computer must perform and the huge quantities of intermediate solutions it must handle, a digital computer must have a place to store data. Some of these data are stored and called for at a much later time, while some data are stored only temporarily and used within the next few steps of the computer operation. Thus, the digital computer has the ability to store data temporarily and also to store data for indefinitely long periods of time. The portions of the machine set aside for data storage are referred to as the *memory* of the machine. The machine must store large quantities of data and must have the ability to gain access to these data quickly and easily.

Input-Output Devices Figure 26-1 is a block diagram of a digital computer. Since the computer is called upon to handle large amounts of data quickly and perform many mathematical operations, it is of utmost importance that a control of data traffic be arranged for. The *central control unit* is the portion of the machine which performs this function. The *input-output device* permits communication with the computer. This device may be a card reader, a card puncher, a typewriter, a printer, or some other machine which permits communication between the inside of the computer and the outside world. Note that the arrows in the diagram indicate the possible signal flow paths.

THE PROGRAM

In order for a digital computer to produce the solution to a problem it must be fed information of two types. First, the *program* must be submitted to the machine, and, second, the raw data for the particular problem must be submitted. The program is a set of instructions which communicate to the computer what steps must be done and in what order. Both the program and the data are placed into the input-output device by the machine operator. This information is then stored in the memory section of the computer until it is called for. The solution of the problem is begun with

FIGURE 26-1 *Block diagram of a digital computer.*

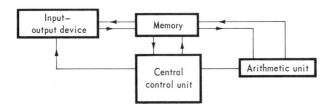

the control section calling for the first instruction of the program and then interpreting what the machine is now required to do in order to carry out this instruction. Any data required for this operation are then called for from the memory. These data are then fed into the appropriate part of the arithmetic unit in order for the necessary arithmetic operations to be completed. After the arithmetic operation is carried out the solution, whether final or intermediate, is then fed back to the memory for storage. It can be called upon in the future to supply some necessary information and/or be sent on to the input-output device at the end of the problem.

LOGIC CIRCUITS

In order to get the proper data into and out of the memory the data must first be located. This is no mean task when it is realized that the computer is storing millions of bits of data in its memory. A *bit* is the smallest discernible amount of information. Bit is a contraction of the two words, binary digit. In order to facilitate the locating of data after they have been stored, each data location is given an address. A given address can be located electrically by the use of circuits known as *logic circuits*. Logic circuits also are used in the arithmetic unit of the computer, where they implement the processes of binary addition and binary subtraction.

Logic circuits are circuits which are known by the following names:

> AND circuits
> OR circuits
> NOT circuits (also called inverters)
> NAND circuits
> NOR circuits

Except for the NOT circuit, all these circuits have multiple inputs and a single output. The following discussion will be limited to what is commonly referred to as positive logic.

The AND Circuit An AND circuit is one which will produce an output voltage if and only if *all* inputs are acted upon by an input voltage (see Fig. 26-2*a*).

The OR Circuit An OR circuit is one which provides an output voltage if *any* of the inputs are acted upon by an input voltage or if all the inputs are acted upon by a voltage (see Fig. 26-2*b*).

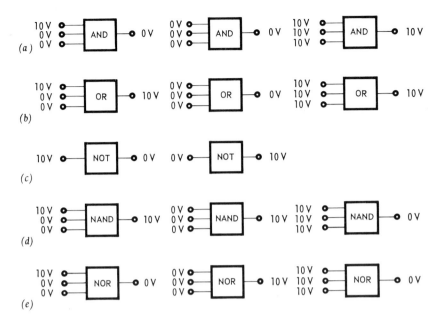

FIGURE 26-2 *Logic circuits under various input conditions.*

The NOT Circuit (Inverter) A NOT circuit is one which will provide an output voltage only if the input *is not* acted upon by a voltage and will not provide an output voltage if the input *is* acted upon by a voltage (see Fig. 26-2c).

The NAND Circuit A NAND circuit is one which will not provide an output if and only if all the inputs are being activated by a voltage. It is a combination of a NOT and an AND (see Fig. 26-2d). It is really an AND-NOT circuit.

The NOR Circuit A NOR circuit is one which will not provide output voltage if any or all the inputs are activated by an input voltage. It is a combination of a NOT and an OR (see Fig. 26-2e). It is really an OR-NOT circuit.

Logic circuits can be implemented in a number of different ways using various components. The simplest of the circuits is that group referred to as *diode logic circuits.*

DIODE LOGIC CIRCUITS

Diode logic circuits are those circuits which can be used to implement any of the above mentioned logic functions and which consist of only resistors and diodes, as well as sources of voltage.

The AND and OR functions can be implemented by such diode logic circuits. Figure 26-3a is a schematic diagram of a diode logic OR circuit, and Fig. 26-3b is a schematic diagram of a diode logic AND circuit.

Those people who work with logic circuits have designated two conditions which are allowable, *one*, and *zero*. The *zero* condition can be any reference level, but for simplicity we will consider it as zero voltage $V(0)$. The other level, the one condition, is taken as any positive voltage reference $V(1)$.

THE OR CIRCUIT

Refer now to the schematic of the OR circuit shown as Fig. 26-3a. Note that a voltage applied to terminals A, B, or C which is equal to $V(1)$ will forward-bias the associated diode, thus causing it to conduct. By doing so the input voltage $V(1)$ is then directly coupled to the output and the output terminal is presented with a voltage corresponding to $V(1)$. In the event that no signal appears at any of the input terminals, the output terminal is coupled to ground through R and no voltage appears across the output.

THE AND CIRCUIT

Let us now turn to the diode logic AND circuit of Fig. 26-3b. Note that with all the input terminals returned to zero voltage, a current flows through R which is great enough for Kirchhoff's voltage law to be satisfied, making the voltage drop across R equal to the supply voltage $V(1)$. This causes the voltage from the output terminal to ground to be zero. Note that not only must one diode be opened to change this condition but all the diodes must be made to open, thereby eliminating all the possible paths for the current which is now flowing through R. To cause one of the diodes to appear as an open circuit its corresponding input terminal must have a voltage applied to it which is at least equal to $V(1)$. It is of the utmost significance to note that *all* the input terminals must have such a voltage applied in order to eliminate paths for the flow of current which is providing the voltage drop across R. Therefore in order to get the voltage corresponding to $V(1)$ between the output termi-

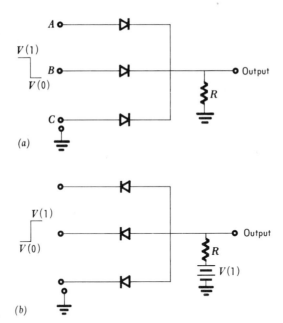

FIGURE 26-3 (a) *Diode logic* OR *circuit (positive logic).* (b) *Diode logic* AND *circuit (positive logic).*

nal and ground it is necessary for all the input terminals to have a voltage applied to them of at least $V(1)$.

SYMBOLS

Since it is obviously quite cumbersome to draw a complete diagram of an AND or an OR circuit whenever going through a preliminary logic design, symbols are used to represent the OR and the AND function, as shown in Fig. 26-4.

Note that the AND and the OR circuit can have as many input terminals as the designer chooses to provide, the only limiting factor being the power drain and diode capabilities. The limiting factors due to the diode characteristics will not be discussed in this book.*

* More about such limiting conditions can be found in J. Millman and H. Taub, "Pulse, Digital, and Switching Waveforms," McGraw-Hill Book Company, New York, 1965.

THE NOT CIRCUIT

The NOT circuit is also known as an inverter circuit since its function is to convert $V(1)$'s to $V(0)$'s and vice versa. A simple single-stage common-emitter amplifier can be used to perform this function. An inherent property of the single-stage amplifier is its ability

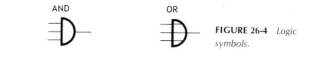

AND   OR

FIGURE 26-4 *Logic symbols.*

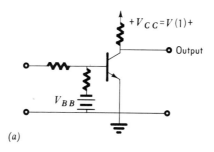

(a)

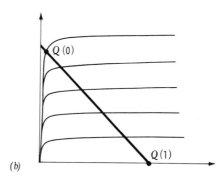

(b)

FIGURE 26-5 (a) *Schematic circuit of an inverter* (NOT *circuit*). (b) *Characteristic curve and load line indicating the zero and one points of operation.*

to invert the input signal when providing the output signal. Remember the 180° phase shift of the single-stage amplifier when dealing with sine waves.

A circuit often used to perform the NOT function is shown in Fig. 26-5. The circuit components are so chosen that when the input is presented with a $V(1)$ signal, the amplifier conducts fully, providing an output voltage as indicated by $Q(0)$ in Fig. 26-5b. When the circuit is provided with a $V(0)$ input, the transistor goes to cutoff, indicated as $Q(1)$ in Fig. 26-5b.

Thus it is seen that the circuit indicated in Fig. 26-5 performs the NOT function, providing a $V(0)$ output when excited by a $V(1)$ input and providing a $V(1)$ output at all other times.

There is no neutral time. The input to all the logic circuits is either recognized as a $V(1)$ signal or as a $V(0)$ signal.

Symbolically a NOT function is indicated as a small circle at the input or output of another function (see Fig. 26-6).

COMPUTERS AND DIODE LOGIC CIRCUITS   369

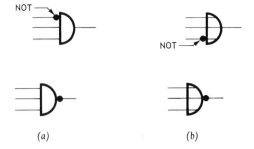

FIGURE 26-6 *Logic symbols with an inverter on one input.*

FIGURE 26-7 *Symbol for* (a) NAND *circuit and* (b) NOR *circuit.*

(a)   (b)

THE NAND AND NOR CIRCUITS

A NAND circuit is a combination of an AND and a NOT circuit. This is shown symbolically as Fig. 26-7*a*. Obviously a NOR circuit is then as shown symbolically in Fig. 26-7*b*.

A NAND circuit will provide a $V(0)$ output only if all the inputs are $V(1)$, while a NOR circuit will provide a $V(1)$ output only if all the inputs are a $V(0)$.

TRUTH TABLES AND ALGEBRA TYPE OF EQUATIONS

Are you beginning to get confused? It is difficult to keep track of whether only one $V(1)$ appearing on the input of an AND circuit will provide either a $V(1)$ or a $V(0)$, considering that there are five different circuits involved (OR, AND, NOR, NAND, NOT). When we consider that these are just the building blocks we will use when we design the implementation for complex logic designs, it becomes obvious that some simplified bookkeeping scheme is necessary.

One technique is the use of truth tables. In a truth table all the possible combinations of inputs are written down and the expected output is determined. All this is done in a tabular form, as shown in Fig. 26-8. The 0s indicate $V(0)$'s and the 1s indicate $V(1)$'s.

In addition to truth tables for keeping track of logic design requirements, we can use algebra type of equations in which the plus sign indicates the OR function and the product sign indicates the AND function. For example,

$$F = (A+B+C)(D)$$

A three-input AND circuit is indicated as $A \cdot B \cdot C$, while a three-input OR circuit is indicated as $A+B+C$. Inversion is indicated by a prime following whatever is to be inverted or a bar over whatever is to be inverted (see Fig. 26-8).

$A \cdot B \cdot C = D$

A	B	C	D
0	0	0	0
0	0	1	0
0	1	0	0
0	1	1	0
1	0	0	0
1	0	1	0
1	1	0	0
1	1	1	1

(a)

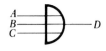

$A + B + C = D$

A	B	C	D
0	0	0	0
0	0	1	1
0	1	0	1
0	1	1	1
1	0	0	1
1	0	1	1
1	1	0	1
1	1	1	1

(b)

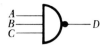

$(A \cdot B \cdot C)' = D$

A	B	C	D
0	0	0	1
0	0	1	1
0	1	0	1
0	1	1	1
1	0	0	1
1	0	1	1
1	1	0	1
1	1	1	0

(c)

$(A + B + C)' = D$

A	B	C	D
0	0	0	1
0	0	1	0
0	1	0	0
0	1	1	0
1	0	0	0
1	0	1	0
1	1	0	0
1	1	1	0

(d)

FIGURE 26-8 (a) Three-input AND circuit. (b) Three-input OR circuit. (c) Three-input NAND circuit. (d) Three-input NOR circuit.

Illustrative Problem 26-1

In a particular system five signal lines are available. It is desired that an output pulse be provided only if the following conditions prevail *simultaneously.*

1 A pulse appears on line A.
2 A pulse does not appear on line B.
3 A pulse appears on either line C or D.
4 A pulse appears on line E.

(a) Write an equation for the requirements of this design.
(b) Sketch the logic symbol diagram needed to provide the above function.
(c) Make a truth table that specifies the effect of the OR circuit used.
(d) Sketch the circuitry required to implement the above function.

SOLUTION
(a) $(A)(B')(C+D)E = F$
(b) See Fig. Prob. 26-1a.
(c) See Fig. Prob. 26-1b.
(d) See Fig. Prob. 26-1c.

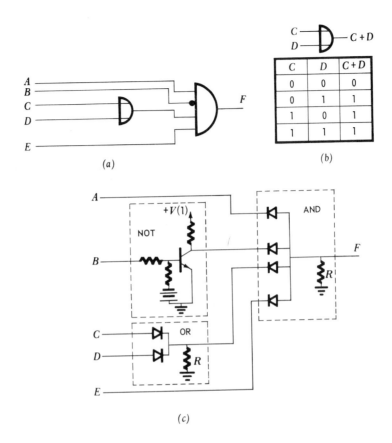

FIGURE PROB. 26-1

PROBLEMS

26-1 What are the three main computer classifications?

26-2 On what general finding is the analog computer based?

26-3 Which type of computer would you prefer to use for simulation purposes, the analog or the digital? Why?

26-4 Being quite dumb, why does the digital computer find as much usefulness as it does?

26-5 What is meant when we refer to a computer memory?

26-6 What function is performed by each of the following units?

    (a) Central control unit

    (b) Input-output device

    (c) Arithmetic unit

26-7 What is a program?

26-8 List the different types of logic circuits. Which of these have multiple inputs and which only a single input? Define the function of each basic logic circuit.

26-9 What kind of circuit using an active device is used to implement the NOT function? Why is it used?

26-10 (*a*) Construct a truth table to describe $(A + B) \cdot C' = D$.

(*b*) Sketch the logic symbol diagram necessary for implementing this function.

(*c*) Draw a schematic diagram for the circuitry necessary to implement this function.

(*d*) Describe in words the conditions necessary for an output pulse to appear.

THE ASTABLE MULTIVIBRATOR

So far in our dealings with pulses and pulse trains, we have taken for granted the ability of producing pulses with any combination of pulse duration and rest time. One way we have been able to produce a waveshape resembling a pulse train is by generating a sine wave and then passing it through a two-level slicer. This has a great many limitations. First, the pulse duration and the rest period are not independent. Second, the slope of the sides leaves a great deal to be desired.

Let us now examine a circuit which can be used as a primary source for the generation of pulse trains, one in which the pulse duration and the rest time are independently variable.

THE BARKHAUSEN CRITERION
Let us backtrack a bit to the first circuit we considered when developing primary signal sources in Chap. 22. The block diagram of such a circuit, a two-stage capacitor-coupled amplifier with 100 percent feedback, is shown in Fig. 27-1. Recalling the Barkhausen criterion for oscillation and referring to Fig. 27-2,

$$A' = \frac{A}{1 - AB} \quad \text{and} \quad A' = \infty \quad \text{when } AB = +1$$

Comparing Figs. 27-1 and 27-2,

$$A = A_1 A_2 \quad \text{and} \quad B = 1$$

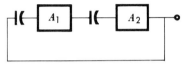

FIGURE 27-1 *A two-stage capacitor-coupled amplifier with 100 percent feedback.*

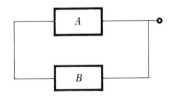

FIGURE 27-2 *A basic feedback loop.*

In Fig. 27-3 we have a schematic diagram of a two-stage transistor amplifier which can be used to implement this description. Figure 27-4 is simply a copy of Fig. 27-3 with components rearranged for ease of analysis.

$AB > +1$

Designing the two stages so that $AB > +1$, then breadboarding it and letting it run in the laboratory provides an output at each of the two collectors, as shown in Fig. 27-5. These are good approximations of pulse trains.

What is the meaning of making AB greater than $+1$? It means that only a very small disturbance is needed to create a situation in which each time the disturbance makes a pass around the loop it gets bigger. It keeps getting bigger and bigger until it exceeds the two extreme points on the load line. We then say that the amplifier is going into cutoff on one extreme of the load line and into saturation on the other extreme. More will be said about these two extremes shortly.

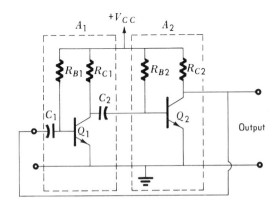

FIGURE 27-3 *Schematic diagram of a two-stage capacitor-coupled amplifier with 100 percent feedback.*

THE ASTABLE MULTIVIBRATOR   375

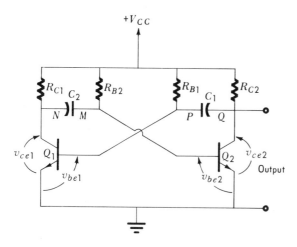

FIGURE 27-4 *The astable multivibrator.*

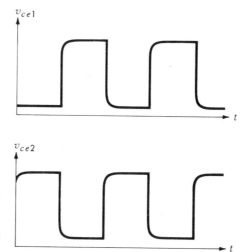

FIGURE 27-5 *The voltage waveshapes available at the collector of each of the transistors of the astable multivibrator of Fig. 27-4.*

QUASI-STABLE STATES

The two-stage capacitor-coupled amplifier with 100 percent feedback of Fig. 27-4 proves to be a good primary source of pulse trains. Note from Fig. 27-5 that the collector voltage for each transistor comes up to a particular level, stays for a given length of time, and then changes value instantaneously, holding its new value for another period of time, at the end of which it again changes value instantaneously, returning to its original value.

Thus, the circuit is said to have two semistable or quasi-stable states, and it alternates between the two at a fixed rate. The amount of time spent in each of the two states is independently variable and depends upon component values. Because of the manner in which this circuit operates, it is given the name *astable multivibrator.*

CUTOFF AND SATURATION

Considering the important role played by the cutoff and saturation conditions in the astable multivibrator circuit, it is appropriate at this point to study them in detail.

Referring to Fig. 27-6, note that the two extreme points of operation on the load line are called the *cutoff point* and the *saturation point.* The cutoff point gets its name from the fact that at this point on the load line no collector current flows. Increasing the base voltage in the reverse bias direction has no effect. The reason for naming the other extreme point the saturation point is less obvious. At the saturation point so much collector current is flowing that the voltage drop across the resistor R_C is so great that very little voltage is left to appear across the collector-to-emitter terminals of the transistor. Remember that Kirchhoff's voltage law requires that the sum of the voltage drops be equal to the sum of the voltage rises. Thus, the saturation point for the particular circuit is that point on the load line at which the collector-to-emitter voltage has taken on the smallest allowable voltage of v_{ce} for the particular load line. The reason for calling this the saturation point is that at this point the capability of the collector circuit to provide current is saturated. Increasing the base current has no effect on collector current once saturation has been reached.

For the sake of simplicity the actual transistor characteristics of Fig. 27-6 can be approximated by the set of characteristics shown

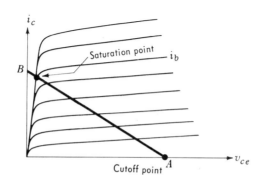

FIGURE 27-6 *Transistor characteristic curves showing load line and cutoff and saturation points.*

THE ASTABLE MULTIVIBRATOR   377

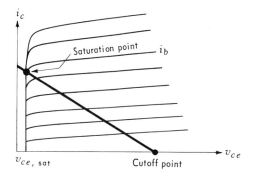

FIGURE 27-7 *Simplified transistor characteristic curves showing load line and cutoff and saturation points.*

in Fig. 27-7. Note in Fig. 27-7 that the collector-to-emitter voltage v_{ce} can be taken as approximately constant regardless of the load line. This saturation voltage $V_{CE,sat}$ depends on the chemical makeup of the transistor. The collector-to-emitter voltage at the saturation point can be approximated as 0.3 volt for a silicon transistor and 0.1 volt for a germanium transistor. The associated base-to-emitter voltage at saturation is approximately 0.7 volt for silicon transistors and 0.3 volt for germanium transistors.

TABLE 27-1
VOLTAGES AT SATURATION

	$V_{BE,sat}$, **volts**	$V_{CE,sat}$, **volts**
Si	0.7	0.3
Ge	0.3	0.1

To ensure that the transistor is cut off or saturated when desired, the designer usually provides for a collector voltage greater than the marginal value required for cutoff and for base currents greater than the marginal value for saturation.

ANALYSIS OF THE CIRCUIT

By providing the proper conditions we can cause each of the transistors of Fig. 27-8a (Fig. 27-4 reproduced) to alternate between cutoff and saturation, each transistor's action being the complement of the other. Let us investigate the effect this has on other circuit components. A study of the capacitors will prove interesting since

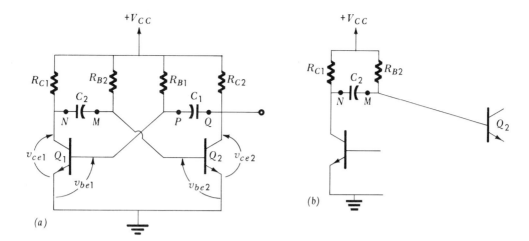

FIGURE 27-8   (a) The
astable multivibrator.   (b)
Section of the astable multivibrator which is in the
environment of C_2.

the rate of change of the voltage across them is dependent on the
RC time constant of their charge and discharge paths.

Figure 27-8b is one section of the astable multivibrator whose
complete schematic diagram was shown as Fig. 27-8a.   This section of the total schematic has been chosen so that we can investigate the effect the various circuit conditions have on the voltage
across C_2.

In order to simplify the analysis let us make the assumption
that the voltages across the collector to emitter and that across the
base to emitter during saturation are negligible compared to V_{CC}
and therefore during saturation both the collector-to-emitter and
the base-to-emitter junctions can be considered short circuits.
With this in mind we can sketch the circuits of Fig. 27-9, which
shows the circuit conditions during the two possible quasi-stable
states.   In Fig. 27-9a we have the conditions for the quasi-stable
state in which Q_1 is cut off and Q_2 is saturated, while in Fig. 27-9b
we have the conditions for Q_1 saturated and Q_2 cut off.

In order to see how these schematics of Fig. 27-9 were developed let us concentrate on the capacitor C_2 of Fig. 27-8a during
each of the two quasi-stable states.   First let us take the case of
Fig. 27-9a, Q_1 cut off and Q_2 saturated.   With Q_1 cut off its collector-to-emitter section can be considered an open circuit and thus

eliminated from the diagram while the base to emitter of Q_2 has the very small saturation voltage which we have chosen to consider as a short circuit for simplicity. Thus Fig. 27-9a represents the capacitor C_2 and the components in its immediate environment during the quasi-stable state in which Q_1 is cut off and Q_2 is saturated.

What about the quasi-stable state depicted in Fig. 27-9b? In this case Q_1 is saturated and Q_2 is cut off. Thus the collector-to-emitter section of Q_2 can now be taken as an open circuit and eliminated from the diagram while the base-to-emitter section of Q_1 has the small saturation voltage across it that we have chosen to consider negligible and represent as a short circuit.

Combining the two circuits of Fig. 27-9, we can represent them as shown in Fig. 27-10, where we have depicted a switching arrangement to switch from the condition of Fig. 27-9a to b and vice versa.

As a general rule we will find that R_C is much smaller than R_B in astable multivibrator circuits. Thus we will find that the time constant $R_C C$ is much smaller than the time constant $R_B C$.

Let us assume that when we start, the switch of Fig. 27-10 is in position 1. The switch being in this position causes the capacitor to charge very rapidly to V_{CC} with *point M negative*. Assume that

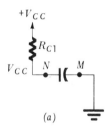

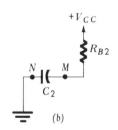

(a)   (b)

FIGURE 27-9 *The environment of capacitor C_2 during each of the quasi-stable states. (a) Q_1 cut off and Q_2 saturated; (b) Q_1 saturated and Q_2 cut off.*

FIGURE 27-10 *Switching arrangement for studying the voltage across C_2 during each of the two quasi-stable states. Position 1: Q_1 cut off, Q_2 saturated; position 2: Q_2 cut off, Q_1 saturated.*

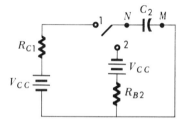

380   PULSES AND THEIR APPLICATIONS

the switch remains in position 1 long enough for the capacitor to become fully charged. Now assume that the switch is thrown to position 2. The capacitor now begins to charge to the condition of having V_{CC} across it, this time however with *point N negative and point M positive* (see Fig. 27-11).

Let us now recall what position 2 on the switch represented for the total astable-multivibrator circuit of Fig. 27-8a. Q_1 was to be saturated, and Q_2 was to be cut off. This is true only so long as the base of Q_2 is reverse-biased. This means with *NPN* transistors that point *M*, which is connected to the base of transistor Q_2, must be negative. Therefore, as the curve of Fig. 27-11 crosses the horizontal axis, the conditions of the circuit change and the switch is sent back into position 1, its other quasi-stable state.

Thus the curve of Fig. 27-11 can come up to the horizontal axis but cannot cross it. Once it starts to cross it, a change of state is initiated. Thus we can see how one of the state changes is caused. How about the other state change? We need only remember that the circuit is symmetrical to recognize that the other state change is initiated by an exact duplicate of the situation just described but having to do with the other capacitor C_1 and its charge and discharge paths.

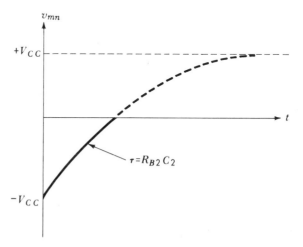

FIGURE 27-11 *Graph of voltage across C_2 vs. time. Switch is thrown from position 1 to position 2 at $t = 0$.*

TIMING

The major question at this point is: How long does the circuit remain in either of the two possible quasi-stable states? Look at the graph of the capacitor voltage shown in Fig. 27-11. The time constant of this RC charge curve is $R_{B_2}C_2$. An exact construction of this curve will show that the curve crosses the horizontal axis in 0.69 time constant after the charging has begun. Thus, the circuit remains in the state of Q_1 saturated and Q_2 cut off for a length of time equal to $0.69R_{B_2}C_2$. Because of the symmetry of the astable multivibrator circuit (Fig. 27-8a) we see that the circuit remains in the other state, Q_1 cut off and Q_2 saturated, for a length of time equal to $0.69R_{B_1}C_1$.

The output, if taken from across the collector-to-emitter terminals of Q_2, thus remains at V_{CC} for a length of time equal to $0.69R_{B_2}C_2$ and *approximately zero* for a length of time equal to $0.69R_{B_1}C_1$. The inverse of this waveshape is available if the output is taken from across the collector-to-emitter terminals of transistor Q_1.

Illustrative Problem 27-1

Transistors having the characteristics shown in Fig. Prob. 27-1a are to be used in the design of an astable multivibrator. The output of the circuit is to be a pulse train having a pulse duration of 2 msec and a rest time of 5 msec. During the duration of the pulse, it is to have a value of 15 volts. The collector current during saturation is to be limited to 7 ma.

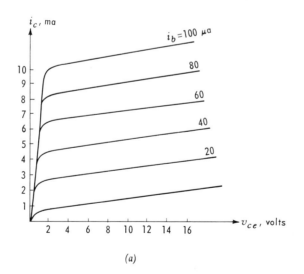

FIGURE PROB. 27-1a

(a)

(a) What should the value of V_{CC} be?
(b) Draw a load line for the operation as described.
(c) Determine the value of R_C.
(d) Determine the necessary values of $R_B C$.

SOLUTION

(a) Since the cutoff transistor has a voltage from collector to emitter equal to V_{CC} *across* it and the output voltage is taken there,

$$V_{CC} = 15 \text{ volts}$$

(b) See Fig. Prob. 27-1b.

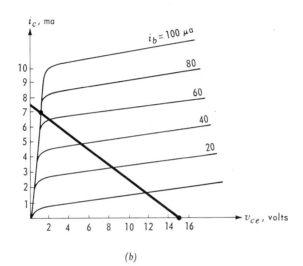

(b)

FIGURE PROB. 27-1b

(c) $I_{C,\text{intercept}} = 7.5$ ma

$$\frac{V_{CC}}{R_C} = 7.5 \text{ ma}$$

$$\frac{15}{R_C} = 7.5 \times 10^{-3}$$

$$R_C = \frac{15}{7.5 \times 10^{-3}}$$

$$R_C = 2000 \text{ ohms}$$

(d) $t_{\text{rest}} = 0.69 R_{B_1} C_1$

$$5 \times 10^{-3} = 0.69 R_{B_1} C_1$$

$$R_{B_1} C_1 = \frac{5 \times 10^{-3}}{0.69}$$

$$\boxed{R_{B_1}C_1 = 7.25 \times 10^{-3}}$$

$$t_p = 0.69R_{B_2}C_2$$
$$2 \times 10^{-3} = 0.69R_{B_2}C_2$$
$$R_{B_2}C_2 = \frac{2 \times 10^{-3}}{0.69}$$

$$\boxed{R_{B_2}C_2 = 2.9 \times 10^{-3}}$$

DESIGN TECHNIQUE

Because Illustrative Problem 27-1 can be used to develop a technique for designing astable multivibrators, a more detailed analysis of it will now be undertaken.

To start, V_{CC} was determined by the description of the maximum value of the pulses in the pulse train, $V_{CC} \approx V_{\text{pulse max}}$. The determination of R_C was then made, once we decided on the value for collector current during saturation. Frequently, the characteristic curves are not provided for transistors that are intended for use in pulse circuits. This need not present too great a problem in determining R_C. The simplest way to handle this is to apply Kirchhoff's law and Ohm's law to the saturated transistor (see Fig. 27-12).

$$\boxed{R_C = \frac{V_{CC} - V_{CE,\text{sat}}}{I_{C,\text{sat}}}}$$

We neatly avoided having to determine the required values of R_B and C in the illustrative problem by finding merely their product R_BC from a consideration of the required time constant.

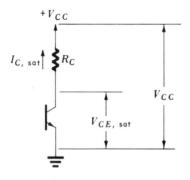

FIGURE 27-12 *Determining the value of R_C.*

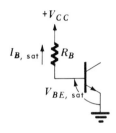

FIGURE 27-13 *The Kirchhoff loop containing R_B.*

How do we determine independent values for R_B and C? Refer to the characteristic curve with the load line that was used in the solution of the illustrative problem. Examine the load line at various points. Note that for values of base current less than about 70 μa, the transistor is not saturated. Any value of base current larger than 70 μa will keep the transistor saturated. In the event that the characteristic curves are not provided, as we just postulated, the manufacturer will provide a parameter $h_{FE,\text{sat}}$ which will relate the collector current to the minimum value of the base current necessary to cause saturation for a particular value of collector current

$$h_{FE,\text{sat}} = \frac{I_{C,\text{sat}}}{I_{B,\text{sat min}}}$$

A limitation on R_B can now be determined. Applying Kirchhoff's voltage law in the loop containing R_B, as in Fig. 27-13,

$$R_B I_{B,\text{sat}} = V_{CC} - V_{BE,\text{sat}}$$

and because minimum base current is provided when maximum R_B is used,

$$R_{B,\text{max}} I_{B,\text{sat min}} = V_{CC} - V_{BE,\text{sat}}$$

A minimum allowable value for R_B is usually set by the manufacturer's maximum allowable rating for base current.

Finally, exact values of R_B and C are determined by the timing requirements of the pulse train to be generated and the standard values of components available for R_B and C.

For quick estimates, we can neglect the collector-to-emitter and the base-to-emitter voltage drops during saturation and develop the following approximation:

$$R_C \approx \frac{V_{CC}}{I_{C,\text{sat}}}$$

$$h_{FE,\text{sat}} \approx \frac{I_{C,\text{sat}}}{I_{B,\text{sat}}}$$

THE ASTABLE MULTIVIBRATOR 385

$$R_{B,\max} I_{B,\text{sat min}} \approx V_{CC}$$
$$\approx R_C I_{C,\text{sat}}$$

$$\boxed{R_{B,\max} \approx R_C h_{FE,\text{sat}}}$$

Illustrative Problem 27-2

A pair of silicon transistors that have an $h_{FE,\text{sat}}$ of 50 are to be used in an astable multivibrator. The rated collector current is 100 ma, and the maximum allowable base current is 10 ma. The required pulse train is to have a pulse duration of 8 msec and a rest time of 4 msec. The duration value of the pulse is 20 volts.

SOLUTION

Given: $h_{FE,\text{sat}} = 50$; $I_{C,\text{rated}} = 100$ ma; $I_{B,\max} = 10$ ma; $t_p = 8$ msec; $t_{\text{rest}} = 4$ msec; $V_{\text{duration}} = 20$ volts

Find:

(a) V_{CC}
(b) R_C
(c) R_{B_1}
(d) C_1
(e) R_{B_2}
(f) C_2

(a) $\boxed{V_{CC} = 20 \text{ volts}}$

(b) $R_C = \dfrac{V_{CC} - V_{CE,\text{sat}}}{I_{C,\text{sat}}} = \dfrac{20 - 0.3}{100 \times 10^{-3}} = \dfrac{19.7}{10^{-1}}$

$$\boxed{R_C = 197 \text{ ohms}}$$

(c) $0.69 R_{B_2} C_2 = 8 \times 10^{-3}$
$R_{B_2} C_2 = 11.6 \times 10^{-3}$
$0.69 R_{B_1} C_1 = 4 \times 10^{-3}$
$R_{B_1} C_1 = 5.8 \times 10^{-3}$
$R_{B,\max} I_{B,\text{sat min}} = V_{CC} - V_{BE,\text{sat}}$

$$I_{B,\text{sat min}} = \frac{I_{C,\text{sat}}}{h_{FE,\text{sat}}}$$
$$= \frac{100 \times 10^{-3}}{50} = 2 \times 10^{-3}$$

$R_{B,\max} I_{B,\text{sat min}} = V_{CC} - V_{BE,\text{sat}}$
$R_{B,\max} \times 2 \times 10^{-3} = 20 - 0.7$
$$= \frac{19.3}{2 \times 10^{-3}}$$

$$\boxed{R_{B,\max} = 9.65 \text{ kilohms}}$$

$$R_{B,\min}I_{B,\max} = V_{CC} - V_{BE,\text{sat}}$$
$$R_{B,\min} \times 10 \times 10^{-3} = 20 - 0.7$$
$$R_{B,\min} = \frac{19.3}{10 \times 10^{-3}}$$

$$\boxed{R_{B,\min} = 1.93 \text{ kilohms}}$$

$R_{B_1}C_1 = 5.8 \times 10^{-3}$
$R_{B,\max} = 9.65$ kilohms
$R_{B,\min} = 1.93$ kilohms

Let

$$\boxed{R_{B_1} = 4700 \text{ ohms} \qquad \text{a standard resistance value}}$$

(d) $R_{B_1}C_1 = 5.8 \times 10^{-3}$
$4700 \times C_1 = 5.8 \times 10^{-3}$
$$C_1 = \frac{5.8 \times 10^{-3}}{4700}$$

$$\boxed{C_1 = 1.23 \ \mu f}$$

(e) Let

$$\boxed{R_{B_2} = 4700 \text{ ohms}}$$

(f) $R_{B_2}C_2 = 11.6 \times 10^{-3}$
$4700 \times C_2 = 11.6 \times 10^{-3}$
$$C_2 = \frac{11.6}{4700} \times 10^{-3}$$

$$\boxed{C_2 = 2.46 \ \mu f}$$

PROBLEMS

27-1 Where does the astable multivibrator get its name?
27-2 In Fig. 27-14, the switch is in position 1 for an indefinitely long time.   At $t = 0$, the switch is moved into position 2.
(a) Draw a V_C-vs.-time graph to scale.
(b) How long does it take for the voltage across the capacitor to become zero after the switch is thrown?

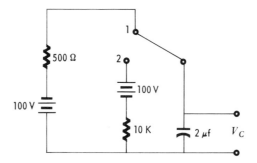

FIGURE 27-14 *Diagram for Prob. 27-2.*

27-3 Determine the time constants of $R_{B_1}C_1$ and $R_{B_2}C_2$ for an astable multivibrator whose output is to be a pulse train with a pulse duration of 600 μsec and a rest time of 900 μsec. What is the PRR of the pulse train?

27-4 A pair of transistors whose characteristics are shown in Fig. 27-15 are to be used in an astable multivibrator. The collector current during saturation is to be 50 ma. The voltage levels of the output pulse are to be 20 volts and approximately zero volts.
  (*a*) Draw a schematic diagram of the circuit.
  (*b*) What should the value of V_{CC} be?
  (*c*) Draw a load line that describes the operation of this circuit.
  (*d*) Indicate the saturation and cutoff points on the load line.
  (*e*) Determine the necessary value of R_C.

27-5 Why are the cutoff and the saturation points called what they are?

27-6 Why is it necessary to know whether the transistors being considered for use in an astable multivibrator are silicon or germanium when the characteristic curves are not available? What else is it necessary to know about the transistors?

27-7 A pair of germanium transistors is being considered for use in an astable multivibrator. Each has an $h_{FE,\text{sat}}$ of 80. The collector current is to be 15 ma. The maximum permitted base current is 1 ma. The output is to have an upper level of 12 volts, a 200-μsec

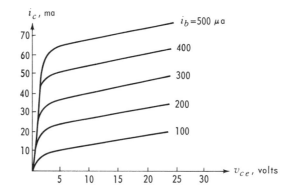

FIGURE 27-15 *Diagram for Prob. 27-4.*

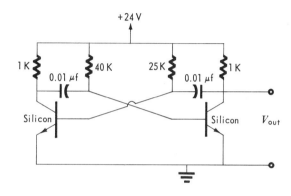

FIGURE 27-16 *Diagram for Prob. 27-9.*

rest time, and a 150-μsec pulse duration. Draw a schematic of the circuit and choose values for all components.

27-8   Estimate the maximum values of the base bias resistors in an astable multivibrator that uses a transistor having an $h_{FE,sat}$ of 110 and an R_C of 1 kilohm.

27-9   Determine the following quantities for the circuit shown in Fig. 27-16.
   (*a*) Pulse duration
   (*b*) Rest time
   (*c*) Collector current during saturation
   (*d*) Base current during saturation
   (*e*) Minimum permitted value of $h_{FE,sat}$
   (*f*) How can we get an output in which the pulse duration and the rest time are interchanged?
   (*g*) Determine the necessary power rating for the R_C's and R_B's.

27-10 (*a*) Design a symmetrical (pulse duration equal to the rest time) astable multivibrator having a pulse repetition rate of 2 pps and maximum pulse level of 10 volts. Specify as many component values as possible.
   (*b*) How can a premature change from one astable state to the other be triggered?

THE ASTABLE MULTIVIBRATOR   389

28

THE BISTABLE MULTIVIBRATOR

Let us discuss an electrically operated memory device capable of storing either a zero or a one. The need for such a device arises in digital computers when it is necessary to store data after calling them up from permanent storage or after having generated them as an intermediate solution in solving a problem. These data consist of a set of digits. Each digit of the set can have a value of either zero or one. Thus, we need a way of storing information that can have only one of two possible values.

A Multivibrator? The first idea that comes to mind is to use the astable multivibrator of Fig. 28-1 because it also has only two possible states. In one state transistor Q_1 is cut off and transistor Q_2 is saturated, while in the other state Q_2 is cut off and Q_1 is saturated. The only problem is that the astable multivibrator changes from one state to the other periodically of its own accord. However, if we were to alter the circuit to eliminate this automatic change of state, we would have a solution to our problem. We also have to provide some means to write in and read out the stored data.

In computers, collections of circuits for the temporary storage of data are called *registers*. Thus we are seeking circuits which can be combined to form a register.

What is it in the astable multivibrator of Fig. 28-1 that causes the circuit to change automatically from one state to the other? The RC circuits R_BC cause these automatic changes. Merely

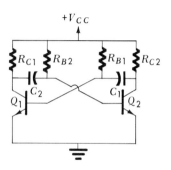

FIGURE 28-1 *The astable multivibrator.*

eliminating the capacitor altogether, thereby eliminating the coupling between the two stages, is not a good idea because we would then be unable to drive one transistor into cutoff and another into saturation. Instead, let us try to replace the capacitors of the astable multivibrator with resistors.

In Fig. 28-2 we have replaced the coupling capacitors with resistors, thus eliminating the timing action of the circuit yet still maintaining its feedback aspects. However, a new difficulty has arisen. Examine the base circuitry of both transistors. Now that the capacitors have been replaced by resistors (Fig. 28-2), we have eliminated the possibility of developing a reverse bias at either of the bases and thus eliminated the capability of cutting off either of the transistors. Previously, in the original astable multivibrator, the capacitors allowed *decreases* in collector-emitter voltage of one transistor to appear as a negative voltage at the base of the other transistor because the voltage across a capacitor could not change instantaneously. Now that we have eliminated the capacitors, we have also eliminated the ability of the circuit to provide reverse bias to the base-emitter junction of either transistor.

We can attempt to correct this difficulty by providing a separate bias supply for the base-emitter junction and return the base bias resistors R_{B1} and R_{B2} to it, as shown in Fig. 28-3.

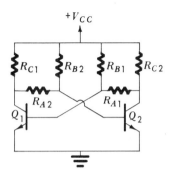

FIGURE 28-2 *Capacitors of the astable multivibrator replaced by resistors.*

THE BISTABLE MULTIVIBRATOR   391

ANALYSIS OF THE CIRCUITS

Will this circuit in Fig. 28-3 be able to hold one of the two states and function as a temporary storage element? As a starting point let us take a naïve approach and assume that the two stages are operating at the same operating point on the load line somewhere other than at cutoff or saturation. There really is no reason to assume otherwise in our first analysis since the two stages appear to be identical. Assume that the collector-to-emitter voltages are equal. Now assume that due to some slight disturbance, the collector current of transistor Q_1 increases slightly. This causes the collector-to-emitter voltage of Q_1 to drop slightly. This slight drop in voltage is transmitted to the base of Q_2 through the voltage divider R_{A2} and R_{B2}. This decrease in voltage between the base and emitter of Q_2 causes the collector current through transistor Q_2 to decrease, which in turn causes the collector voltage of Q_2 to increase.

The decreased collector current then causes a reduced voltage drop across R_{C2} and allows an increase in the collector-to-emitter voltage of Q_2. This increase in collector voltage of Q_2 is transmitted through the voltage divider $R_{A1}R_{B1}$ and appears on the base of Q_1 as an increase in base voltage. In turn the increase in base voltage of Q_1 causes an increase in the base current and collector current of Q_1. Remember that it was an increase in collector current of Q_1 that originally triggered off the chain of events. Thus, if the voltage-divider ratios are chosen in relation to the amplifier gains in such a way that the loop gain is greater than unity, the chain of events continues until one of the transistor collector currents reaches zero (cutoff) or until one of the transistors reaches saturation.

One of our design objectives will be to provide for the saturation of one transistor and the cutoff of the other to occur simultaneously.

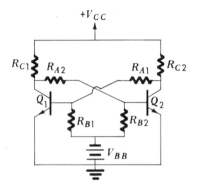

FIGURE 28-3 A fixed-bias NPN transistor binary.

A similar analysis can be performed assuming that the disturbance originated at the other transistor. With this new assumption we still get one transistor cut off and the other driven into saturation. The only difference is that the roles of the two transistors are interchanged.

STABLE STATES

Thus we have developed a system which has two *stable states*, one with Q_1 cut off and Q_2 in saturation and the other with Q_1 saturated and Q_2 cut off. Once driven into one of the two stable states, the circuit will remain there until acted upon by a relatively sizable externally applied signal.

Because the circuit has two stable states, it takes the name *bistable multivibrator*. Other names by which the circuit is known are *flip-flop*, *binary*, and the *Eccles-Jordan circuit*, after its originators.

THE DETERMINATION OF COMPONENT VALUES
FOR THE TRANSISTOR BISTABLE MULTIVIBRATOR

To develop our design technique we must first examine the requirements set by the system into which the circuit must be integrated. The system usually requires a particular voltage level to indicate the presence of a pulse in storage. When the circuit is storing a pulse, the transistor whose collector is the one from which the output is taken is in the condition of cutoff and the output is V_{CC}. Thus the V_{CC} for the circuit is determined by the required output voltage level.

Now that we see how the collector supply voltage is determined, let us turn our attention to the choice of R_C, the collector load resistor, knowing the particular collector current rating for the particular transistors to be used. We can apply Kirchhoff's voltage law around the collector-emitter circuit and then use Ohm's law. As in the case of the astable multivibrator,

$$R_C = \frac{V_{CC} - V_{CE,\text{sat}}}{I_{C,\text{sat}}}$$

Once we have determined the required value of the collector supply voltage and the collector resistors, we can turn our attention to determining the required values of the R_B's and R_A's and the necessary value of V_{BB}.

However, before undertaking these determinations, it is necessary to know the required value of the base current to ensure satura-

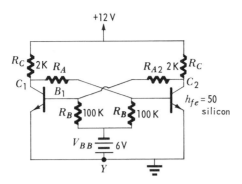

FIGURE 28-4 *The bistable multivibrator.*

tion. This can be found, as in the case of the astable multivibrator, from

$$I_{B,\text{sat min}} = \frac{I_{C,\text{sat}}}{h_{FE,\text{sat}}}$$

Now we can determine the necessary requirements for R_A and R_B and V_{BB}. Any two of the three quantities can be chosen freely. The third value must then be chosen to ensure saturation and also to avoid excessively large base current. An example will show how this can be done.

Assume all quantities as given in Fig. 28-4 and determine the limitations for R_{A1} and R_{A2}. In almost all cases R_{A1} is made equal to R_{A2}. The design study will be made for the conditions of Q_1 OFF and Q_2 ON. (An equally valid design can be undertaken assuming the opposite conditions.)

The determination has to satisfy two conditions. First Q_1 has to be cut off when Q_2 is ON (saturated), and Q_2 must be ON when Q_1 is cut off. Assume that the transistors are of silicon: $V_{CE,\text{sat}} = 0.3$ volt. In Fig. 28-5 a section of the bistable multivibrator of Fig. 28-4 has been isolated for intensive study. With Q_1 cut off V_{B1Y} must be more negative than 0 volts in order to reverse-bias the base-emitter junction. The following equations can now be written for Fig. 28-5:

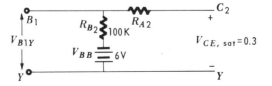

FIGURE 28-5 *Section of the bistable multivibrator of Fig. 28-4 removed for intensive study.*

$$V_{B1Y} = \frac{-R_{A2}}{R_{A2} + R_{B2}} (V_{BB} + V_{CE,\text{sat}}) + V_{CE,\text{sat}}$$

$$= \frac{-R_{A2}}{R_{A2} + R_{B2}} (6 + 0.3) + 0.3$$

$$< 0 \qquad \text{to ensure cutoff}$$

$$V_{B1Y} = \frac{-R_{A2}}{R_{A2} + 100 \text{ kilohms}} \times 6.3 + 0.3 < 0$$

$$\frac{-R_{A2} \times 6.3}{R_{A2} + 100 \text{ kilohms}} < -0.3$$

$$\frac{R_{A2} \times 6.3}{R_{A2} + 100 \text{ kilohms}} > 0.3$$

$$R_{A2} \times 6.3 > 0.3(R_{A2} + 100 \text{ kilohms})$$

$$6R_{A2} > 100 \text{ kilohms}$$

$$\boxed{R_{A2} > 16.7 \text{ kilohms}}$$

This does not complete the determination of R_A. It only indicates a *minimum value* for R_A. The following study of the base circuit of Q_2 will provide the maximum value (see Fig. 28-6 for that section of the circuit which has been isolated for this determination).

Remember Thévenin's theorem: any two-terminal network can be represented by a voltage source in series with an impedance, the voltage source being the open-circuit voltage of the network and the impedance being the impedance seen looking back into the opened terminals with all voltage sources shorted. Applying Thévenin's theorem to terminals B_2 and Y of Fig. 28-6b, R_thev and V_thev are found:

$$V_\text{thev} = -V_{BB} + (V_{CC} + V_{BB}) \frac{R_B}{R_C + R_A + R_B}$$

$$= -6 + (12 + 6) \frac{100 \text{ kilohms}}{102 \text{ kilohms} + R_A}$$

$$= -6 + 18 \times \frac{100 \text{ kilohms}}{102 \text{ kilohms} + R_A}$$

$$R_\text{thev} = (R_{A1} + R_C) \| R_{B2}$$

$$= (R_A + 2 \text{ kilohms}) \| 100 \text{ kilohms}$$

$$= \frac{(R_A + 2 \text{ kilohms}) 100 \text{ kilohms}}{R_A + 2 \text{ kilohms} + 100 \text{ kilohms}}$$

$$= \frac{(R_A + 2 \text{ kilohms})(100 \text{ kilohms})}{102 \text{ kilohms} + R_A}$$

This Thévenin equivalent is shown in Fig. 28-7.

Now let us determine the minimum required current for saturation.

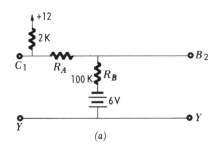

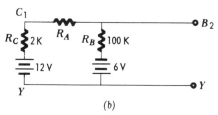

FIGURE 28-6 (a) Another section of the bistable multivibrator of Fig. 28-4 removed for intensive study. (b) A more convenient form of the circuit of part (a).

FIGURE 28-7 The Thévenin equivalent of Fig. 28-6b.

$$I_{C,\text{sat}}R_C = V_{CC} - V_{CE,\text{sat}}$$
$$I_{C,\text{sat}} = \frac{12 - 0.3}{2 \text{ kilohms}} = \frac{11.7}{2 \text{ kilohms}} = 5.85 \text{ ma}$$
$$I_{B,\text{sat min}} = \frac{I_C}{h_{FE,\text{sat}}} = \frac{5.85 \times 10^{-3}}{50} = 0.117 \text{ ma}$$
$$I_{B,\text{sat min}} = 0.117 \text{ ma}$$
$$I_B > 0.117 \text{ ma}$$

Returning to Fig. 28-7,

$$I_B = \frac{V_{\text{thev}} - 0.7}{R_{\text{thev}}}$$
$$= \frac{18 \dfrac{100 \text{ kilohms}}{102 \text{ kilohms} + R_{A1}} - 6 - 0.7}{\dfrac{100 \text{ kilohms}(R_A + 2 \text{ kilohms})}{102 \text{ kilohms} + R_A}}$$

$$= \frac{1800 \text{ kilohms} - 6.7(102 \text{ kilohms} + R_A)}{100 \text{ kilohms}(R_A + 2 \text{ kilohms})}$$

$$= \frac{1800 \text{ kilohms} - 6.7(102 \text{ kilohms} + R_A)}{100 \text{ kilohms}(R_A + 2 \text{ kilohms})} > 0.117 \text{ ma}$$

$$1800 \text{ kilohms} - 6.7(102 \text{ kilohms} + R_A) > 11.7(R_A + 2 \text{ kilohms})$$

$$1800 \text{ kilohms} - 683.4 \text{ kilohms} - 6.7R_A > 11.7R_A + 23.4 \text{ kilohms}$$

$$1093 \text{ kilohms} - 6.7R_A > 11.7R_A$$

$$1093 \text{ kilohms} > 18.4R_A$$

$$59.5 \text{ kilohms} > R_A$$

$$R_A < 59.5 \text{ kilohms}$$

Since R_{A1} and R_{A2} are to be equal, their upper and lower limits are 16.7 kilohms $< R_{A1,2} <$ 59.5 kilohms.

In order to allow for variation in component values some middle value which is available as a standard value is chosen.

Illustrative Problem 28-1

Design a bistable multivibrator which is to be used in a system requiring a 15-volt indication from the cutoff transistor. In addition to the main supply, a 9-volt positive ground supply is available. Silicon transistors are to be used which have an $h_{FE,\text{sat}}$ of 80 and a 10-ma collector current rating. Base current is not to exceed 1 ma.

SOLUTION

Given: $V_{\text{on}} = 15$ volts; 9 volt battery; Si transistors; $h_{FE,\text{sat}} = 80$; $I_{C,\text{rating}} = 10$ ma

Find: Bistable multi

(a) $\boxed{V_{CC} = 15 \text{ volts}}$

See Fig. Prob. 28-1a.

(b) $R_C = \dfrac{V_{CC} - V_{CE,\text{sat}}}{I_{C,\text{sat}}} = \dfrac{15 - 0.3}{10 \times 10^{-3}}$

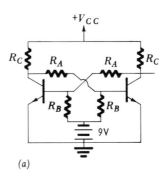

(a)

FIGURE PROB. 28-1a

THE BISTABLE MULTIVIBRATOR   397

$$\boxed{R_C = 1470 \text{ ohms}}$$

(c) $I_{B,\text{sat}} > \dfrac{I_{C,\text{sat}}}{h_{FE,\text{sat}}} > \dfrac{10 \times 10^{-3}}{80}$

$$\boxed{I_{B,\text{sat}} > 125 \ \mu a}$$

(d) With Q_2 saturated design for Q_1 cutoff.   (See Fig. Prob. 28-1b):

$$V_{B_1Y} = \frac{-R_A}{R_A + R_B} \ (9 + 0.3) + 0.3 < 0 \qquad \text{to ensure cutoff}$$

$$\frac{-R_A}{R_A + R_B} \times 9.3 + 0.3 < 0$$

$$\frac{9.3 R_A}{R_A + R_B} > 0.3$$

$$\frac{R_A}{R_A + R_B} > \frac{0.3}{9.3}$$

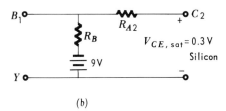

FIGURE PROB. 28-1b (b)

Since either R_A or R_B can be chosen freely, let $R_B = 14.7$ kilohms (a commonly available value).

$$\boxed{R_B = 14.7 \text{ kilohms}}$$

(e) $\dfrac{R_A}{R_A + 14.7 \times 10^3} > \dfrac{0.3}{9.3}$

$$R_A > \frac{0.3}{9.3} \ (R_A + 14.7 \times 10^3)$$

$$> 0.0323 \ (R_A + 14.7 \times 10^3)$$

$$R_A(1 - 0.0323) > 0.0323(14.7 \times 10^3)$$

$$R_A > \frac{0.0323(14.7 \times 10^3)}{1 - 0.0323}$$

$$\boxed{R_A > 488 \text{ ohms}}$$

(f) See Fig. Prob. 28-1c.

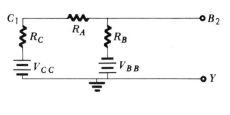

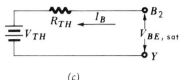

(c)

FIGURE PROB. 28-1c

$$V_{\text{thev}} = -V_{BB} + (V_{CC} + V_{BB}) \frac{R_B}{R_C + R_A + R_B}$$

$$= -9 + (15 + 9) \frac{14.7 \text{ kilohms}}{1470 + R_A + 14.7 \text{ kilohms}}$$

$$\boxed{V_{\text{thev}} = -9 + 24 \frac{14.7 \text{ kilohms}}{R_A + 16.2 \text{ kilohms}}}$$

$$R_{\text{thev}} = (R_A + R_C)\|R_B$$
$$= (R_A + 1470)\|14.7 \text{ kilohms}$$
$$= \frac{(R_A + 1470)(14.7 \text{ kilohms})}{R_A + 16.2 \text{ kilohms}}$$

$$I_{B,\text{sat}} = \frac{V_{\text{thev}} - V_{BE,\text{sat}}}{R_{\text{thev}}}$$
$$> 125 \times 10^{-6}$$

$$\frac{V_{\text{thev}} - 0.7}{R_{\text{thev}}} > 125 \times 10^{-6}$$

$$\frac{-9 + 24 \dfrac{14.7 \text{ kilohms}}{R_A + 16.2 \text{ kilohms}} - 0.7}{\dfrac{(R_A + 1470)(14.7 \text{ kilohms})}{R_A + 16.2 \text{ kilohms}}} > 125 \times 10^{-6}$$

$$\frac{-9.7(R_A + 16.2 \text{ kilohms}) + 24(14.7 \text{ kilohms})}{(R_A + 1470)(14.7 \text{ kilohms})} > 125 \times 10^{-6}$$

$$\frac{-9.7R_A - 9.7(16.2 \text{ kilohms}) + 24(14.7 \text{ kilohms})}{(14.7 \text{ kilohms})R_A + 1470(14.7 \text{ kilohms})} > 125 \times 10^{-6}$$

$$\frac{-9.7R_A + 196 \times 10^3}{14.7 \times 10^3 R_A + 21.6 \times 10^6} > 125 \times 10^{-6}$$

$$-9.7R_A + 196 \times 10^3 > 125 \times 10^{-6}(14.7 \times 10^3 R_A + 21.6 \times 10^6)$$
$$> 1840 \times 10^{-3}R_A + 2700$$

$$-11.5R_A > -193,300$$
$$R_A < \frac{193,300}{11.5}$$

THE BISTABLE MULTIVIBRATOR   399

$$\boxed{R_A < 16.8 \text{ kilohms}}$$

$$\boxed{488 < R_A < 16.8 \text{ kilohms}}$$

Check for limitation on I_B due to maximum rating.

$$I_B < 1 \times 10^{-3}$$
$$\frac{-9.7R_A + 196 \times 10^3}{14.7 \times 10^3 R_A + 21.6 \times 10^6} < 1 \times 10^{-3}$$
$$-9.7R_A + 196 \times 10^3 < 14.7R_A + 21.6 \times 10^3$$
$$-24.4R_A < -174 \times 10^3$$
$$-R_A < \frac{174 \times 10^3}{24.4}$$

$$\boxed{R_A > 7140 \text{ ohms} \qquad \text{due to the base-current rating limitations of the transistor}}$$

$$\boxed{7140 < R_A < 16.8 \text{ kilohms}}$$

Let $R_A = 10$ kilohms, a resistor which is available as a standard value.

TRIGGERING

We have developed a circuit, the bistable multivibrator, which when put into one of its two stable states will remain there until another disturbance comes along and causes it to flip into its other stable state. Since we originally developed this circuit to store information, the circuit must respond to externally applied signals. How can we provide a means of determining which of the two transistors in the bistable multivibrator is cut off and which is saturated? What if provision is made for the application of pulses to the base of each of the transistors, as shown in Fig. 28-8? Assume that we will be applying pulses of such polarity as to cut off the transistor. What if such a pulse were applied to the cut-off transistor? Absolutely nothing would happen, since it would merely reinforce the tendency of the cut-off transistor to remain cut off. But, if such a pulse were applied to the saturated transistor, it would tend to go into cutoff. This would be enough of a disturbance to also cause the cut-off transistor to tend to go into saturation. Thus the circuit of Fig. 28-8 can be used to determine which of the two transistors will be cut off and which will be saturated. The transistor whose base was last to experience a reverse biasing will be the transistor

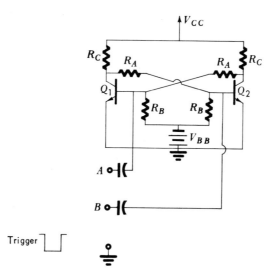

FIGURE 28-8 *The bi-
stable multivibrator with
provisions for triggering.*

which we will find cut off. Thus a negative-going pulse applied
to terminal A in Fig. 28-8 will cause the voltage at the collector of
Q_1 to have a value of approximately V_{CC} and the voltage at the collector of Q_2 to have a voltage associated with a saturated transistor
collector voltage (0.1 or 0.3 volt).

Frequently capacitors are placed across the resistors R_A in
order to speed up the transition from one state to another when the
pulse is applied. Such capacitors are referred to as *speed-up* or
commutating capacitors. They are usually tens or hundreds of
picofarads.

Similar triggering results can be obtained with pulses whose
polarity is such as to forward-bias the transistor. When forward-
biasing pulses are used, the last transistor whose base experienced
such a positive-going pulse is the *saturated* transistor.

In Fig. 28-9 we have a functional diagram of the bistable multivibrator. Two input terminals are provided, one marked SET and
the other marked RESET.

Figure 28-10 is the schematic diagram associated with the functional diagram of Fig. 28-9. Note the points marked SET, RESET,
Y, and $\bar{Y}$. Note that we have both Y and the complement or nega-

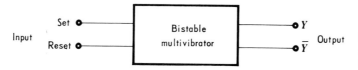

FIGURE 28-9 *Functional
diagram of a bistable multivibrator.*

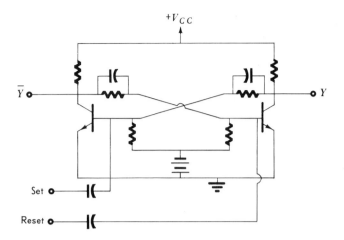

FIGURE 28-10 *Schematic diagram of the circuit associated with the functional diagram of Fig. 28-9.*

tion of Y, $\bar{Y}$, as available outputs. This proves very helpful in a computer where certain mathematical operations, e.g., subtraction, require the complement of the data which represent the number.

OTHER TRIGGER ARRANGEMENTS

The technique just described, in which each of the transistors is separately hit with a trigger pulse, is called *unsymmetrical triggering*. Frequently it is desirable to have just one input which will cause the bistable multivibrator to change from whichever stable state it is in to its other stable state. Such a trigger arrangement is called *symmetrical triggering*. Figure 28-11 (note the

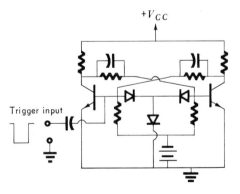

FIGURE 28-11 *A bistable multivibrator with provisions for symmetrical triggering.*

diodes) is a diagram of a circuit which can be used for situations in which symmetrical triggering is required. Such a circuit finds use in binary counting circuits, where we want the bistable multivibrator to flip from one stable state to the other alternately with the same polarity of trigger input.

We have been discussing circuits with only *NPN* transistors and showing only negative trigger pulses. *PNP* transistors can be, and are, used just as well. We have been limiting our discussion to *NPN* to avoid any confusion that might result in visualization due to a negative output of $-V_{CC}$ appearing at the collector of the cut-off transistor. The reason for having shown only negative-going pulses in the diagrams is that negative trigger pulses, when associated with *NPN* transistors and base triggering, are reverse-biasing pulses. In practice it is found that it takes a smaller reverse-direction signal to trigger a flip than is required for a forward-biasing pulse. Because of the tendency for the circuit to flip on both the leading and the trailing edge of the pulses, one being considered as positive- and the other being considered a negative-going trigger, a negative pulse can be made large enough to cause a flip when it seems to be a reverse-going trigger yet small enough so that it can be ignored when it seems to be as a forward-going trigger.

THE MONOSTABLE MULTIVIBRATOR

The astable multivibrator has two quasi-stable states and no stable states, while the bistable multivibrator has two stable states and no quasi-stable states. Let us now consider a circuit which has one of each, one quasi-stable state and one stable state. How would such a circuit behave functionally? Left to itself, one transistor would be cut off and the other saturated, the same one always being cut off and the other always being saturated. Upon the appearance of a properly applied trigger pulse, the circuit would shift into its astable condition. It would remain in this state for a fixed time, after which it would return to its stable state. The amount of time it would remain in the astable state would be determined, as with the astable multivibrator, by component values. How would such a circuit look? Obviously it would look like half of a bistable circuit attached to half of an astable multivibrator, as shown in Fig. 28-12. The amount of time spent in the quasi-state condition being equal to

$$T = 0.69R_2C_2$$

Of what use would such a circuit be? Since such a circuit pro-

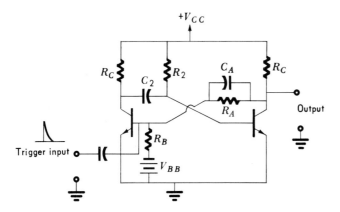

FIGURE 28-12 *The monostable multivibrator.*

duces a single pulse of fixed duration in response to a trigger signal, it is used to establish fixed time intervals and for reshaping pulses.

Frequently after knocking around through many circuits a pulse looses much of its shape, and we want to bring back its once almost perfect shape of near vertical edges and fixed time interval. When the distorted pulse is used as an input to the monostable multivibrator, a new fresh pulse is caused to appear. The monostable multivibrator can also be used to change the pulse duration of a pulse. By passing the distorted pulse through a differentiator circuit it will cause two impulses to appear, one a negative-going one and the other a positive-going one. Passing these two impulses through a diode eliminates one. The other can be allowed to continue, to trigger the monostable multivibrator. Other names by which the monostable multivibrator are known are one-shot, univerter, and delay generator.

PROBLEMS

28-1 Why can't the astable multivibrator be used for data storage?

28-2 What is a register?

28-3 How can an astable multivibrator be converted to a bistable multivibrator?

28-4 By what other names is the bistable multivibrator known?

28-5 When designing a bistable multivibrator, what determines the required value of the collector supply voltage?

28-6 A bistable multivibrator is to be designed which makes use of a 20-volt collector supply. The collector current passing through the saturated transistor is to be 8 ma.

(*a*) Determine the required resistance value and the power rating of the collector resistor.   (The transistor to be used is made of silicon.)

(b) The transistor has an $h_{FE,\text{sat}}$ of 120.   Calculate the minimum required value of base current in order to ensure saturation.

28-7 An incompletely designed bistable multivibrator has the following resistance values and voltages associated with it.   Determine the minimum allowable value of R_A.

$R_B = 50$ kilohms $V_{BB} = 9$ volts $V_{CE,\text{sat}} = 0.3$ volt

28-8 In the circuit discussed in Prob. 28-7 the collector circuit resistor R_C is 2 kilohms, and the collector voltage supply V_{CC} is 24 volts.

(a) Determine the collector current which flows through the saturated transistor.

(b) The transistor has an $h_{FE,\text{sat}}$ of 100.   Find the minimum base current needed to ensure saturation.

(c) Using the data from this problem and from Prob. 28-7, determine the maximum permitted value of R_A.

28-9 Design a bistable multivibrator which is to be used in a system which requires a 12-volt pulse height.   The main supply is a 12-volt supply, a secondary supply of 6 volts being available.   Germanium transistors having an $h_{FE,\text{sat}}$ of 75 are to be used.   The collector current is to be 100 ma.

28-10 Determine the permitted range for the V_{BB} supply of the bistable multivibrator shown in Fig. 28-13.

28-11 Why wouldn't you design a bistable multivibrator without provisions for triggering?

28-12 What is the effect of applying a reverse-biasing pulse to the base of the saturated transistor?   The cut-off transistor?

28-13 What are commutating capacitors?

FIGURE 28-13 *Diagram for Prob. 28-10.*

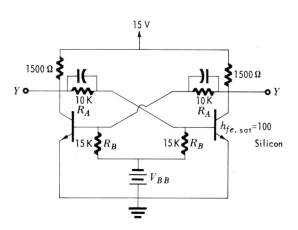

28-14 Distinguish between unsymmetrical triggering and symmetrical triggering.

28-15 What is a monostable multivibrator? Where is it used?

28-16 A circuit is to be designed which will produce a single output pulse of 24 volts having a duration of 10 msec upon the reception of a trigger pulse. A saturated collector current of 24 ma is desired during the stable state.

(*a*) What should the value of V_{CC} be?

(*b*) Calculate R_C.

(*c*) Which transistor will be saturated during the stable state?

(*d*) Determine R_2 for a saturated base current of 0.5 ma. (The transistor is silicon.)

(*e*) Find the necessary value of C_2.

28-17 By what other names is the monostable multivibrator known?

APPENDIX

CHARACTERISTIC CURVES

TYPICAL COLLECTOR CHARACTERISTICS

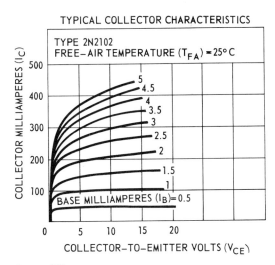

TYPE 2N2102
FREE–AIR TEMPERATURE (T_{FA}) = 25° C

BASE MILLIAMPERES (I_B)= 0.5

COLLECTOR MILLIAMPERES (I_C)

COLLECTOR–TO–EMITTER VOLTS (V_{CE})

TYPICAL BASE CHARACTERISTIC

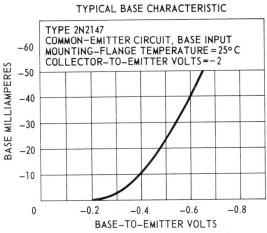

TYPE 2N2147
COMMON–EMITTER CIRCUIT, BASE INPUT
MOUNTING–FLANGE TEMPERATURE = 25° C
COLLECTOR–TO–EMITTER VOLTS = –2

BASE MILLIAMPERES

BASE–TO–EMITTER VOLTS

Source: *RCA.*

407

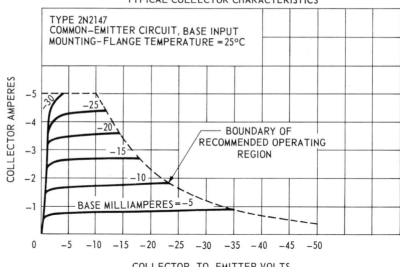

TYPICAL COLLECTOR CHARACTERISTICS

TYPE 2N2147
COMMON–EMITTER CIRCUIT, BASE INPUT
MOUNTING–FLANGE TEMPERATURE = 25°C

BOUNDARY OF
RECOMMENDED OPERATING
REGION

BASE MILLIAMPERES = –5

COLLECTOR–TO–EMITTER VOLTS

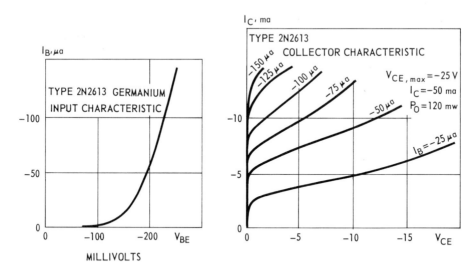

$I_B, \mu a$

TYPE 2N2613 GERMANIUM
INPUT CHARACTERISTIC

MILLIVOLTS

I_C, ma

TYPE 2N2613   COLLECTOR CHARACTERISTIC

$V_{CE, max} = -25$ V
$I_C = -50$ ma
$P_O = 120$ mw

$I_B = -25 \mu a$

Source: *RCA.*

408   APPENDIX: CHARACTERISTIC CURVES

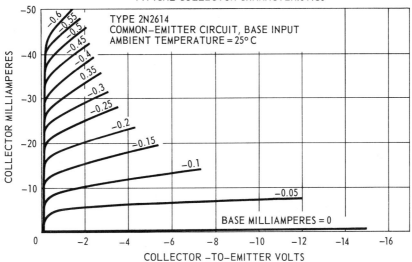

TYPICAL COLLECTOR CHARACTERISTICS

TYPE 2N2614
COMMON–EMITTER CIRCUIT, BASE INPUT
AMBIENT TEMPERATURE = 25° C

COLLECTOR MILLIAMPERES

COLLECTOR –TO–EMITTER VOLTS

BASE MILLIAMPERES = 0

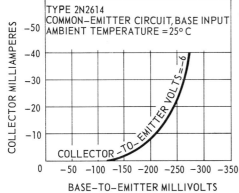

TYPICAL TRANSFER CHARACTERISTIC

TYPE 2N2614
COMMON–EMITTER CIRCUIT, BASE INPUT
AMBIENT TEMPERATURE = 25° C

COLLECTOR MILLIAMPERES

COLLECTOR –TO–EMITTER VOLTS = –6

BASE–TO–EMITTER MILLIVOLTS

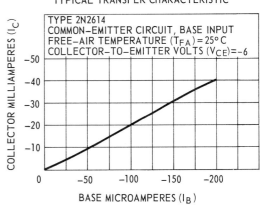

TYPICAL TRANSFER CHARACTERISTIC

TYPE 2N2614
COMMON–EMITTER CIRCUIT, BASE INPUT
FREE–AIR TEMPERATURE (T_{FA}) = 25° C
COLLECTOR–TO–EMITTER VOLTS (V_{CE}) = –6

COLLECTOR MILLIAMPERES (I_C)

BASE MICROAMPERES (I_B)

Source: *RCA.*

APPENDIX: CHARACTERISTIC CURVES   409

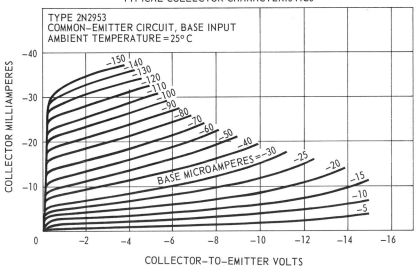

TYPICAL COLLECTOR CHARACTERISTICS

TYPE 2N2953
COMMON–EMITTER CIRCUIT, BASE INPUT
AMBIENT TEMPERATURE = 25° C

COLLECTOR MILLIAMPERES

BASE MICROAMPERES = −30

COLLECTOR–TO–EMITTER VOLTS

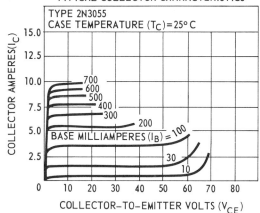

TYPICAL COLLECTOR CHARACTERISTICS

TYPE 2N3055
CASE TEMPERATURE (T_C) = 25° C

COLLECTOR AMPERES(I_C)

BASE MILLIAMPERES (I_B) = 100

COLLECTOR–TO–EMITTER VOLTS (V_{CE})

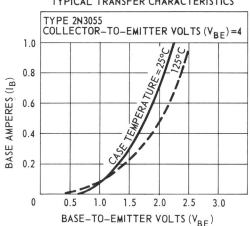

TYPICAL TRANSFER CHARACTERISTICS

TYPE 2N3055
COLLECTOR–TO–EMITTER VOLTS (V_{BE}) = 4

BASE AMPERES (I_B)

CASE TEMPERATURE = 25°C

125°C

BASE–TO–EMITTER VOLTS (V_{BE})

Source: *RCA.*

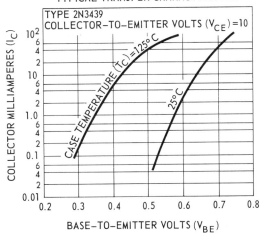

TYPICAL TRANSFER CHARACTERISTICS

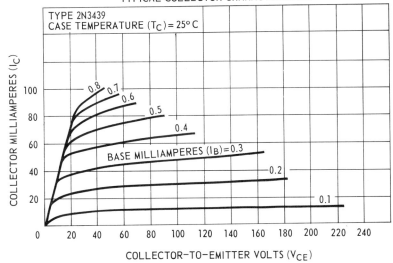

TYPICAL COLLECTOR CHARACTERISTICS

Source: *RCA.*

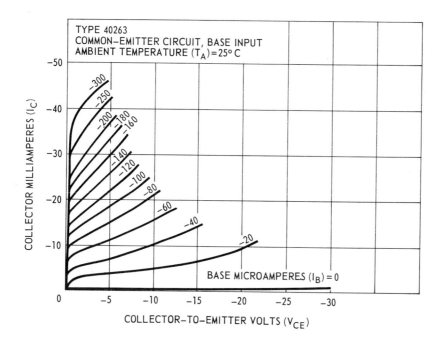

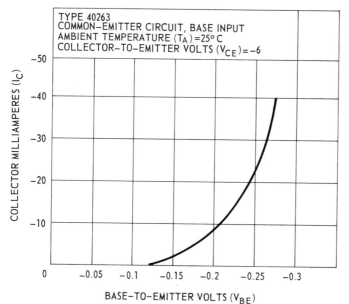

Source: RCA.

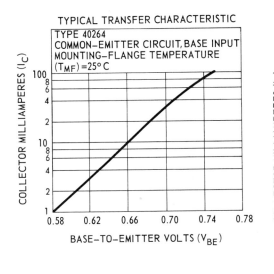

TYPICAL TRANSFER CHARACTERISTIC

TYPE 40264
COMMON-EMITTER CIRCUIT, BASE INPUT
MOUNTING-FLANGE TEMPERATURE
$(T_{MF}) = 25°C$

COLLECTOR MILLIAMPERES (I_C)

BASE-TO-EMITTER VOLTS (V_{BE})

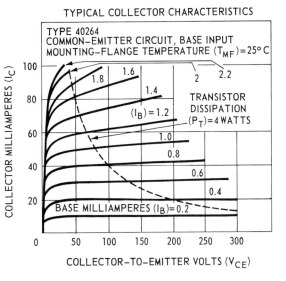

TYPICAL COLLECTOR CHARACTERISTICS

TYPE 40264
COMMON-EMITTER CIRCUIT, BASE INPUT
MOUNTING-FLANGE TEMPERATURE $(T_{MF}) = 25°C$

COLLECTOR MILLIAMPERES (I_C)

TRANSISTOR DISSIPATION $(P_T) = 4$ WATTS

$(I_B) = 1.2$

BASE MILLIAMPERES $(I_B) = 0.2$

COLLECTOR-TO-EMITTER VOLTS (V_{CE})

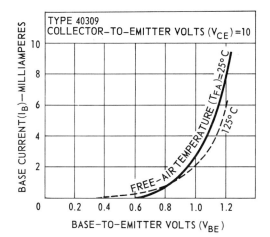

TYPE 40309
COLLECTOR-TO-EMITTER VOLTS $(V_{CE}) = 10$

BASE CURRENT (I_B)—MILLIAMPERES

FREE-AIR TEMPERATURE $(T_{FA}) = 25°C$
$125°C$

BASE-TO-EMITTER VOLTS (V_{BE})

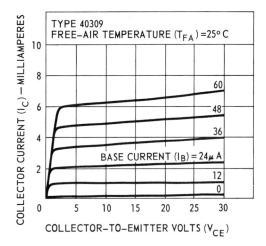

TYPE 40309
FREE-AIR TEMPERATURE $(T_{FA}) = 25°C$

COLLECTOR CURRENT (I_C) — MILLIAMPERES

BASE CURRENT $(I_B) = 24\mu A$

COLLECTOR-TO-EMITTER VOLTS (V_{CE})

Source: *RCA.*

APPENDIX: CHARACTERISTIC CURVES   413

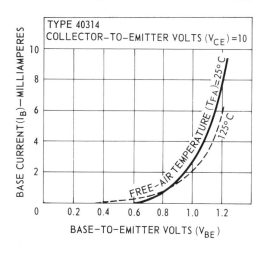

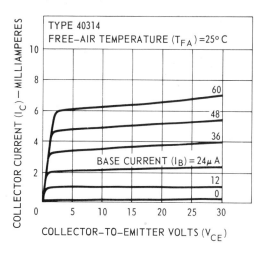

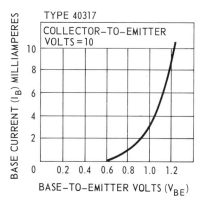

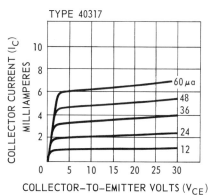

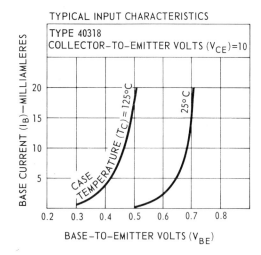

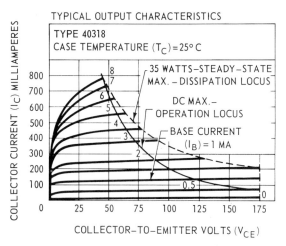

Source: *RCA.*

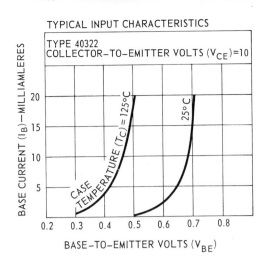

TYPICAL INPUT CHARACTERISTICS

TYPE 40322
COLLECTOR–TO–EMITTER VOLTS (V_{CE})=10

BASE CURRENT (I_B)–MILLIAMLERES

CASE TEMPERATURE (T_C)=125°C

25°C

BASE–TO–EMITTER VOLTS (V_{BE})

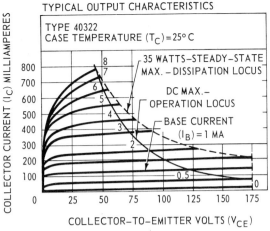

TYPICAL OUTPUT CHARACTERISTICS

TYPE 40322
CASE TEMPERATURE (T_C)=25°C

COLLECTOR CURRENT (I_C) MILLIAMPERES

35 WATTS–STEADY–STATE
MAX.– DISSIPATION LOCUS

DC MAX.–
OPERATION LOCUS

BASE CURRENT
(I_B)=1 MA

COLLECTOR–TO–EMITTER VOLTS (V_{CE})

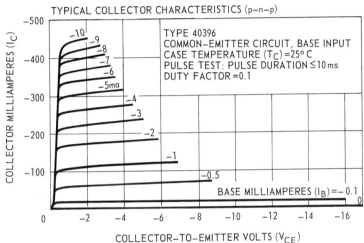

TYPICAL COLLECTOR CHARACTERISTICS (p–n–p)

TYPE 40396
COMMON–EMITTER CIRCUIT, BASE INPUT
CASE TEMPERATURE (T_C)=25°C
PULSE TEST: PULSE DURATION ≤10 ms
DUTY FACTOR =0.1

COLLECTOR MILLIAMPERES (I_C)

BASE MILLIAMPERES (I_B)=– 0.1

COLLECTOR–TO–EMITTER VOLTS (V_{CE})

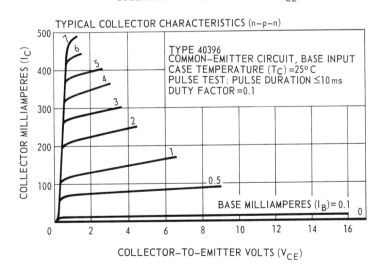

TYPICAL COLLECTOR CHARACTERISTICS (n–p–n)

TYPE 40396
COMMON–EMITTER CIRCUIT, BASE INPUT
CASE TEMPERATURE (T_C)=25°C
PULSE TEST: PULSE DURATION ≤10 ms
DUTY FACTOR =0.1

COLLECTOR MILLIAMPERES (I_C)

BASE MILLIAMPERES (I_B)= 0.1

COLLECTOR–TO–EMITTER VOLTS (V_{CE})

Source: *RCA.*

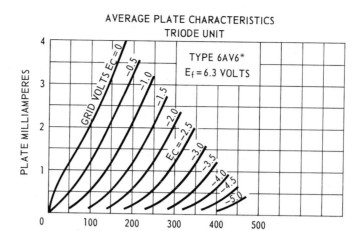

AVERAGE PLATE CHARACTERISTICS
TRIODE UNIT

TYPE 6AV6*
$E_f = 6.3$ VOLTS

PLATE VOLTS

*(THIS CURVE ALSO APPLIES TO THE 12AX7A)

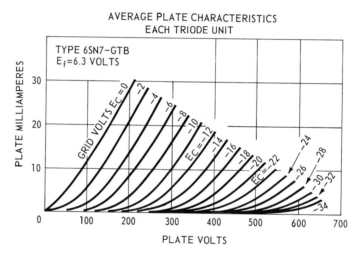

AVERAGE PLATE CHARACTERISTICS
EACH TRIODE UNIT

TYPE 6SN7–GTB
$E_f = 6.3$ VOLTS

PLATE VOLTS

Source: *RCA.*

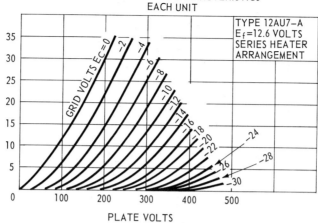

AVERAGE PLATE CHARACTERISTICS
EACH UNIT

TYPE 12AU7–A
E_f=12.6 VOLTS
SERIES HEATER
ARRANGEMENT

PLATE VOLTS

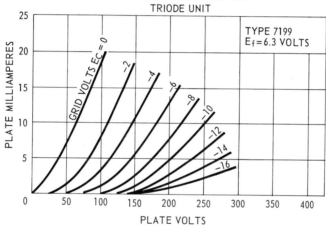

AVERAGE CHARACTERISTICS
TRIODE UNIT

TYPE 7199
E_f=6.3 VOLTS

PLATE MILLIAMPERES

PLATE VOLTS

Source: *RCA.*

APPENDIX: CHARACTERISTIC CURVES   417

ANSWERS

TO SELECTED PROBLEMS

Chapter 1

1-7 (*b*) 1.09 amp
     (*c*) 26.3 volts
     (*d*) 82.5 volts
     (*e*) Transformer: 438 ma;
        120:58.5
        Diode: 438 ma; 1370 ma;
        103 volts

1-9 (*b*) 6.28 amp; 157 volts
     (*c*) 25 ohms
     (*d*) 246 watts

Chapter 2

2-1 (*a*) 78 volts
     (*b*) 78 volts
     (*c*) 156 volts
     (*d*) 110 volts
     (*e*) 6.25 amp

2-7 628 volts

2-3 Diode: 94 ma; 292 ma; 294
     volts
     Transformer: 188 ma;
        120:168 center-tapped

Chapter 3

3-3 (*b*) 0.050 sec
     (*c*) 0.050 sec
     (*d*) 37 volts
     (*e*) 7.4 ma

3-7 (*a*) 500 volts
     (*b*) 500 volts
     (*c*) 250 μa
     (*d*) 34.3 μa

3-5 0.002 coulomb; 0.0005
     coulomb

3-9 (*a*) 0.001 coulomb
     (*b*) 0.012 sec
     (*c*) 0.0833 amp
     (*d*) 0.0833 amp

Chapter 4

4-3 170 volts

4-11 1000 volts

4-9 0.00955; 0.955%

4-13 (a) 1.76 μf
  (b) 321 volts
  (c) 1.88 ma
  (d) 72 ma
  (e) 643 volts
  (f) 1.88 ma; 120:182

4-15 4000 ohms

Chapter 5

5-3 8.7%

5-9 (a) I_z max rated > 450 ma
  (b) 9 watts

Chapter 6

6-11 (a) 625 ma
  (b) 1.96 amp
  (c) 98 volts
  (d) 98 volts
  (e) 120:55.6

Chapter 7

7-13 (c) (10,0) and (0,30)

7-15 (c) 2.3 ma
  (d) 4 ma
  (e) 3750 ohms

7-17 (d) 10 ma; 150 volts

7-23 (c) 636 ohms
  (d) 62.5 μf
  (f) 13.3

7-25 (c) −5 volts
  (d) 667 ohms

Chapter 8

8-3 88 kilohms

8-5 (b) 58.6 kilohms
  (e) 96

8-9 97 kilohms

8-13 250 ohms; 2500 ohms;
  13.3 kilohms

8-15 284 ohms; 2840 ohms; 41
  kilohms

Chapter 9

9-5 15; 2500 μmhos; 6000
  ohms

9-7 (c) 400 ohms
  (d) 0.997; 0.996; 266; 260

Chapter 10

10-5 (d) −58.8
  (e) −0.588

10-7 88.9; 144

10-11   (d) 255
       (e) 90
       (f) 20.2×10^3
       (g) 48 mv
       (h) 10.8 volts
       (i) 3.6 ma
       (j) 0.24 μw

10-13   1150 ohms; 20 kilohms; 13

Chapter 11

11-3   −17.9
11-7   (c) 390 kilohms
     (e) 52 mv

11-11 (d) 20 kilohms; 1.13 watts
      (g) −10

11-5   59.6; 172; 10,300
11-9   (d) 133
     (e) 72 mv
     (f) 132

Chapter 12

12-7   318 Hz

12-9   (a) 877 kHz
     (c) 106 volts
     (d) 0.075 watt
     (e) 0.124 watt

Chapter 13

13-3   1.59 megohms; 159 kilohms;
      15.9 kilohms; 1590
      ohms; 159 ohms
13-7   (b) −16.5
     (d) 75.9 Hz
     (e) 1.94 Hz
     (g) 1.13 MHz
     (h) 910 kHz

13-5   0.272 μf

Chapter 14

14-3   (c) 6.36 Hz
     (d) 2.13 Hz
     (e) −135
14-9   (b) 7.06 MHz
     (c) 916 kHz

14-5   238 Hz; 22.5 Hz

Chapter 15

15-3   (a) 25 watts
     (b) 22.2 watts
     (c) 22.2 watts
15-7   (b) 9 volts
     (c) 100 ohms
     (d) 1.41:1
     (e) 4.6 volts

15-5   10:1; 1 volt rms

15-9   (b) 835 ohms
     (c) 224:1
     (f) 0.49 volt peak-to-peak

Chapter 16

16-1   20%

16-3   (*b*) 13.3%
     (*c*) 65 watts
     (*d*) 75 watts

16-5   (*c*) 3 ohms
     (*d*) 0.866:1
     (*f*) 19 watts
     (*g*) 4.25 watts
     (*h*) 22.3%
     (*i*) 0.29 volt peak-to-peak
     (*j*) 39.7; 147; 5840

Chapter 18

18-7   (*b*) 15.8:1
     (*d*) 7.64 watts
     (*e*) 3.3 watts
     (*f*) 43.2%

18-11   (*c*) 340 ma
      (*d*) 0.836:1
      (*e*) 56.3%

Chapter 20

20-3   85; 86; −136; 0.932; 11,600;
      80.2

20-5   (*b*) 478 ohms
     (*c*) 478 ohms
     (*d*) 4.31 ohms
     (*e*) 51; 0.855; 43.6

20-9   146 ohms; 0.468 volt peak-
      to-peak

Chapter 21

21-3   −0.875; −10.7

21-5   (*a*) −3
     (*b*) −.0429
     (*c*) 17.5

21-7   9.5

Chapter 22

22-1   (*a*) 113 mh
     (*b*) 14.3
     (*d*) 333 ma
     (*e*) 356 volts

22-5   (*a*) 0.0635 μf
     (*b*) 126
     (*c*) 1.58 megohms
     (*d*) 31.7 μa
     (*e*) 3.98 ma

Chapter 23

23-1   (*a*) 0.05 msec
     (*b*) 0.3 msec
     (*c*) 0.35 msec
     (*d*) 2.86×10^3 pps
     (*e*) 0.8 msec
     (*f*) 0.85 msec

23-5   2.2

23-7   20%

23-9   500 nsec; 5 nsec

Chapter 24

24-3 (c) 20 msec

(d) 0.04 μf

Chapter 25

25-1 40 volts

25-3 (b) 200 Hz

Chapter 27

27-3 1300 μsec

869 μsec

66.7×10^3 pps

27-7 12 volts

793 ohms

22 kilohms

17.7 pf

9.8 pf

27-9 (a) 276 μsec

(b) 148 μsec

(c) 23.7 ma

(d) 0.508 ma

(e) 0.536 ma

(g) 567 mw; 1.12 mw; 1.25 mw

Chapter 28

28-7 1670 ohms

INDEX